CAMPING AND
CARAVANNING
GUIDE

Quality Assessment

Credits

Produced by AA Publishing

Maps prepared by the AA's Cartographic Department

Maps © The Automobile Association 1995.

Directory generated by the AA Establishment Database, Information Research and Control, Hotel and Touring Services

Editor: Denise Laing

Advertisements

Head of Advertisement Sales:
Christopher Heard Tel. 01256 20123 ext. 21544

Advertisement Production: Karen Weeks Tel. 01256 20123 ext. 21545

Filmset by Avonset, Midsomer Norton, Bath

Colour origination by LC Repro, Basingstoke

Colour printing by Sussex Litho, Chichester, Sussex

Printed and bound in Great Britain by William Clowes Limited, Beccles & London

The contents of this publication are believed correct at the time of printing. Nevertheless the Publisher cannot be held responsible for any errors or omissions or for changes in the details given in this guide or for the consequences of any reliance on the information provided in the same. Although every effort has been made to ensure accuracy we always welcome any information from readers to assist in such efforts and to keep the book up to date.

Assessments of caravan and camping parks are based on the experience(s) of the AA's team of experienced camping park officers on the occasion(s) of their visit(s) and therefore the descriptions given in this guide may contain an element of subjective opinion which may not dictate a reader's experience on another occasion.

A CIP catalogue record for this book is available from the British Library Published by AA Publishing which is a trading name of Automobile Association Developments Limited whose registered office is Norfolk House, Priestley Road, Basingstoke, Hampshire RG24 9NY, Registered number 1878835

AA Ref 52896

ISBN 0 7495 1113 3

CAMPING AND
CARAVANNING
GUIDE

Contents

CAMPING AND
CARAVANNING
GUIDE

Cover photograph is Harford Bridge Holiday Park at Tavistock, Devon

Symbols & Abbreviations

England

♣♠♠☺	AA qualitative assessment symbols (see p 14)
▶	AA pennant classification (see p 15)
▷	Venture Site (see p 14)
☎	Site telephone number
🐕	No dogs
★	1995 prices
🚐	Touring caravans
🚍	Motor caravans
▲	Tents
⊕	Electric hook up
🛁	Bath(s)
🚿	Shower(s)
⊙	Electric shaver point(s)
🔲	Launderette
🔳	Hairdrier
🏊	Indoor swimming pool
🏊	Outdoor swimming pool
⚲	Tennis court
●	Games room
🖵	Separate TV room
❄	Cold storage
♉	Licensed bar
⚠	Children's playground
▮	Calor Gas
⌀	Camping Gaz
⊞	Battery charging
Ⓣ	Toilet fluid
✕	Café/restaurant
♿	Disabled facilities
☏	Public telephone
🛒	Shop on site or within 200 yds (except where it appears after ➜)
⊡	Mobile shop calls at the site at least 5 days a week
➜	Facilities within three miles of site
∪	Stables
⛳	9 hole/18 hole golf course
⛵	Boats for hire
🎬	Cinema
🎣	Fishing
🍼	Baby care
🍖	Barbeque area
🏞	Picnic area
🍔	Fast food/take away
🐕	Dog exercise area on site
◎	Mini golf
⛴	Watersports
all year	Site open all year
C	Century
cdp	Chemical closet disposal point
Etr	Easter
fr	From
hrs	Hours
m	Mile
mdnt	Midnight
nc	No children (with age limit)
rs	Restricted service
Sign-posted	Officially prescribed sign to site
supervised	Site supervised 24hrs a day
wk	Week
wknd	Weekend

Français

♣♠♠☺	Symboles AA d'évaluation qualitative (voir p 14)
▶	Classification drapeau AA (voir p 15)
▷	Venture Site (voir p 14)
☎	Numéro de téléphone due site
🐕	Chiens non permis
★	Prix 1995
🚐	Caravanes die tourisme
🚍	Caravanes à moteur
▲	Tentes
⊕	Branchements éléctriques
🛁	Bain(s)
🚿	Douche(s)
⊙	Prise(s) pur rasoirs éléctriques
🔲	Machine à laver
🔳	Sechoir pour cheveux
🏊	Piscine couverte
🏊	Piscine extérieure
⚲	Court de tennis
●	Salle de jeux
🖵	Télévision
❄	Congrélateur
♉	Bar
⚠	Terrain de récréation
▮	Calor Gas
⌀	Camping Gaz
⊞	Batterie
Ⓣ	Fluide pour WC chimique
✕	Café/restaurant
♿	Facilités pour invalides
☏	Téléphone public
🛒	Magasin au site ou endéans de 180m (sauf où le symbole est indiqué après ➜)
⊡	Magasin ambulant visitant le site au moins 5 jours par semaine
➜	Agréments endéans de 5km du site
∪	Ecuries d'équitation
⛳	Terrain de golf à 9 trous ou 18 trous
⛵	Bateaux en location
🎬	Cinéma
🎣	Péche
🍼	Soins aux enfants
🍖	Zone de barbecue
🏞	Zone de pique-nique
🍔	Plats préparés/à emporter
🐕	Zone de promenade des chiens
◎	Mini golf
⛴	Sports nautiques
all year	Emplacement ouvert toute l'année
C	Siècle
cdp	Lieu d'evacuation pour W-C chimiques
Etr	Pâques
fr	À partir de
hrs	Heures
m	Mile
mdnt	Minuit
nc	Pas d'enfants (avec limite d'âge)
rs	Service limité
Sign-posted	Indicateur officiellement recommandé vers le site
supervised	Gardien en service au site
wk	Semaine
wknd	Fin de semaine

Deutsch

AA Katagorisierung der Qualität (siehe p 14)
AA Fahnchenklassifizierung (siehe p 15)
Venture Site (siehe p 14)
Telefonnummer des Campingplatzes
Hundeverbot
1995 Preise
Reisewohnwagen
Campingwagen
Zelt
Stromschluss
Bad(e)
Dusche(n)
Stromanschluss für Rasierapparate
Waschmaschine
Haartrockner
Hallenbad
Freibad
Tennisplatz
Spielzimmer
Fernsehen
Gefriermaschine
Bar
Spielplatz (Kinder)
Calor Gas
Camping Gaz
Batterieladung
Chemikal für Toiletten
Café/restaurant
Für Körperbehinderte geeignet
Öffentliche Telefonzelle vorhanden
Lebensmittelgeschäft am Platz oder nicht weiter entfernt als 180m (ausgenommen wenn das Zeichen nach → aufgeführt wird)
Autoladen besucht den Platz wenigstens fünfmal in der Woche
→ Freizeitmöglichkeiten nicht weiter entfernt als 5km
U Reitstall
Golf platz 9/18 holes
Bootverleih
Kino
Fischen
Babywickelraun
Grillstelle
Picknickstelle
Schnellimbiss/Essen zum Mitnehmen
Auslaufbereich für Hunde
Minigolf
Wassersport
all year Ganzjährig geöffnet
C Jahrhundert
cdp Ausgus für Chemikaitoiletten
Etr Ostern
fr Von
hrs Stunden
m Meile
mdnt Mitternacht
nc Kinder nicht gestattet (mit Altersgrenze)
rs Beschränkte Bienstleistungen
Sign-posted Amtlicher Strassenchild zum Platz
supervised Aufseher am Piatz anwesend
wk Woche
wknd Wochenende

Español

Simbolo de evaluación calitativa de la AA (Véase p 14)
Classificacion insignias AA (Véase p 15)
Venture Site (Véase p 14)
Numero de téléfono del camping
Se prohiben los perros
Precios de 1995
Rulotas
Coches-rulotas
Tiendas
Acoplamientos elétricos
Baño(s)
Ducha(s)
Toma(s) de corriente para maquinillas eléctricas
Lavanderia
Secar cabello
Piscina cubierta
Piscina descubierta
Cancha de tenis
Sala de juegos
Television
Congelador
Bar
Terreno de recreos
Calor Gas
Camping Gaz
Bateria
Liquido para retretes quimicos
Café/restaurant
Facilidades para invalidos
Teléfono público
Almacén en el camping o en un radio de 180 metros (a menos que el almacén figure después del simbolo →)
Un almacén ambulante pasa por el camping al menos 5 veces a la semana
→ Servicios públicos en un radio de 3 millas
U Escuela hipica
Campo de golf de 9 o 18 hoyos
Se alquilan botes
Cine
Pesca
Cuidado de los niños
A la parilla/bar-b-cu
Area de recreo
Comida al expresso
Area de ejercicio para los perros
Campo de minigolf
Departes de agua
all year El camping está abierto todo el ano
C Siglo
cdp Punta de recogida de inodoros quimicos
Etr Pascua de Resurrección
fr Desde
hrs Horas
m Milla
mdnt Medianoche
nc Se prohibe la entrada a los niños (más el limite de edad)
rs Servicio limitado
Sign-posted Indicator de dirección de camping oficial
supervised Guardian de servicio en el camping
wk Semana
wknd Fin de Samana

Italiano

Simbolo di valu tazione qualitativa della AA (Vedi p 14)
Classificazione stendardi dell AA (Vedi p 15)
Venture Site (Vedi p 14)
Numero telefonico del campeggio
Proibito ai canis
Prezzi de 1995
Roulotte
Campers
Tende
Collegamenti elettrici
Bagno(i)
Doccia(e)
Presa(e) di corrente per rasoi
Lavandaria
Asciuga capelli
Piscina coperta
Piscina scoperta
Campo da tennis
Sala di giuoco
Televisione
Congelatore
Bar
Campo di giuoco por figli
Calor Gas
Camping Gaz
Batteries
Liquido por toelettas chimicas
Café/restaurant
Attrezzature per invalidi
Telefono pubblico
Negozio nel campeggio o in un raggio di 180 metri (a meno che non venga indicato dopo il segno →)
Un furgone provviste passa per il campeggio al meno 5 giorni alla settimana
→ Comodità in un raggio di 3 miglia dal campeggio
U Scuola d'jequitazione
Campo da golf a 9 to 18 buche
Affittansi bare he
Cinema
Pesca
Area cura bambini
Area per barbecue
Area per picnic
Fastfood/Cibi da asporto/Takeaway
Area riservata ai canis
Minigolf
Sport acquatici
all year Campeggio aperto tutto l'anno
C Secolo
cdp Punto di eliminazione a gabinetto chimico
Etr Pasqua
fr Da
hrs Orario
m Miglio
mdnt Mezzanotte
nc Proibito ai bambini (con il limite d'età)
rs Servizio limitato
Sign-posted Indicazione ufficiale per il campeggio
supervised Guardiane di servizio nei campeggio
wk Settimana
wknd Fine de Settimana

How to Use the Guide

Whether you are a newcomer to camping and caravanning or an old hand, it is probable that what attracted you in the first place was the 'go-as-you-please' freedom of being able to set off on the merest whim. However, in practice, especially during holiday periods, parks in popular parts of the country get dreadfully crowded, and if you choose somewhere off the beaten track, you may go for miles without finding anywhere.

When you do find somewhere, how do you know that it will have the facilities you need? How do you know whether they will be maintained to an acceptable standard? This is where you will find the AA guide invaluable in helping you to choose the right park. Please also read the section on the Pennant Rating Scheme so that you know what the classification symbols used in this guide mean.

The directory of parks is organised by county, with locations listed in alphabetical order of location. Locations on islands are listed alphabetically under the island name, e.g. Wight, Isle of. Parks are listed in descending order of pennant rating. There is a location map for every county and the map normally appears after the county heading; if it does not, there is a page reference.

Town Name
appears in alphabetical order within counties

Name of Site
followed by 6-figure Ordnance Survey map reference. If printed in italics, details given have not been confirmed by the park. If the words 'Apply to' follow the map reference this is the contact number for details and bookings.

Pennant Rating and Quality Awards
See the section on the AA pennant rating scheme for explanation.

Quality symbols mean:
♦♦ excellent sanitation facilities; ✿ excellent leisure facilities
♣ attractive environment
Parks with the Sanitation and one or both of the other awards have the highlighted Q for quality entry.

ANYTOWN

AWARD

Pleasant Caravan Park (NZ626182)
Skelton Rd TS14 6QA
☎ 01287 610182 Signposted
► ► ► ♦ ♦♦ ⊞ £8-£10 ⊞ £8-£10 ▲ £8-£10
Open Mar-Oct Booking advisable bank hols & high season Last arrival 21.00hrs Last departure noon
Situated in a private wooded valley alongside a stream, the site is centred around a preserved watermill. A 7-acre site with 30 touring pitches and 75 statics.

🔌 📶 ⊙ 🗑 ✳ ♀ 🏔 🛈 📞 🛒 ♿
→ ∪ 🛠

Price Guide
for caravans, motor vans and tents. Not every park accepts all three

Facilities
All facilities and amenities on or within 3 miles of the park are listed. Please refer to the explanation of symbols and abbreviations at the start of the directory. The arrow indicates 'within 3 miles of the park'

Important note.

Telephone the park before you travel. In the caravan and camping world there are many restrictions and some categories of visitor are banned. On many sites unaccompanied young people, single-sex groups, single adults, and motorcycle groups will not be accepted. Do not assume that you can take your dog or other family pet. Some parks have no suitable areas for exercise. On the other hand, some parks cater well for teenagers with magnificent sporting and leisure facilities as well as discos; others have only very simple amenities.

LOOK OUT FOR THE NUMBER 1, LET THE NUMBER 1 LOOK AFTER YOU.

- Your No. 1 choice for Tenting and Touring Holidays.
- 26 scenic locations for 1996, in England and Wales.
- From only £5 per pitch per night, it's great value for money. Many special offers, including 7 nights for the price of 6 and special ferry prices to the Isle of Wight.
- Now more Main Service Pitches, more Disabled and Family Suites and more Electrical Hook-ups.
- **FREE** family daytime activities with fun pools and the Tiger Club for 5-11 year olds. **FREE** sparkling evening entertainment.
- Plus excellent touring facilities, including showers, shaver and hairdryer points, disposal points and washing-up sinks.

Call 0191 417 4141 for your free 1996 Touring brochure, quoting TMA01. Or complete the coupon.

How to Use the Guide

Special Offers

In the front of this book you will find a reply-paid card and details of how to enter our prize draw for a Luxury Weekend. Please don't forget to fill it in, with your name and address, and return it to us so that we can enter it in one of the draws.

Booking

It is advisable to book in advance during peak holiday seasons and at school or public holidays. Where an individual park requires advance booking, 'advance bookings accepted' or 'booking advisable' (followed by dates) appears in the entry. It is also wise to check whether a reservation entitles you to a particular pitch. It does not necessarily follow that an early booking will get you the best pitch; you may just have the choice of what is available at the time you check in.

The words 'Advance bookings not accepted' indicate that a park does not accept reservations. Some parks may require a deposit on booking which may well be non-returnable if you have to cancel your holiday. If you have to cancel, notify the proprietor at once because you may be held legally responsible for partial or full payment unless the pitch can be re-let. Do consider taking out insurance such as AA Travelsure to cover lost deposit or compensation. Some parks will not accept overnight bookings unless payment for a full minimum period (e.g. two or three days) is made. If you are not sure whether your camping or caravanning equipment can be used at a park, check beforehand.

Please note: The AA does not undertake to find accommodation or to make reservations.

Chemical Closet Disposal Point (CDP)

You will usually find one on every park, except those catering only for tents. It must be a specially constructed unit, or a WC permanently set aside for the purpose with adjacent rinsing and soak-away facilities. However, some local authorities are concerned about the effect of chemicals on bacteria in cesspools etc, and may prohibit or restrict provision of cdps in their areas.

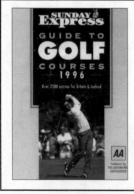

Over 2,500 courses

This guide has something to suit every golfer – from the novices to the most proficient player

Packed with useful information – it gives you –

- The latest information about visitors, green fees, entry restrictions and club and refreshment facilities
  - Descriptions of each course – especially the more challenging aspects.
- Full page features of twenty major Championship Courses.
- NEW for 1996 – a national directory of Driving Ranges.

Cold Storage

A fridge and/or freezer for the use of holidaymakers.

Complaints

Speak to the park proprietor or supervisor immediately if you have any complaints, so that the matter can be sorted out on the spot. If this personal approach fails, you may decide, if the matter is serious, to approach the local authority or tourist board. AA members may write to:

**The Editor,
The AA Camping and Caravanning Guide,
AA Publishing,
Norfolk House,
Priestley Road,
Basingstoke, Hants RG24 9NY.**

CAMPING AND
CARAVANNING
GUIDE

The AA will look into any reasonable complaints from members but will not in any circumstances act as negotiator or enter into further correspondence. The AA will not guarantee to take any specific action.

Directory

If the name of a park is printed in italics this indicates that we have not been able to get details or prices confirmed by the owners.

Electrical Hook-up

This is becoming more widely available at parks with three or more pennants, but if it is important to you, you must check before booking. The voltage is generally 240v AC, 50 cycles, although variations between 200v and 250v may still be found. All parks in the AA scheme which provide electrical hook-ups do so in accordance with International Electrotechnical Commission

The table below gives the amperage used by appliances in common use.

Portable black & white TV 50 watts approx. 0.2 amp	**100 watt light bulb** approx. 0.4 amp	**Small domestic kettle** 2000 watts approx. 8.3 amp *N.B. A fast-boil jug kettle rates much higher and should only be used on 16amp circuits.*
Small colour TV 90 watts approx. 0.4 amp	**Battery charger** 100 watts approx. 0.4 amp	
Small fan heater 1000 (kW) approx. 4.2 amp	**Small refrigerator** 125 watts approx. 0.4 amp	5 amp circuits are not suitable for anything above 600 watts.
One-bar electric fire NB each extra bar rates 1000 watts	**Domestic microwave** 600 watts approx. 2.5 amp	
60 watt table lamp approx. 0.25 amp	**Toaster or electric iron** 1300 watts approx. 5.4 amp	

How to Use the Guide

regulations. Outlets are coloured blue and take the form of a lidded plug with recessed contacts, making it impossible to touch a live point by accident. They are also waterproof. A similar plug, but with protruding contacts which hook into the recessed plug, is on the end of the cable which connects the caravan to the source of supply, and is dead.

These cables can usually be hired on site, or a plug supplied to fit your own cable. You should ask for the male plug; the female plug is the one already fixed to the power supply.

This supply is rated for either 5, 10 or 16 amps and this is usually displayed on a triangular yellow plate attached to source of supply. If it is not, be sure to ask at Reception. This is important because if you overload the circuit, the trip switch will operate to cut off the power supply. The trip switch can only be reset by a park official, who will first have to go round all the hook-ups on park to find the cause of the trip. This can take a long time and will make the culprit distinctly unpopular with all the other caravanners deprived of power, to say nothing of the park official.

It is a relatively simple matter to calculate whether your appliances will overload the circuit. The amperage used by an appliance depends on its wattage and the total amperage used is the total of all the appliances in use at any one time. See the table on page 9.

Last Arrival

Unless otherwise stated, parks will usually accept arrivals at any time of the day or night but some have a special 'late arrivals' enclosure where you have to make temporary camp so as not to disturb other people on park. Please note that on some parks access to the toilet block is by key or pass card only, so if you know you will be late, do check what arrangements can be made.

Last Departure

As with hotel rooms and self-catering accommodation, most parks will specify their overnight period - e.g. noon to noon. If you overstay the departure time you can be charged for an extra day. Do make sure you know what the regulations are.

Maps

A map of each county, highlighting the locations, usually appears as near as possible to the county heading, or if one or more county maps have been grouped together, there will be a cross-reference under the county heading to the appropriate page. These maps will make a good first reference point to show you everything the AA lists in that county. If you have a specific destination in mind you can quickly see if we list any parks there, and if not, what alternatives there may be.

Please note that these are not road maps and have been designed to show you a quick overall picture of the county. When you are driving to a park, you must use a good road atlas - the AA publishes several - or the appropriate Ordnance Survey 1: 50 000 sheet map if the location is really remote. We give you the National Grid map reference (see 'Explanation of a directory entry', page 6) and outline route directions but space in the directory is limited and we cannot go into exhaustive detail.

Motor Caravans

At some parks motor caravans are only accepted if they remain static throughout the stay. Also check that there are suitable, level pitches at the parks where you plan to stay.

Parking

Some park operators insist that cars be put in a parking area separate from the pitches; others will not allow more than one car for each caravan or tent.

Park Rules

Most parks display a set of rules which you should read on your arrival. A No Dogs symbol in the directory means that dogs are banned (guide dogs for the blind may still be accepted, however). On other parks, dogs are allowed at the park operators' discretion as long as they are kept on a lead and under control. However, please note that some proprietors ban certain breeds or restrict the number per unit. Sleeping in cars is not encouraged by most proprietors. Some parks will not accept the following categories of people: single-sex groups, unsupervised youngsters and motorcyclists whether singly or in groups, even adults travelling on their own. If you are not a family group or a conventional couple, you would be well advised to make sure what rules apply before you try to book.

CAMPING AND
CARAVANNING
GUIDE

How to Use the Guide

Pitches and Charges

The number of touring pitches is included in the description.
Charges given immediately after the appropriate symbol (caravan,
tent, motorvan) are the overnight cost for one tent or caravan, one
car and two adults, or one motor caravan and two adults. The price
may vary according to the number of people in your party, but
some parks have a fixed fee per pitch regardless of the number of
people. Please note that some parks may charge separately for some
of the park's facilities, including the showers. Please note that prices
have been supplied to us in good faith by the park operators and are
as accurate as possible. They are, however, only a guide and are
subject to change at any time during the currency of this book.

When parks have been unable to forecast their 1996 prices, those
for 1995 may be quoted, prefixed by an asterisk. See also
Directory above.

Campsites are legally entitled to use an overflow field which is
not a normal part of their camping area for up to 28 days in any
one year as an emergency method of coping with additional
numbers at busy periods.

When this 28 day rule is being invoked site owners must increase
the numbers of sanitary facilities accordingly when these become
insufficient to cope with extra numbers.

Rabies

Rabies warning: because of quarantine requirements (for instance,
six months isolation for dogs and cats) it is not a practical
proposition to bring an animal with you from your own or a
foreign country on holiday to Britain. Penalties for trying to avoid
this regulation are severe, and if you do have to bring an animal
into Britain, you must have an import licence, obtainable from
Ministry of Agriculture, Fisheries and Food, Hook Rise South,
Tolworth, Surbiton, Surrey KT6 7NF. Tel: 0181-330 4411.

Restricted Service

Restricted service means that full amenities and services
are not available during the period stated – for example a
swimming pool or bar/restaurant may open only in the
summer. Restrictions vary greatly from park to park, so
you must check before setting off.

Shop

The range of food and equipment in shops is usually in
proportion to the size of the park. As far as our pennant
requirements are concerned, a general store within easy
walking distance of the park entrance is acceptable for a
three-pennant rating, but four or five-pennant parks must
have a well equipped shop on park unless there is a
supermarket so close as to make a shop pointless. If a
mobile shop calls at least five days a week, this is shown in
the entry.

Signposted

This does not refer to AA signs but indicates that there is an International Direction Sign on the nearest main road. These signs have not yet been erected for all parks. They show whether the park accepts caravans, tents or both.

Static Van Pitches

We give the number of static van pitches available in the entries in our guide in order to give a picture of the nature and size of the park. The AA pennant rating system is based on an inspection of the touring pitches and facilities only. AA inspectors do not visit or report on the fixed types of accommodation. The AA takes no responsibility for the condition of rented caravans or chalets and will take no action whatsoever about complaints relating to them.

Supervised

If this word appears in a directory entry it means that the park has someone in attendance 24 hours a day. Other parks may have less comprehensive cover.

Telephone

The telephone authorities are liable to change some telephone numbers during the currency of this guide. If you have difficulty in contacting a park, please check with directory enquiries.

The AA Pennant-Rating Scheme

The AA pennant-rating scheme is based on annual inspection and classification of facilities. It is designed for touring holiday makers who travel with their own tents, trailers or motorvans. Our Officers visit camping and caravan parks to assess the facilities available to tourers but do not inspect any static caravans, chalets or ready-erected tents available for hire. All such accommodation is outside the scope of the pennant-rating scheme and outside the scope of this guide.

How the AA Classifies Parks

The basic requirement for all camping and caravan parks in the AA pennant-rating scheme is that they reserve a minimum number of pitches for the use of touring campers or caravanners and that the facilities provided for tourers are well maintained and comply with our standards for classification. All parks receive an annual visit and report. The pennant rating is based on this report, and pennants are awarded on a rising scale of one to five, depending on the range of facilities. There is also a special category known as Venture Sites. These are very quiet rural parks suitable for the self-contained camper who travels with his own toilet facilities and needs only a water tap. They are identified in the gazetteer by the symbol ▷. A five-pennant park (holiday centre) may be no more attractive than a one-pennant park, but it will have far more amenities. Many parks in the AA scheme display a yellow and black sign showing their pennant rating, but not all parks choose to have one, and in some areas local authority regulations prohibit the display of signs.

Awards for Excellence

Pennant ratings provide an objective guide to the basic range of facilities and equipment available on a park. If amenities are of outstandingly high quality, we give Awards for Excellence in three categories. These awards are shown in the guide by three special symbols which appear after the pennant rating:

♠ a tree for attractive environment

♦♦ a man/woman symbol for first class washing and sanitary facilities

✪ a wheel for an outstanding range of sports and recreational facilities

Window stickers are sent to the parks to display in their reception office, and the appropriate symbols appear in the guide after the pennant rating; those with two or more awards are highlighted by a Q for quality symbol and a tint band at the end of the entry, as shown on page 6.

There is also a quick-reference list of parks with awards for excellence on pages 34-39.

Basic Requirements for AA Pennant Rating

All parks must have a local authority site licence (unless specially exempted) and must have satisfied local authority fire regulations. All parks at the higher pennant ratings must satisfy all the one-pennant requirements and have extra facilities, summarised below. Please note that campsites are legally entitled to use an overflow field which is not a normal part of their camping area for up to 28 days in any one year as an emergency method of coping with additional numbers at busy periods.

When this 28 day rule is being invoked site owners must increase the numbers of sanitary facilities accordingly when these become insufficient to cope with extra numbers.

One Pennant ▶

- No more than 30 (reasonably spaced) pitches per acre of land suitable for camping
- At least 6 pitches allocated to tourers or 10% of the total if there are more than 60 pitches
- Separate flush toilets with 2 washbasins and 2 WCs (ladies), 2 washbasins, 1 WC and 1 urinal (men) for every 30 pitches
- Tap water supply of good quality and quantity
- Waste water disposal facilities within reasonable walking distance of any touring pitch
- Adequate arrangements for disposal of refuse, clearly indicated
- Well-drained ground and some level pitches suitable for tents and motor-caravans
- Entrance and access roads of adequate width and surface

Two Pennants ▶▶

- At least 15% of pitches allocated to tourers
- Separate washrooms with hot and cold water direct to each basin
- Point for disposal of chemical closet contents with adjacent flushing and rinsing facilities (as some local authorities will not allow such contents to mix with cesspools, there are exceptions to this rule)
- Externally lit toilet blocks
- Warden available at certain times of the day, to be clearly indicated

Three Pennants ▶▶▶

- Some hardstandings and some pitches with electrical hook ups

- One shower or bath each sex with hot and cold water per 35 pitches
- Deep sinks for hand washing clothes, plus provision of spin or tumble dryers and washing machines
- Electric shaver points (men's), mirrors and sockets for hair dryers (ladies) in washrooms
- All-night lighting of toilet blocks, time-switches acceptable if time clearly indicated
- Shop stocking basic foods either on the park or within short (half a mile) walking distance
- Adequate roads to perimeter and services
- Warden on site during day; contact number clearly indicated for night time emergencies
- Public telephone on site and available 24 hours
- Five per cent of touring pitches with hard standings; some with electrical hook up

Four Pennants ▶▶▶▶

- At least 25% of pitches allotted for tourers
- 2 washbasins per sex for 25 pitches, 1 shower per sex for 30 pitches
- All-night permanent lighting of toilet blocks
- Washing-up facilities with hot and cold water separate from sinks for clothes washing
- Signed reception office
- Signposted late-arrivals enclosure, appropriately sited to prevent disturbing others
- Dedicated first-aid room with washbasin and ventilation, ensuring comfort and privacy
- Park shop offering a wide

selection of food, household and domestic products, and camping and caravanning spares
- Access routes to and from essential facilities, lit after dark
- Children's playground, fenced or in a safe area, with a suitable surface. Area for ball games away from pitches and tents
- Some landscaping of park
- 10% of touring pitches with hard standings; 50% with electrical hook-ups

Holiday Centres (Five pennants) ▶▶▶▶▶

These parks are also designated as 'Holiday Centres' because of the range of leisure facilities they offer on site. See also the quick reference list on page 16
- A comprehensive range of services and equipment
- At least 40% of pitches allocated to tourers
- 24hr supervision by warden on site
- Automated laundry with at least 2 each of the following permanently installed: washing machines, tumble-dryers, irons and ironing boards
- 2 washbasins per sex for 20 pitches, 1 free shower per sex per 25pitches
- Heated washrooms if park open between October and Easter
- Range of facilities for indoor and outdoor recreation for adults
- Indoor recreational facilities for children separate from those provided for adults
- Cafe or restaurant
- Visitors' car park

Two parks are new to the list this year, **Killigarth Manor Holiday Estate** at Polperro in Cornwall and **Bainland Country Park** at Woodhall Spa, Lincolnshire, this year's Central England Winner of the AA Campsite of the Year Award.

Holiday Centres

The five-pennant classification denotes parks which cater for holidaymakers who like to have a very wide range of leisure facilities and recreational equipment on site, so that they need never range far afield for entertainment either during the day or in the evenings, unless they choose to do so. We have given these parks the additional title of 'Holiday Centres', and set out below is a complete, quick-reference list, in county order. You will find all the details about the parks under the appropriate county and location in the directory.

Crantock (Newquay), Cornwall
Trevella Tourist Park

Holywell Bay, Cornwall
Trevornick Holiday Park

Looe, Cornwall
Treble B Holiday Centre

Newquay, Cornwall
Hendra Holiday Park
Newquay Holiday Park

Perranporth, Cornwall
Perran Sands Holiday Centre

Polperro, Cornwall
Killigarth Manor Holiday Estate

Rejerrah, Cornwall
Newperran Tourist Park

White Cross, Cornwall
White Acres Holiday Park

Chudleigh, Devon
Finlake Leisure Park

Paignton, Devon
Beverley Parks Caravan and Camping Park

Woolacombe, Devon
Golden Coast Holiday Village

South Cerney, Gloucestershire
Cotswold Hoburne

Skipsea, Humberside
Far Grange Park

St Helens, Isle of Wight
Nodes Point Holiday Park

Woodhall Spa, Lincolnshire
Bainland Country Park

Hunstanton, Norfolk
Searles of Hunstanton

Selsey, West Sussex
Warner Farm Touring Park

Filey, North Yorkshire
Flower of May Holiday Park,

SCOTLAND

Brighouse Bay, Dumfries & Galloway
Brighouse Bay Holiday Park

IRELAND

Crookhaven, Co Cork
Barley Cove Caravan Park

Ballylickey, Co Cork
Eagle Point Caravan and Camping Park

Killarney, Co Kerry
Fossa Caravan Park

Killaloe, Co Clare
Lough Derg Caravan and Camping Park

Red Cross, Co Wicklow
River Valley Caravan Park

CAMPING AND
CARAVANNING
GUIDE

CAMPSITE
OF THE
YEAR
1995/96

Everybody loves a winner, and there is no doubt that those sites which this year receive the Automobile Association's highest accolade will be a popular choice with campers and caravanners. All except one of the sites offers outstanding recreational opportunities for all the family, with children very much in mind, and the odd one out is in such a gorgeous location next to the sea that it would still be a natural winner regardless of recreational facilities These sites are this year's cream of what we already consider to be the best in the country, and we recommend that you make a reservation and pay them a visit as soon as you can!

Winners

THIS YEAR'S CAMPSITE OF THE YEAR AWARD WINNER FOR 1995-6
Seaview International, Boswinger, Cornwall

REGIONAL AWARD WINNERS

SOUTHERN ENGLAND
Old Oaks Touring Park. Glastonbury, Somerset

CENTRAL ENGLAND
Bainland Country Park, Woodhall Spa, Lincolnshire

NORTHERN ENGLAND
Holgate's Caravan Park, Silverdale, Lancashire

WALES
Cei Bach Country Club, New Quay, Dyfed

SCOTLAND
Castle Cary Holiday Park, Creetown, Dumfries & Galloway

LAST YEAR'S AWARD WINNERS
Campsite of the Year –
Stanmore Hall Touring Park, Bridgnorth, Shropshire

REGIONAL AWARD WINNERS
Eastern England: Cherry Hinton Caravan Club Site, Cherry Hinton, Cambridgeshire
Southern England: Sun Haven Valley Caravan & Camping Site, Mawgan Porth, Cornwall
Northern England: Flower of May Holiday Park, Filey, N. Yorkshire
Scotland: Camping & Caravanning Club Site, Barcaldine, Strathclyde
Wales: Camping & Caravanning Club Site, Cardigan Bay, Cross Inn, Dyfed

Campsite of the Year

AND BEST CAMPSITE

FOR THE SOUTH-WEST

Sea View International,
Boswinger, Cornwall

The outstanding impression one gets of this site is its superb order and cleanliness. The whole park is rich with the colour of shrubs and flowers, and even those sometimes intruding service blocks are beautifully screened with hanging baskets. The Michell family – Anne and Donovan and their children Elaine and Gary – have been running the park for over 30 years, and they have put a polish on everything which makes this an absolutely outstanding park. This park is aptly named, too, as from most areas there are stunning views of the ocean. Whether you choose to sit on the sun terraces beside the swimming pool, play some of the giant games like chess and chequers, or take part in some of the many sports and recreational activities available on site, you are surrounded by quality, and offered a standard of service that is second to none. Don't forget to book well in advance, because pitches will be in greater demand than ever this year!

Best Campsite for Southern England

The Old Oaks Touring Park,
Glastonbury, Somerset

Amongst the top small parks in the country, Old Oaks is certainly one of the best, and undoubtedly one of the most popular. The emphasis here is on relaxation and friendliness, and the White family make excellent hosts. They are Jim and Sally White, and their brood of four sons who help keep things running smoothly - Daniel, Tom, James, and the youngest Nicholas who keeps the grass manageably short. This working farm east of Glastonbury Tor is in a lovely setting with panoramic views of the Mendip Hills. The camping park is spacious and well managed, and every year there are new improvements to marvel at. This year a spacious reception office and shop, and next year terracing of the slightly sloping park. The swimming pool is a mecca for all whatever the weather, and there is a playground and games room which are guaranteed to amuse. This is definitely a worthy winner!

Best Campsite for Central England

Bainland Country Park,
Woodhall Spa, Lincolnshire

More a country club than a purely touring park, Bainland Park is one of the best-equipped parks in the country. Indoor and outdoor sporting enthusiasts are well catered for, with an impressive array of activities and facilities to choose from. The floodlit tennis courts are covered in winter, and there is a full-size all weather bowling strip, an 18-hole golf course, trampoline with safety barrier, crazy golf and badminton to name just a few activities which may be indulged in. A heated indoor swimming pool is understandably in great demand, and there are three eating outlets in the form of a restaurant, a bistro and a coffee bar, plus a licensed bar, amusement room and those triple attraction of sauna, solarium and jacuzzi. All this, and a very well maintained touring area and facilities makes this our wholehearted choice for the Midlands. Congratulations to David Dain, the managing director of this family-run site on such a fine achievement!

Best Campsite for Northern England

Holgate's Caravan Park,
Silverdale, Lancashire

The success of this park belongs to a family that really works well together, and the results of their combined efforts are something they are justifiably proud of. Frank and Judith Holgate, along with daughter Susan and sons Mick and Roger, have developed the park over 39 years, and it covers some 100 acres of woodland, park and moorland. Attractively designed stone buildings house the essential facilities, and the quality of equipment and standard of cleanliness is as high as could be. The extensive amenities include an indoor heated swimming pool, 9-hole pitch and putt course, restaurant, lounge bar, games room and sauna. And as if all that were not enough, there are panoramic views to be enjoyed from the park's outstanding location overlooking Morecambe Bay towards Grange-over-Sands. Visit it and see!

Best Campsite for Wales

Cei Bach Country Club,
New Quay, Dyfed

This little camping park is in such a lovely setting that words like 'magnificent' and 'glorious' spring immediately to mind. Set high on the cliffs overlooking the sweep of Cardigan Bay, it offers extensive views which it would be impossible to tire of. The pitches are spread over the gently undulating site, and there are hedges and newly planted trees which have the dual role of providing privacy and shelter from the wind. Coupled with this naturally attractive setting is a site which is continually improving, thanks to the Wynne family which owns it. The facilities are excellent, including a licensed bar and restaurant, and the nearby coastal path is perhaps the finest recreational activity of all. Don't take our word for it, just book your holiday now!

Best Campsite for Scotland

Castle Cary Holiday Park,
Creetown, Dumfries & Galloway

Set in the grounds of a 16th-century baronial castle, on the shores of the Solway Firth between the coast road and a magnificent backdrop of wooded hills, Castle Cary presents an idyllic picture. Screened by mature trees, its presence is hardly discernable until the pillared entrance to the drive is reached. The Henryson-Caird family have lived here for six generations, and the site has been very well developed and managed by the present owner, Alastair, his mother and his partner Sheila Marshall. Thoughtful landscaping and excellent equipment make this an ideal spot for a camping holiday, and there are 18 fully serviced pitches for those who relish the ultimate in luxury. Recreational facilities include both indoor and outdoor swimming pools, games room, children's playground, and a private coarse fishing loch. So when you choose this place for your holiday, don't forget the rods!

Welcome to
fallbarrow 🌳 park
On the shore of Lake Windermere

An English Tourist Board
Rose award park

- **Spectacular location** in wooded parkland on shore of Lake Windermere . . . only a five minute walk to the village with its restaurants, shops, lake cruises, boat hire and recreational facilities.

- **Lake and Glade Touring Sites** — all with free electric hook-ups, individual hard standings and grass surrounds — Lake sites with individual water points.

- **First Class toilet and shower facilities.**

- **Extensive foreshore with slipway and jetties.**

- **Your own licensed bar** with meals, family lounge, childrens facilities and pop bar.

- **Luxury holiday caravans** with full facilities including colour televisions.

- **All usual park facilities** Mini-market with off-licence. Tourist Information, childrens play-area, laundrette, etc.

 Rose award park   **AA** ▸▸ acsi RAC

The Discerning Choice For Over 25 Years — Fallbarrow Park

For full colour brochure write to Fallbarrow Park, Windermere, The Lake District, LA23 3DL or telephone (015394) 44427

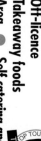

WE'VE GOT ONE WORD FOR PEOPLE LIKE YOU

Whether you are a member or not, a warm welcome is one of the many benefits you will find when you visit our Club sites.

We have over 70 sites open to non-members in England, Scotland and Wales and all of these are excellent value. We offer special rates for families throughout the season but it's even better to be a member, because you can save up to £3.50 per night on pitch fees and for those members over 60, there are further concessions.

You'll find our sites on the coast, in the mountains near famous sites and even on Royal Estates. And our friendly wardens, will ensure that all the sites are run to the same high standard – and they are a superb source of information making your stay even better.

The Camping and Caravanning Club

The friendly Club

For our free colour guide of Club sites open to non-members or membership details, please call **01203 694995** and ask for our Sites Department (quote 9264). Alternatively write to our Sites Department, Camping and Caravanning Club, FREEPOST 9264, Greenfields House, Westwood Way, Coventry CV4 8BR.

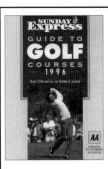

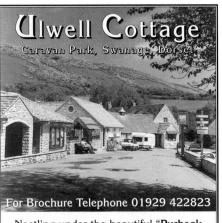

CAMPING AND CARAVANNING GUIDE

BRITAIN'S BEST PARKS

Britain's Best Parks

On page 14 we give details of the three awards for excellence for parks which excel in three categories: attractive environment; sanitation facilities; leisure and recreational equipment. This list covers all the parks which have awards for environment or sanitation or both. A ❁ symbol beside a site shows it has awards for both attractive environment and sanitation facilities.

CHANNEL ISLANDS

Catel, Guernsey
Fauxquets Valley Farm
St Martin, Jersey
Rozel Camping Park

AVON

Bath
Newton Mill Caravan & Camping Park

BERKSHIRE

Finchampstead
California Chalet & Touring Park

CAMBRIDGESHIRE

Cherry Hinton
❁*Caravan Club Site*
Comberton
❁*Highfield Farm Camping Park*
Great Shelford,
Camping & Caravanning Club Site
Houghton
Houghton Mill Caravan & Camping Park

CLEVELAND

Guisborough
❁*Tockett's Mill Caravan Park*

CORNWALL

Ashton
❁*Boscrege Caravan Park*
Boswinger
❁*Sea View International Caravan & Camping Park*
Bude
❁*Budemeadows Touring Holiday Park*
Camelford
Juliot's Well Holiday Park
Carlyon Bay
Carlyon Bay Caravan Park
Crantock
❁*Trevella Tourist Park*
Goonhavern
❁*Silverbow Park*
Helston
Trelowarren Chateau Park
Leedstown
❁*Calloose Caravan Park*
Looe
Polborder House Caravan & Camping Park
Lostwithiel
❁*Powderham Castle*
Mawgan Porth
❁*Sun Haven Valley*
Pentewan
Sun Valley Holiday Park
Porthtowan
Porthtowan Tourist Park
Rose Hill Park
Rejerrah
Newperran Tourist Park
Relubbus
❁*River Valley Caravan Park*
Ruthernbridge
Ruthern Valley Holidays
St Ives
Trevelgan Farm
Truro
❁*Leverton Place*
Thretheake Manor
Liskey Touring Park
Summer Valley

CUMBRIA

Ambleside
Skelwith Fold Caravan Park
Appleby in Westmorland
❁*Wild Rose Park*

Eskdale
Fisherground Farm Campsite
Keswick
Low Manesty Caravan Club Site
Kirkby Lonsdale
Woodclose Caravan Park
Lamplugh
Dockray Meadow Caravan Club Site
Inglenook Caravan Park
Mealsgate
Larches Caravan Park
Milnthorpe
❀ *Fell End Caravan Park*
Watermillock
❀ *Cove Caravan & Camping Park*
The Quiet Site
Windermere
Fallbarrow Park
❀ *Limefitt Park*

DERBYSHIRE
Bakewell
Chatsworth Park Caravan Club Site
Castleton
❀ *Lose Hill Caravan Club Site*
Crowden
Camping & Caravanning Club Site
Hayfield
Camping & Caravanning Club Site
Matlock
❀ *Darwin Forest Park*
Pinegrove Caravan Park

DEVON
Ashburton
❀ *Ashburton Caravan Park*
River Dart Country Park
Blackawton
❀ *Woodland Leisure Park*
Brixham
Hillhead Holiday Camp
Chudleigh
Finlake Leisure Park
Holmans Wood Park
Clifford Bridge
Clifford Bridge Park

Combe Martin
Stowford Farm Meadows
Dolton
Dolton Caravan Park
East Worlington
Yeatheridge Farm Caravan Park
Hawkchurch
Hunters Moon Touring Park
Kentisbeare
Forest Glade Holiday Park
Lydford
Camping & Caravanning Club Site
Lynton
Camping & Caravanning Club Site
Modbury
Camping & Caravanning Club Site
Newton Abbot
❀ *Dornafield*
Paignton
Widend Camping Park
Plymouth
❀ *Riverside Caravan Park*
Sidmouth
❀ *Oakdown Touring Park*
Slapton
❀ *Camping & Caravanning Club Site*
Stoke Gabriel
❀ *Ramslade Touring Park*
Tavistock
Langstone Manor Camping & Caravan Park
Woodovis Caravan Park
West Down
Hidden Valley Coast & Country Park
Whiddon Down
Dartmoor View Caravan & Camping Park

DORSET
Bere Regis
❀ *Rowlands Wait Touring Park*
Blandford Forum
The Inside Park
Bridport
Binghams Farm Touring Caravan Park
Highlands End Farm Caravan Park

CAMPING AND
CARAVANNING
GUIDE

Charmouth
Monkton Wylde Farm Caravan Park
Chickerell
Bagwell Farm Touring Park
Corfe Castle
Woodland Camping Park
Wimborne Minster
Wilksworth Farm Caravan Park

CO DURHAM
Wycliffe
Thorpe Hall

ESSEX
Colchester
Colchester Camping

HAMPSHIRE
Bransgore
Harrow Wood Farm Caravan Park
Brockenhurst
Hollands Wood Campsite
Fordingbridge
✻*New Forest Country Holidays*

HEREFORD & WORCESTER
Wythall
Chapel Lane Caravan Club Site

HUMBERSIDE
Rudston
Thorpe Hall Caravan & Camping Park
Skipsea
✻*Far Grange Park*

ISLE OF WIGHT
Newbridge
✻*Orchards Holiday Caravan Park*
Newchurch
✻*Southland Camping Park*
Sandown
Adgestone Camping Park
Wroxall
Appuldurcombe Gardens Caravan & Camping Park

KENT
Ashford
✻*Broad Hembury Holiday Park*
Harrietsham
Hogbarn Caravan Park
Hoath
South View
Martin Mill
✻*Hawthorn Farm Caravan & Camping Site*
Sevenoaks
Camping & Caravanning Club Site

LANCASHIRE
Croston
Royal Umpire Caravan Park
Silverdale
✻*Holgate's Caravan Park*
Thornton
Kneps Farm

LINCOLNSHIRE
Fleet Hargate
Matopos Caravan & Campsite
Woodhall Spa
✻*Bainland Country Park*

LONDON
London E4
Lee Valley Leisure Centre Camping & Caravan Site

NORFOLK
Barney
✻*The Old Brick Kilns*
Clippesby
Clippesby Holidays
Sandringham
✻*Camping & Caravanning Club Site*
Scratby
Scratby Hall Caravan Park
Trimingham
Woodlands Caravan Park
West Runton
Camping & Caravanning Club
Wortwell
Little Lakeland Park

NORTHUMBERLAND
Bamburgh
Waren Caravan Park
Bellingham
Brown Rigg Caravan & Camping Par
Berwick-upon-Tweed
Seaview Caravan Club Site
Haltwhistle
Camping & Caravanning Club Site
Kielder
Kielder Water Caravan Club Site

NOTTINGHAMSHIRE
Worksop
Clumber Park Caravan Club Site

OXFORDSHIRE
Banbury
Barnstones Caravan & Camping Site
Bletchington
Diamond Farm Caravan & Camping Park
Charlbury
✻*Cotswold View*
Oxford
Oxford Camping International
Standlake
✻*Lincoln Farm Park*

SHROPSHIRE
Bridgnorth
✻*Stanmore Hall Touring Park*
Haughton
Camping & Caravanning Club Site
Lyneal
Fernwood Caravan Park

SOMERSET
Bawdrip
Fairways International Touring Carava & Camping Park
Bruton
Batcombe Vale Caravan Park
Crowcombe
Quantock Orchard Caravan Park
Exford
Westermill Farm

Glastonbury
❀*Old Oaks Touring Park*
Martock
Southfork Caravan Park
Minehead
Camping & Caravanning Club Site
North Wootton
Greenacres Camping

STAFFORDSHIRE
Cannock Chase
Camping & Caravanning Club Site
Leek
❀*Blackshaw Moor Caravan Club Site*

SUFFOLK
East Bergholt
❀*Grange Country Park*
Waldringfield
Moon & Sixpence

SURREY
East Horsley
Camping and Caravaning Club Site

SUSSEX, EAST
Battle
Normanhurst Court Caravan Club Site

SUSSEX, WEST
Bognor Regis
Bognor Regis Caravan Club Site
Graffham
Camping & Caravanning Club Site
Southbourne
Chichester Camping
Southwater
Raylands Park

WARWICKSHIRE
Aston Cantlow
Island Meadow Caravan Park

WILTSHIRE
Marston Meysey
Second Chance Caravan Park

YORKSHIRE, NORTH
Allerston
❀*Vale of Pickering Caravan Park*
Allerton Park
Allerton Park Caravan Site
Aysgarth
Westholme Caravan Park
Bolton Abbey
❀*Strid Wood CaravanClub Site*
Cawood
Cawood Holiday Park
Coneysthorpe
Castle Howard Caravan & Camping Site
Cropton
❀*Spiers House Campsite*
Fylingdales
Grouse Hill Caravan Park
Harrogate
❀*Rudding Holiday Park*
Helmsley
Foxholme Caravan Park
Golden Square Touring Caravan Park
North Stainley
Sleningford Water Mill Caravan Site
Richmond
Brompton-on-Swale Caravan Park
Ripley
❀*Ripley Caravan Park*
Sheriff Hutton
Camping & Caravan Club Site
Snainton
Jasmine Caravan Park
Sutton-on-the-Forest
❀*Goosewood Caravan Park*
Threshfield
❀*Wood Nook Caravan Park*
Whitby
Northcliffe Holiday Park
Winksley
❀*Woodhouse Farm Caravan & Camping Park*
Wykeham
❀*St Helens Caravan Park*
York
❀*Rawcliffe Manor Caravan Site*
Rowntree Park Caravan Club Site

WALES

CLWYD
Betws-yn-Rhos
Hunters Hamlet Caravan Park
Llanddulas
Bron Y Wendon Caravan Park
Llandrillo
Hendwr Caravan Park
Llangollen
Ty-Ucha Caravan Park

DYFED
Cross Inn
❀*Camping & Caravanning Club Site*
Hasguard Cross
Redlands Touring Caravan Site
Llandre
Riverside Park
New Quay
Cei Bach Country Club
Newcastle Emlyn
Afon Teifi Caravan & Camping Park
Cenarth Falls Holiday Park
Rhandirmwyn
❀*Camping & Caravanning Club Site*
St David's
Lleithyr Meadow Caravan Club Site
Tenby
Rowston Holiday Park
Trefalun

GWENT
Dingestow
Bridge Caravan Park & Camping Site

GWYNEDD
Abersoch
❀*Bryn Cethin Bach Caravan Park*
Bala
Camping & Caravanning Club Site
Beddgelert
Beddgelert Forest Campsite
Betws Garmon
Bryn Gloch Caravan & Camping Park
Brynteg
Nant Newydd Caravan Park

Conwy
Conwy Touring Park
Dulas (Isle of Anglesey)
Tyddyn Isaf Caravan Park
Llanrwst
Bodnant Caravan Park
Llanystumdwy
Camping & Caravanning Club Site
Porthmadog
*Tyddyn Llwyn Caravan Park &
Camping Site*
Talsarnau
*Barcdy Touring Caravan & Camping
Park*

SCOTLAND

BORDERS
Peebles
🌼*Crossburn Caravan Park*

CENTRAL
Aberfoyle
Trossachs Holiday Park
Doune
Blair Drummond Caravan Club Site
Luib
Glendochart Caravan Park

DUMFRIES AND GALLOWAY
Balminnnoch
Three Lochs Caravan Park
Brighouse Bay
🌼*Brighouse Bay Holiday Park*
Creetown
Castle Cary Holiday Park
Crocketford
🌼*Park of Brandedleys*
Ecclefechan
Hoddom Castle Caravan Park
Glen Trool
Caldons Campsite
Kirkcudbright
🌼*Seaward Caravan Park*
Parton
Loch Ken Holiday Centre

Port Logan
New England Bay Caravan Club Site
Portpatrick
Galloway Point Holiday Park
Sandyhills
Sandyhills Bay Leisure Park

FIFE
Letham Feus
Letham Feus Caravan Park
St Andrews
🌼*Craigtoun Meadows Holiday Park*

GRAMPIAN
Aboyne
Aboyne Loch Caravan Park
Alford
Haughton House Caravan Site
Braemar
🌼*Invercauld Caravan Club Site*

HIGHLAND
Ardmair
Ardmair Point Caravan Park
Aviemore
Glenmore Forest
Balmacara
Balmacara Woodland Campsite
Reraig Caravan Site
Corpach
🌼*Linnhe Caravan Park*
Culloden Moor
Culloden Moor Caravan Club Site
Dingwall
Camping & Caravanning Club Site
Fort William
Glen Nevis Caravan & Camping Park
Invergarry
🌼*Faichem Park*
Nairn
Spindrift Caravan & Camping Park
Onich
🌼*Bunree Caravan Club Site*
Resipole
🌼*Resipole Farm*

LOTHIAN
Dunbar
Camping & Caravanning Club Site
Musselburgh
Drum Mohr

STRATHCLYDE
Arduaine
Arduaine Caravan Park
Barcaldine
Camping & Caravanning Club Site
Carradale
Carradale Bay
Craignure (Isle of Mull)
Shieling Holidays
Culzean
Camping & Caravanning Club Site
Glendaruel
Glendaruel Caravan Park
Inveruglas
Loch Lomond Holiday Park
Oban
Oban Divers Caravan Park
Tarbolton
Middlemuir Park
Tayinloan
Point Sands CaravaPark

TAYSIDE
Auchterarder
Auchterarder Caravan Park
Blair Atholl
🌼*Blair Castle Caravan Park*
River Tilt Caravan Park
Bridge of Cally
🌼*Corriefodly Holiday Park*
Carnoustie
Woodlands Caravan Park
Inchture
Inchmartine Caravan Park & Nurseries
Kirriemuir
Drumshademuir Caravan Park
Perth
🌼*Cleeve Caravan Park*

IRELAND'S BEST CAMPING AND CARAVAN PARKS

CO CLARE
Killaloe
✿*Lough Derg Caravan & Camping Park*
Kilrush
Aylevarroo Caravan Park
Lahinch
Lahinch Camping & Caravan Park
O'Brien's Bridge
Shannon Cottage Caravan & Camping Park

CO CORK
Ballylickey
✿*Eagle Point Caravan & Camping Park*
Crookhaven
✿*Barley Cove Caravan Park*
Glandore
Meadow Camping Park

CO DONEGAL
Portsalon
Knockalla Caravan Park

CO KERRY
Castlegregory
Anchor Caravan Park
Killarney
✿*Fleming'sWhite Bridge Caravan Park*
Flesk Caravan & Campsite

CO ROSCOMMON
Boyle
✿*Lough Key Forest Park*

CO. TIPPERARY
Aherlow
Ballinacourty House Camping and Caravan Park

CO WATERFORD
Clonea
Casey's Caravan Park

CO WESTMEATH
Mullingar
✿*Lough Ennell Holiday Village*

CO WEXFORD
Wexford
✿*Ferry Bank Caravan Park*

CO WICKLOW
Redcross
✿*River Valley Caravan Park*
Roundwood
✿*Roundwood Caravan Park*

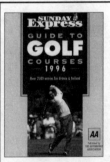

Castaway

Cast away
the pressures
of life on
mainland
Britain and
explore
an island
adventure

CAMPING AND CARAVANNING GUIDE

There can be no doubt that islands arouse expectations in most people that are triggered long before the mainland shore has been left behind. Whether the conjured images are romantic, adventurous or purely escapist depends on the individual nature of the traveller. Yet anyone seeking an island holiday will probably be attracted by a variety of qualities ranging from simple old-fashioned unworldliness through remoteness and isolation to the most godforsaken wilderness. Whatever the degree of seclusion sought, the goal is the same: detachment from normal life and its ubiquitous problems. While any holiday might be expected to offer this temporary balm to the weary soul, an island retreat tacitly promises a more loaded package than just sun, sea and whatever turns you on in the evening.

Whether your choice can take in the palm-fringed islands of the Caribbean, the heat-baked hideaways of the Aegean, or the unpredictable Scottish Isles, the effect will always be a severing of the link with the rest of the world. 'They won't be able to get at me here' may be an extreme attitude to take, but this sentiment in diluted form is behind the lure.

OFF SCOTLAND'S SHORES

How much more unreachable you are, then, if you eschew those baronial hotels and stone-built bed and breakfast cottages, and opt instead to camp or to 'rough it' it some other way. The Scottish island authorities have observed a growing taste for a cheap, basic, rural experience, and come up with an innovative way of satisfying this market. The authorities of other islands mentioned in this article are more concerned with preserving the interests of residents and other holiday makers, and impose many restrictions on those characters who enjoy self-sufficiency under canvas or in a caravan.

The Shetland Islands are the farthest-flung outpost of the British Isles, taking 14 hours to reach by boat from Aberdeen, and as far away from London as Milan. The archipelago of Shetland consists of over 100 islands and skerries (reefs of rock), though only 15 are permanently inhabited. At no point on the mainland are you more than three miles from the sea, and with its impressively rugged coastline it follows that the islands' scenery is stunning. Here is the ultimate escape from clock-watching, noise and pollution.

Campers and caravanners are welcome on Shetland, the only restrictions being on Noss and Fair Isle, and the Tresta Links in Fetlar, where camping is not allowed at all. Elsewhere there are four official campsites, but visitors are by no means restricted to these. Campers can stray into the wilds if they wish to, and the only requisite is that they seek permission from the owner of the land on which they intend to stay. The Shetlanders are a hospitable lot, and they understand this need for seclusion and peace. Caravans and motor caravans must stick to the public roads, but there are many places where they too can get away from it all, and they are urged only to check their maps carefully so that they don't find themselves in an intractable situation.

Camping 'Böds' are the ideal alternative to sleeping outdoors, and for those who don't mind spending the night cheek by jowl with strangers of the opposite sex, they are a good way of seeing Shetland on a budget. The Shetland böd was traditionally a building to house fishermen and their gear during the fishing season, and the idea has been adopted to provide low-cost, basic accommodation, with the emphasis on 'basic'. Some have no electricity, and none has hot water. You need to bring your own sleeping bag and bed roll, camping stove and cooking utensils. What you get is a toilet, table and benches, and a roof over your head.

Castaway

The Orkney Islands, closer to the mainland of Scotland, are far less rugged and wild than the Shetlands, and in fact this remarkably fertile land is extremely productive. The Vikings found it a less hostile environment to colonise, and Orcadians still provide a warm welcome for strangers from the sea. There are no restrictions on access for camping and caravanning, and plenty of beautiful spots to pitch camp. Here it is an easy matter to avoid the crowds, although Orkneys incredible bird population is never very far away. Only on the tiny island of Fair Isle between Shetland and Orkney is camping not allowed, and there is no car ferry.

The Western Isles, or Outer Hebrides, are a group of over 200 islands – only 13 of them inhabited – linked by a network of ferries and causeways. Most of the population live on Lewis, with Harris, home of the famous tweed, being another major centre. That leaves miles and miles of unpopulated space including spectacular mountains, golden beaches and rolling hills to explore. Again there are official campsites, but wild camping is allowed anywhere within reason, and with the landowner's prior permission.

Tucked in against the mainland behind North and South Uist is that most nostalgic of islands, *Skye*. With its sister isles of *Rhum* and *Eigg,* it remains as alluring and atmospheric as it must have done hundreds of years ago to Bonnie Prince Charlie when he fled across the water from his enemies. These days he could take the road bridge from Kyle of Lochalsh, which does lessen the romantic impact, but there is still a car ferry from Mallaig for those who prefer to make a more traditional crossing. No such ferry goes to Rhum and Eigg, so the only camping possible on these islands is for the backpacking tenter.

The *Isle of Bute* is a much more sheltered place than the first three

sea level. There are some excellent beaches, but many of them are a long way down, and a long climb back up again. One delightful aspect of both these small islands is that the air is truly fresh and free of petrol fumes. There are three campsites, and all are so attractively located that it would be difficult to recommend one over the other.

Alderney is the third largest Channel Island, closest to France, and small enough to get around by foot for those who relish a slow pace of life. There are plenty of opportunities to get off the beaten track, and the island is a haven for wildlife, flora and fauna. The clear seas are ideal for snorkelling, and sailboarding and surfing are popular in the bays. Visitors have a good choice of beaches, and the clean white sand is perfect for making sandcastles. Like the other islands, caravans are not permitted, and camping is only allowed on the one official camp site. Campers must have a confirmed booking before they arrive.

CAMPING AND CARAVANNING GUIDE

ISLE OF MAN

Trailer caravans are only allowed on the Isle of Man if they are to be used in connection with trade shows and exhibitions, or for demonstration purposes. They must not be used for living accommodation. Written application for permission should be made to the Secretary, Planning Committee, Isle of Man Local Government Board, The Government Offices, Murray House, Mount Havelock. The shipping line will not accept a caravan without this written permission. Motor caravans may enter without prior permission.

ISLES OF SCILLY

Caravans and motor caravans are not allowed on the Scilly Isles, and campers may only stay at officially licensed sites. Booking is advisable on all sites, especially during school holidays. For details about licensed sites on St Mary's write to: Mrs J Burrows, Garrison Farm, St Mary's. For details about sites on Bryher write to: Mrs J Stedeford, Jenford Bryer. For St Agnes write to: Mrs S J Hicks, Troy Town, St Agnes. For St Martin's write to: Mr C A Savill, Middletown, St Martin's. Note: strict control is kept on the landing of animals on these islands.

So, if your urge to escape to a less hectic way of life encompasses an exotic but essentially British experience, choose one or more of the above mentioned islands, and you will not regret it.

DENISE LAING

EDITOR

All that's spoilt at our caravan and campsites is your choice of things to do.

rock climbing

hillwalking

birdwatching

mountain biking

horseriding

historical sites

canoeing

fishing

swimming

wind surfing

Not only that, we offer you a huge choice of places to go. Forest Enterprise has 29 touring sites in all corners of the country — from Glenmore in the Highlands to The New Forest, Beddgelert in Snowdonia to Thorpe Woodlands in the Fens. Each site is as picturesque as the next, and is sure to offer something different for everyone. To help you decide which of our sites you would like to visit, just fill in the coupon or phone 0131-334-0066 (24 hr. answering machine) or 0131-334-0303, and we'll send you our free brochure.

Forest Enterprise is part of the Forestry Commission

- -

To: Forest Holidays, (AA), Forest Enterprise, Freepost, Edinburgh EH12 7AT (no stamp required).

Name _____

Address _____

_____ Postcode _____

Directory

ENGLAND

FORESTRY COMMISSION CARAVAN AND CAMPSITES

Forestry Commission sites which come within the scope of the Automobile Association's Caravan and Campsite classification scheme are listed in this guide. In addition there are entries for minimum-facility sites suitable for the camper or caravanner who prefers to be self-sufficient and carries his own chemical toilet.

ISLE OF

Places incorporating the words 'Isle of' or 'Isle' will be found under the actual name, eg Isle of Wight is listed under Wight, Isle of.

AVON

For the map of this county, see Somerset

BATH

Newbridge Caravan Park (ST719655)
Brassmill Ln, Newbridge BA1 3JT
☎ 01225 428778 & 424301
Signposted
▶ ▶ ▶ ▶ ⊕ £9.50-£13.50 ⊕ £9.50-£13.50
Open all year Booking advisable bank hols & Jun-Sep
Last departure noon
A very pleasant site on the edge of Bath in park-like grounds among maturing trees and shrubs. From city head for suburb of Newbridge, and site is signed. A 3-acre site with 88 touring pitches.

🎮 🐾 ⊙ 🖥 🍴 ✳ ♀ ⚠ 🛢 ⊘ 🚼 T ✗ 📞 🛒 🚿 🐕
🏖 ♿

➔ ∪ ▶ ⊙ ⤱ 🎥 🎵

🛗

Credit Cards ◼ 💳 💳 💳

Newton Mill Caravan and Camping Park (ST715649)
Newton St Loe BA2 9JF ☎ 01225 333909 (3m NW off A4)
Signposted
▶ ▶ ▶ ▶ ♦ ⊕ ⊕ Å
Open all year Booking advisable public hols & Jul-Aug
Last arrival 21.00hrs Last departure noon

Tranquil terraced site with excellent facilities by trout stream and partially bordered by woodland. Situated within easy reach of main routes. Follow Bath-Bristol rd, turn L at rndbt in Bath and site 1m on L. A 23-acre site with 180 touring pitches.
Satellite T.V hook ups.

🎮 🐾 ⊙ 🖥 🍴 ◀ ⊏ ✳ ♀ ⚠ 🛢 ⊘ 🚼 T ✗ 📞 🛒
🐕 🏖 ♿

➔ ∪ ▶ ⤱ 🎥 🎵

Credit Cards ◼ 💳 💳

BRISTOL

Baltic Wharf Caravan Club Site (ST573722)
Cumberland Rd BS1 6XG ☎ 0117 926 8030
▶ ▶ ▶ ★ ⊕ fr £11 ⊕ fr £11 Å fr £11
Open all year Booking advisable bank hols & Jul-Aug
Last arrival 20.00hrs Last departure noon
A waterside site, right in the heart of the redeveloped dockland. Linked in the summer to the city centre by a river ferry. Because of steep camber outside site, care is needed when towing in or out. Follow signs for SS Great Britain, and site about 500yds over dock bridge. A 2.5-acre site with 58 touring pitches.

🎮 🐾 ⊙ 🖥 🍴 ✳ 🛢 🚼 📞 🏖

➔ ∪ ▶ ⚠ ⤱ 🎥 🎵

Credit Cards ◼ 💳 💳

REDHILL

Brook Lodge Caravan Park (ST485620)
BS18 7RD ☎ 01934 862311 Signposted
► ► 🖵 🚐 🛦
Open Mar-Nov Booking advisable 22 May-4 Sep & bank hols Last arrival 10.00hrs Last departure 11.00hrs
A pleasant, well-screened touring site, hidden from the A38 by hedging and trees. A 3-acre site with 29 touring pitches and 1 static.

🕹 🐾 ⊙ ? ✳ 🅰 ⊞ 🆃 📞 🐾
➜ ∪ ♪ 🔲

SEVERN BEACH

Salthouse Farm Caravan & Camping Park (ST543854)
BS12 3NH ☎ 01454 632274 & 632699 Signposted
Nearby town: Bristol
► ► ► ★ 🚐 £6.70-£8.30 🚐 £6.70-£8.30 🛦 £6.70-£8.30
Open Apr-Oct Booking advisable public hols Last arrival 22.00hrs Last departure 14.00hrs ✿
Level, grassy site in meadowland adjacent to Severn Estuary and beach, off A403. Well-protected from winds. A 3-acre site with 40 touring pitches and 50 statics.

🕹 🐾 ⊙ 🔍 ✳ 🅰 🔋 🖊 ⊞ 🆃 📞 🐾
➜ ∪ ► ♪
💷

SIDCOT

Netherdale Caravan & Camping Site (ST426567)
Bridgwater Rd BS25 1NH ☎ 01934 843481 & 843007 Signposted
Nearby town: Cheddar
► ★ 🚐 £5-£7 🚐 £5-£7 🛦 £5-£7
Open Mar-Oct Booking advisable public hols Last arrival 22.00hrs Last departure noon
A pleasant site with a sloping southerly aspect and lower level pitches. An ideal touring centre, close to the A38 but well screened. A 1.5-acre site with 30 touring pitches and 37 statics.

🕹 🐾 ⊙ ✳ 🅰 🔋 🖊
➜ ∪ ♪ 🐾

WESTON-SUPER-MARE

Country View Caravan Park (ST335647)
Sand Rd Sand Bay BS22 9UJ ☎ 01934 627595 Signposted
► ► ► ★ 🚐 £6.50-£12 🚐 £6.50-£12 🛦 £4-£12
Open Mar-Oct Booking advisable bank hols & peak periods Last arrival 21.00hrs Last departure noon
A pleasant, flat, open site in a country area not far from the coast. A 4-acre site with 120 touring pitches and 65 statics.
Dishwashing facilities.
See advertisement under Somerset

🕹 🐾 ⊙ 🔲 🖫 ? 🔍 ✳ 🖟 🅰 🔋 🖊 ⊞ 📞 🚿 🐾 ♿
➜ ∪ ► ⚴ 🍴 ♪
Credit Cards 🃏 💳

West End Farm Caravan & Camping Park (ST354600)
Locking BS24 8RH ☎ 01934 822529 (3m E off A371) Signposted
► ► ► 🖵 🚐 🛦
Open all year Booking advisable peak periods Last arrival 22.00hrs Last departure noon
A flat, hedge-bordered site by helicopter museum with good clean facilities and landscaping. Good access to Weston-super-Mare and the Mendips. A 2.5-acre site with 75 touring pitches and 20 statics.

🕹 🐾 ⊙ 🔲 🖫 🔍 ✳ 🅰 🔋 🖊 ⊞ 🆃 📞 🐕 🐾 ♿
➜ ∪ ► ⊙ 🔺 🌾 📽 ♪

Weston Gateway Caravan Site (ST370621)
West Wick BS24 7TF ☎ 01934 510344 Signposted
► ► ► ★ 🚐 £4.50-£7.50 🚐 £4.50-£7.50 🛦 £4.50-£7.50
Open all year (rs Nov-Mar chem wc disposal only, shop & club closed) Booking advisable Jul-Aug Last arrival mdnt Last departure 14.00hrs
A pleasant site set among trees and shrubs close to the A370 and junc 21 of M5. Plenty of entertainment but basic toilet block. A 15-acre site with 175 touring pitches.

🕹 🐾 ⊙ 🔲 🔍 🔲 ✳ 🍷 🅰 🔋 🖊 ⊞ 🆃 📞 🐕 🐾
➜ ∪ ► ⚴ ♪

BERKSHIRE

FINCHAMPSTEAD

California Chalet & Touring Park (SU785650)
Nine Mile Ride RG11 3NY ☎ 01734 733928 Signposted
Nearby town: Wokingham
► ► ► ♠ ★ 🚐 £8.50-£10 🚐 £8.50-£10 🛦 £5-£8.50
Open Mar-Oct Booking advisable bank & school hols & Ascot wk Last arrival 22.00hrs Last departure noon
A secluded site in a delightful country park, with well-spaced pitches giving a good degree of privacy. From A321 to Sandhurst turn right on B3016, and after .75m turn right onto Nine Mile Ride. Signposted. A 6-acre site with 35 touring pitches.
Fishing on site.

🕹 🐾 ⊙ 🔲 🖫 ✳ 🅰 ⊞ 🏠 🐕 🐾 ♿
➜ ∪ ► ⚴ ♪

NEWBURY

Oakley Farm Caravan & Camping Park (SU458628)
Washwater RG20 0LP ☎ 01635 36581
► ► 🖵 🚐 🛦
Open Mar-Oct
An open farmland site, well maintained and clean, S of Newbury. From rndbt S of Newbury on A34, take A343 Andover rd. About 300yds past Hants/Berks boundary bridge, turn left at car sales garage into Penwood Rd. Site on L. A 3-acre site with 30 touring pitches.

🕹 🐾 ⊙ 📞 🐾

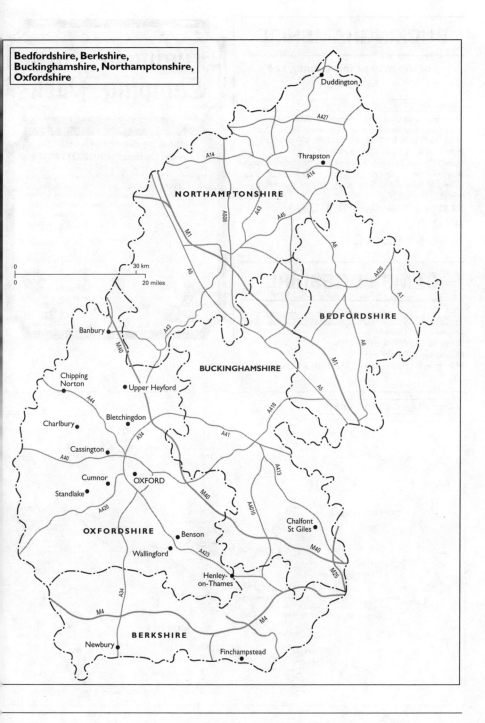

Bedfordshire, Berkshire, Buckinghamshire, Northamptonshire, Oxfordshire

Duddington

A427

A14

Thrapston

A14

NORTHAMPTONSHIRE

A508

A43

A45

A6

M1

A5

A428

A1

0   30 km
0   20 miles

BEDFORDSHIRE

Banbury

A43

M40

BUCKINGHAMSHIRE

A6

Chipping Norton

Upper Heyford

M1

A44

A5

Charlbury

Bletchingdon

A418

Cassington

A34

A41

A40

Cumnor

OXFORD

A413

Standlake

M40

A4010

A420

Chalfont St Giles

OXFORDSHIRE

Benson

M40

Wallingford

A423

M25

Henley-on-Thames

A34

M4

M4

BERKSHIRE

Newbury

Finchampstead

BUCKINGHAMSHIRE

For the map of this county, see Berkshire

CHALFONT ST GILES

Highclere Farm Country Touring Park (SU977927)
Highclere Farm, Newbarn Ln, Seer Green HP9 2QZ
☎ 01494 874505 & 875665 (1.25m SW) Signposted
► ► ► ★ ⊞ £7-£8 ⊞ £7-£8 ▲ £6-£8
Open Mar-Jan Booking advisable Last departure noon
A small, level touring park situated between Chalfont St Giles and Seer Green. Toilets immaculate. A 2.5-acre site with 60 touring pitches.

🔡 📞 📶 🔲 🍽 ✳ ⚟ 🛢 ⊘ 🖭 🅣 📞 🛒 ♿
➜ ∪ ⛟ 📽 🎵

Credit Cards 🪪 💳 💳 🅖

CAMBRIDGESHIRE

BURWELL

Stanford Park (TL578675)
Weirs Rd CB5 0BP ☎ 01638 741547
Nearby town: Cambridge
► ► ► ★ ⊞ £7.50-£8.50 ⊞ £7.50-£8.50 ▲ £7.50-£8.50

Highfield Farm Camping Park

Comberton, Cambridge CB3 7DG
Tel/Fax: Cambridge (01223) 262308

An excellent Award Winning Park close to the historic University City of Cambridge for touring Caravans, Motorcaravans and Tents, featuring modern shower and toilet blocks, laundry room with automatic washing machines, tumble dryers and iron, small shop, Calor Gas/Camping Gaz sales, 90 electrical hook-ups, hard standings, public telephone, battery charging and ice pack freezing facilities.

Leave M11 exit 12, take A603 (Sandy) for half mile, turn right on B1046 to Comberton.
From A428 turn south at Hardwick roundabout and follow International Caravan & Camping signs to Comberton.

Proprietors: Mr & Mrs B. H. Chapman
Write or phone for colour brochure

AA ◑ **AA Campsite of the Year 1991-92 (Midlands Area Winners)**

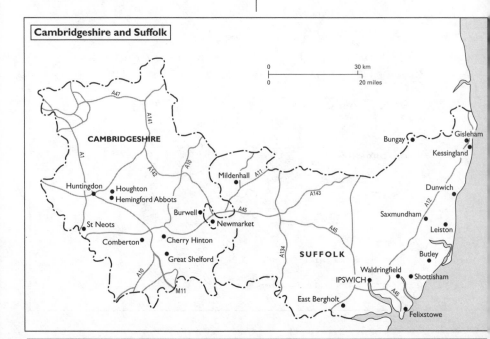

Cambridgeshire and Suffolk

0   30 km
0   20 miles

CAMBRIDGESHIRE

A47
A141
A1
A142
A10
A11
Mildenhall
A143
A45
A45
A134
A12

Huntingdon
Houghton
Hemingford Abbots
St Neots
Burwell
Newmarket
Comberton
Cherry Hinton
Great Shelford
M11

SUFFOLK

Bungay
Gisleham
Kessingland
Dunwich
Saxmundham
Leiston
Butley
Waldringfield
Shottisham
IPSWICH
East Bergholt
Felixstowe

STANFORD PARK
Cambridge

▶▶▶ AA

Weirs Road, Burwell, Cambs
Telephone:
(01638) 741547 & (0374) 152741
Fax: (01638) 743508

Conveniently situated at Burwell for visiting Cambridge, Newmarket and Ely. Several places of interest within easy reach, Wicken Fen National Trust, Newmarket Races, Ely Cathedral and Cambridge University. Camp site includes: modern toilet block with hot showers, hair & iron point, laundry room, electric hook-ups, fishing close by, disabled facilities and open all year.

Open all year Booking advisable bank hols Last arrival 20.30hrs
A secluded site on outskirts of Burwell with modern amenities including purpose-built disabled facilities. Signed from B1102. A 14-acre site with 100 touring pitches and 3 statics.

CAMBRIDGE

See **Burwell & Comberton**

CHERRY HINTON

Cherry Hinton Caravan Club Site
(TL483558)
Lime Kiln Rd CB1 4NQ
☎ 01223 244088
▶▶▶ ♠ ♦♦ 🚐 🚗 Å
Open Mar-Nov Booking advisable bank hols & Jun-Aug Last arrival 20.00hrs Last departure noon
A delightful site with small groups of pitches separated by trees and shrubs and linked by a winding road. Imaginatively landscaped with good views. Winner of the 1995 Campsite of the Year Award for the East of England. From junc 11 of M11 take A1309 signed

Cambridge. In 1.5m after 4 traffic lights turn R into A1134 Long Rd. In 1.5m at rndbt continue into Queen Edith's Way, turn R in 1m into Lime Kiln Rd & site 200yds on R. A 5.5-acre site with 90 touring pitches. Veg prep area.

Credit Cards 🔲 💳

COMBERTON

Highfield Farm Camping Park
(TL389572)
Long Rd CB3 7DG ☎ 01223 262308
Signposted
Nearby town: Cambridge
▶▶▶▶ ♠ ♦♦ 🚐 £6.75-£8.25 🚗 £6.50-£8 Å £6.50-£8
Open Apr-Oct Booking advisable bank hols wknds Last arrival 22.00hrs Last departure 14.00hrs
A first class site with good quality facilities, set in farmland and screened by conifers and hedges. 3m W of Cambridge between A45 and A603. From junc 12 of M11 take A603 Sandy road for .5m, then B1046 to Comberton. An 8-acre site with 120 touring pitches. Dishwashing facility, postbox & hardstanding.
See advertisement under CAMBRIDGE

£

GREAT SHELFORD

Camping & Caravanning Club Site (TL455539)
19 Cabbage Moor CB2 5JU
☎ 01223 841185 (in season) & 01203 694995
Signposted
Nearby town: Cambridge
▶▶▶ ♦♦ ★ 🚐 £9.30-£10 🚗 £9.30-£10 Å £9.30-£10
Open end Mar-early Nov Booking advisable bank hols & Jul-Aug Last arrival 21.00hrs Last departure noon
An attractive site with good landscaping and excellent toilet blocks. From junc 11 of M11 take A1309, then R at traffic lights on to A1301; site .5m on L. Please see the advertisement on page 27 for details of Club Members' benefits. A 12-acre site with 120 touring pitches.

Credit Cards 🔲 💳 💳

HEMINGFORD ABBOTS

Quiet Waters Caravan Park (TL283712)
PE18 9AJ ☎ 01480 463405 Signposted
Nearby town: St Ives
▶▶▶ ★ 🚐 £7.50-£8.50 🚗 £7.50-£8.50 Å £7.50-£8.50
Open Apr-Oct Booking advisable high season Last arrival 20.00hrs Last departure noon

This attractive little riverside site is found in a most charming village just 1m from the A604 making an ideal centre to tour the Cambridgeshire area. A 1-acre site with 20 touring pitches and 40 statics.
Fishing & boating.

🖥 🐾 ☉ 🔧 ✳ 🛈 🌿 📞 🎱
➜ ∪ ▶ 🛬 🎱 🎵 ▣

HOUGHTON

Houghton Mill Caravan & Camping Park (TL284721)
Mill St PE17 2BJ ☎ 01480 462413 & 492811
Signposted
Nearby town: St Ives
▶ ▶ ♣ ★ 🚐 £8.50-£9 🚐 £8.50-£9 🅰 £8.50-£9
Open Etr-Sep Booking advisable at all times Last arrival 20.00hrs Last departure noon
A most attractive meadow location alongside the River Great Ouse and adjacent to the National Trust's Houghton Mill. From Huntingdon on A604 take A1123 into Houghton village and site is at end. A 5-acre site with 65 touring pitches.
Boating & fishing.

🖥 🐾 ☉ ✳ 🛈 🌿 ⊞ 📞 ♿
➜ ▶ 🛬 🎱 🎵 🎱

HUNTINGDON

Park Lane Touring Park (TL245709)
Godmanchester PE18 8AF ☎ 01480 453740
Signposted
▶ ▶ ▶ 🚐 £7.50 🚐 £7.50 🅰 £7.50
Open Mar-Oct Booking advisable bank hols Last arrival 22.00hrs
Small, level site with modern toilet facilities. Situated just off the B1043 between Godmanchester and Huntingdon; turn into Park Lane by the Black Bull Inn. A 3-acre site with 50 touring pitches.
Enclosed dishwashing & preparation area.

🖥 🐾 ☉ 🔧 ✳ 🏔 🌿 ⊞ 🆃 📞 🎱 ♿
➜ ▶ 🛬 🎱 🎵
£

ST NEOTS

Camping & Caravanning Club Site (TL178594)
Rush Meadow PE19 2UD
☎ 01480 474404 (in season) & 01203 694995
Signposted
▶ ▶ ▶ ★ 🚐 £9.30-£10 🚐 £9.30-£10 🅰 £9.30-£10
Open end Mar-early Nov Booking advisable bank hols & peak periods Last arrival 21.00hrs Last departure noon
A level meadowland site adjacent to the River Ouse on the outskirts of St Neots. A well-maintained club site with helpful and attentive staff. Signed from B1043 in town. Please see the advertisement on page 27 for details of Club Members' benefits. A 10-acre site with 180 touring pitches.
Coarse fishing.

🖥 🐾 ☉ 🔧 ✳ 🛈 🌿 ⊞ 🆃 📞 🎱 ♿
➜ ▶ 🛬 🎵

Credit Cards 🔲 🔲

CHESHIRE

For the map of this county, see Shropshire

CHESTER

Chester Southerly Caravan Park (SJ385624)
Balderton Ln, Marlston-Cum-Lache CH3 6QW
☎ 01829 270791 & 270697 Signposted
▶ ▶ ▶ ★ 🚐 £6-£7.80 🚐 £6-£7.80 🅰 £6-£7.80
Open Mar-Nov (rs Dec-Feb open for caravan rallies only)
Booking advisable for periods of 1 wk or more & bank hols Last arrival 23.00hrs Last departure noon
A well-tended site in rural area, on S side of city close to the bypass, and just off the A55/A483 roundabout. A 6-acre site with 90 touring pitches.
Duck pond & breeding cage.

🖥 🐾 ☉ 🔧 🔧 ✳ 🏔 🛈 🌿 📞 🎱 ♿
➜ ∪ ▶ 🛬 🎱 🎵

MACCLESFIELD

Capesthorne Hall (SJ840727)
Siddington SK11 9JY ☎ 01625 861779
Signposted
▶ ▶ ★ 🚐 £4.50-£6.50 🚐 £4.50-£6.50 🅰 £3.50-£5.50
Open Mar-Oct Booking advisable public hols Last arrival dusk Last departure noon no cars by tents
Set in grounds and gardens of Capesthorne Hall in the heart of the Cheshire countryside. The pitches are on level ground close to the Hall, off the A34. Immaculate toilets in old stable block. A 5.5-acre site with 100 touring pitches.
Capesthorne Hall, gardens, fishing. Laundry room.

🖥 🐾 ☉ ✳ 📞 🐕
➜ 🎵 🎱

RIXTON

Holly Bank Caravan Park (SJ693904)
Warburton Bridge Rd WA3 6HU ☎ 0161 775 2842
Signposted
Nearby town: Warrington
▶ ▶ ▶ 🚐 🚐 🅰
Open all year Booking advisable bank hols & wknds Apr-Oct Last arrival 21.00hrs Last departure noon
Attractive site with spotlessly clean facilities. Just off A57 close to the Manchester Ship Canal and convenient to M6 and Manchester. A 9-acre site with 70 touring pitches.
Lending library.

🖥 🐾 ☉ 🔧 ✳ 🏔 🛈 🌿 ⊞ 🆃 📞 🐕 🎱
➜ ∪ ▶ 💧 🎱 🎵

CLEVELAND

For the map of this county, see Northumberland

GUISBOROUGH

Tockett's Mill Caravan Park (NZ626182)
Skelton Rd TS14 6QA
☎ 01287 610182 Signposted
▶▶▶ ♠♠♠ ⊞ £8-£10 ⊞ £8-£10 Å £8-£10
Open Mar-Oct Booking advisable bank hols & high
season Last arrival 21.00hrs Last departure noon
*Situated in a private wooded valley alongside a stream,
the site is centred around a preserved watermill. A 7-
acre site with 30 touring pitches and 75 statics.*

🎮👤📶⊙📖☀️🍷🏍🔋📵♿⚒️❤️

➔∪🏧

CORNWALL & ISLES OF SCILLY

ASHTON

Boscrege Caravan Park (SW595305)
TR13 9TG ☎ 01736 762231
▶▶▶ ♠♠♠ ⊞⊞Å
Open Apr-Oct Booking advisable Jul-Aug Last arrival
22.00hrs Last departure 11.00hrs
*A much improved site in an isolated rural area with very
good screening. From Helston take A394 signed
Penzance, turn right in Ashton on unclass rd, and follow
signs to Boscreage. A 4-acre site with 50 touring pitches
and 26 statics.*
Recreation field.

🎮👤📶⊙📖☀️🔋📵♿⚒️📵🛠️❤️🐕🏧

➔∪🏧🔱⚓🎣

BLACKWATER

Chiverton Caravan & Touring Park (SW743468)
East Hill TR4 8HS ☎ 01872 560667 (jct A30/A390)
Signposted
Nearby town: Truro
▶▶▶ ⊞ £4-£6 ⊞ £4-£6 Å £4-£6
Open Good Fri/Apr-Oct (rs Apr-May & mid Sep-Oct
limited stock kept in shop) Booking advisable mid Jul-
Aug Last arrival 22.00hrs Last departure noon

*A small, well maintained, level, grassy site recently laid
out and run by enthusiastic owners. A 2-acre site with
30 touring pitches and 24 statics.*
Covered sink area, drying lines.

🎮👤📶⊙📖☀️🏍🔋📵⚒️❤️🏧

➔∪🏧🔱⚓🎣

💷

Trevarth Holiday Park (SW744468)
TR4 8HR ☎ 01872 560266 Signposted
▶▶▶ ⊞⊞Å
Open Etr or Apr-Oct Booking advisable Jul-Aug Last
arrival 20.00hrs Last departure noon
*A compact, well screened site on high ground adjacent
to A30/A39 junction. A 2-acre site with 30 touring
pitches and 21 statics.*

🎮👤📶⊙📖☀️🍷☀️🏍🔋📵⚒️🅃❤️

➔∪🎣🏧

BODINNICK

Yeate Farm Camp & Caravan Site (SX134526)
PL23 1LZ ☎ 01726 870256 Signposted
Nearby town: Fowey
▶▶ ★ ⊞ £4.50-£6.50 ⊞ £4.50-£6.50 Å £4.50-£6.50
Open Apr-Oct Booking advisable mid Jul-mid Aug Last
arrival 21.30hrs Last departure 11.00hrs
*A small, level grass site adjacent to a working farm
overlooking the R Fowey. From A390 at East Taphouse
take B3359 signed Looe and Lanreath. Follow signs for
Bodinnick on unclass rd. A 1-acre site with 33 touring
pitches and 2 statics.*
Private slipway/quay, storage of small boats.

🎮👤📶⊙📖☀️🔋📵⚒️🐕🏹

➔⚓🎣🏧

💷

BODMIN

Camping & Caravanning Club Site (SX081676)
Old Callywith Rd PL31 2DZ
☎ 01208 73834 (in season) & 01203 694995 Signposted
▶▶ ★ ⊞ £8.40-£9 ⊞ £8.40-£9 Å £8.40-£9
Open end Mar-early Oct Booking advisable bank hols &
Jul-Aug Last arrival 21.00hrs Last departure noon
*Undulating grassy site with trees and bushes set in
meadowland within urban area, close to main road and
river. Please see the advertisement on page 27 for
details of Club Members' benefits. An 11-acre site with
175 touring pitches.*

🎮👤📶⊙🏍🔋📵⚒️❤️🏧

➔∪

Credit Cards 🟦 💳 💳

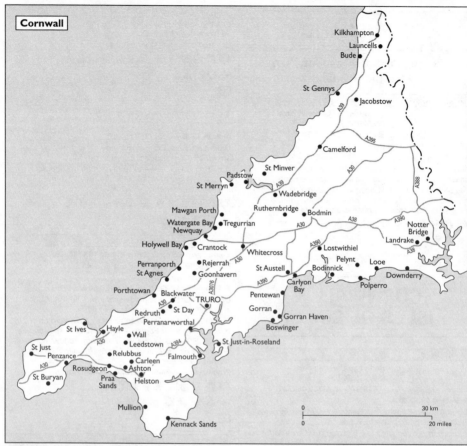

Cornwall

Kilkhampton
Launcells
Bude
St Gennys
Jacobstow
Camelford
St Minver
Padstow
St Merryn
Wadebridge
Mawgan Porth
Ruthernbridge
Bodmin
Notter Bridge
Watergate Bay
Tregurrian
Newquay
Landrake
Holywell Bay
Crantock
Whitecross
Lostwithiel
Pelynt
Looe
Perranporth
Rejerrah
St Austell
Bodinnick
St Agnes
Goonhaven
Downderry
Porthtowan
Blackwater
Carlyon Bay
Polperro
TRURO
Pentewan
Redruth
St Day
Gorran
St Ives
Hayle
Perranarworthal
Boswinger
Gorran Haven
Wall
Leedstown
St Just-in-Roseland
St Just
Penzance
Relubbus
Falmouth
Carleen
St Buryan
Rosudgeon
Ashton
Helston
Praa Sands
Mullion
Kennack Sands

0   30 km
0   20 miles

BOSWINGER

Sea View International Caravan & Camping Park (SW990412)

PL26 6LL ☎ 01726 843425 Signposted
Nearby town: St Austell

▶ ▶ ▶ ▶ ♣ ♦♦ ⊕ ★ ⊕ £5-£13.90 ⊕ £5-£13.90
Å £5-£13.90

Open Mon before Good Fri-Sep Booking advisable Jul-Aug Last arrival 22.00hrs Last departure 11.00hrs

This level, grassy site has been colourfully landscaped with flowers and shrubs and overlooks Veryan Bay. Many times a winner of AA awards in previous years for its beautiful environment and its dedication to high standards of maintenance, we are delighted to announce it as the 1996 National Winner of the Campsite of the Year Award. For full details of award winners, see the colour section at the front of the book. 3.5m SW of Mevagissey harbour and .5m from beach and sea. A 7-acre site with 165 touring pitches and 41 statics.

Crazy golf, volleyball, badminton courts, putting.

See advertisement on page 61

🕹 🚐 🛎 ⊙ 🖥 🐟 ⚓ ✂ 🔍 ⚡ ✳ ⚙ 🔋 🌿 🔲 ☎ 📞 🧺
🏕 🐕 🐖 ♿
→ ∪ ⚑ ⚡ 🎣
£

Credit Cards 🔲 🔲

◎◎◎◎◎◎◎◎◎◎◎

BUDE

Budemeadows Touring Holiday Park (SS215012)

EX23 0NA ☎ 01288 361646
(3m S of Bude on A39) Signposted

▶ ▶ ▶ ▶ ♣ ♦♦ ★ ⊕ £7-£10 ⊕ £7-£10 Å £7-£10

Open all year (rs Oct-Spring bank hol shop closed (ex papers/milk) pool closed) Booking advisable Jul-Aug Last arrival 21.00hrs Last departure 11.00hrs

A very well kept site of distinction, with good quality facilities. A 9-acre site with 100 touring pitches and 1 static.

Outdoor table tennis & giant chess.

🔌 ➡️ ⚡ 🔥 ⊙ 🗄 ❎ ⟋ 🔍 🚻 □ ✳️ ⚠️ 🗑 ⌀ 🎣 ⊞ T 📞
🛗 ⛲ 🌲 🐎 🐕 ⛽ ♿
➜ ∪ ▶ ⊙ ⬙ ⤴ 🍴 ⚓ ✈
£

⊙⊙⊙⊙⊙⊙⊙⊙

Wooda Farm Camping & Caravanning Park (SS229080)
Poughill EX23 9HJ ☎ 01288 352069 (2m E) Signposted
▶ ▶ ▶ ▶ 🚐 £4.50-£8.50 🚗 £4.50-£8.50 ▲ £4.50-£8.50
Open Apr-Oct (rs Apr-end May & mid Sep-end Oct shop
hrs, laundrette/restaurant limited) Booking advisable
Jul-Aug Last arrival 20.00hrs Last departure noon
There are sea views from this site set on raised grounds
overlooking Bude Bay. From the A39 at the edge of
Stratton follow the unclassified Coombe Valley road. A
12-acre site with 160 touring pitches and 52 statics.
Coarse fishing, clay pigeon shoots, pets corner.

🔌 🔥 ⊙ 🗄 ❎ ✳️ ⚠️ 🗑 ⌀ 🎣 ⊞ T ✂ 📞 🛒 🛗 🌲
🐎 ⛽ ♿
➜ ∪ ▶ ⊙ ⬙ ⤴ 🍴 ⚓ ✈
£

Credit Cards 🔺 ⬛ ⬛

Juliot's Well Holiday Park (SX095829)
PL32 9RF ☎ 01840 213302 Signposted
Nearby town: Tintagel
▶ ▶ ▶ ▶ ♠ ★ 🚐 £5-£9.50 🚗 £5-£9.50 ▲ £5-£9.50
Open Mar-Oct (rs Mar-Apr & Oct swimming pool closed)
Booking advisable bank hols & Jul-Aug Last arrival
21.30hrs Last departure 11.00hrs
A quiet site in the grounds of an old manor house. From
A39 in Camelford turn right onto B3266, at T junc turn
left and go straight across crossroads. Site 300yds on
left. A 6-acre site with 60 touring pitches and 48 statics.
Skittle alley & boules.

🔌 🔥 ⊙ 🗄 ❎ ⟋ 🔍 ⚡ ✳️ ⚠️ 🗑 ⌀ 🎣 ⊞ T ✂ 📞
🛗 🐎 ⛽
➜ ∪ ▶ ✈
£

Lakefield Caravan Park (SX095853)
Lower Pendavey Farm PL32 9TX ☎ 01840 213279
Signposted
▶ ▶ ▶ 🚐 🚗 ▲
Open Etr or Apr-Oct Booking advisable Jul-Aug Last
arrival 22.00hrs Last departure noon
An isolated working farm site, newly landscaped and
with very good quality services. From A39 in Camelford ➡

turn right onto B3266, turn right at T junc, and site on left in 1.5m. A 5-acre site with 30 touring pitches. Own lake, farm animal corner on working farm.

🔌 🐾 ☉ ❄ ✳ 🅰 🛢 🍃 ⬆ 🆃 🦮 ➡ ⛲

→ ∪ ▶ 🔺

CARLEEN

Lower Polladras Camping (SW617308)
TR13 9NX ☎ 01736 762220 Signposted
Nearby town: Helston
▶ ▶ ▶ ★ 🏠 fr £6.50 🏠 fr £6.50 🅰 fr £6.50
Open Etr-Oct Booking advisable Jul-Aug Last arrival 22.00hrs Last departure noon
A farm site with good facilities. From A394 turn onto B3302 Hayle road at Hilltop Garage, then take 2nd turning on L to Carleen for site, about 2m on R. A 4-acre site with 60 touring pitches.

🔌 🐾 ☉ 🗄 ❄ ✳ 🅰 🛢 🍃 ⬆ 🆃 ⛲

→ ∪ ✂ 🎵

💷

Poldown Caravan Park (SW629298)
Poldown TR13 9NN ☎ 01326 574560 Signposted
Nearby town: Helston
▶ ▶ 🏠 £3.50-£8 🏠 £3.50-£8 🅰 £3.50-£8
Open Apr-Oct Booking advisable Jul-Aug Last arrival 22.00hrs Last departure noon
A small, quiet site set in attractive countryside. From A394 turn off onto the B3302 Hayle road at Hilltop Garage, then take second left to Carleen for site which is .75m on right. A 2-acre site with 10 touring pitches and 5 statics.

🔌 🐾 ☉ 🗄 ❄ ✳ 🅰 🛢 🍃 ⬆ 🆃 ⛲

→ ∪ ▶ ✂ 🎵

CARLYON BAY

Carlyon Bay Caravan & Camping Park (SX052526)
Bethesda, Cypress Av PL25 3RE ☎ 01726 812735 Signposted
Nearby town: St Austell
▶ ▶ ▶ ♣ ✦ 🏠 £6-£12 🏠 £5-£11 🅰 £6-£12
Open Etr-3 Oct (rs Etr-mid May & mid Sep-3 Oct swimming pool/take-away/shop closed) Booking advisable mid Jul-mid Aug Last arrival anytime Last departure 11.00hrs
An attractive, secluded site set amongst a belt of trees with background woodland. Off A390 W of St Blazey, turn left on A3092 for Par, and right again in .5m. On private rd to Carlyon Bay. A 16-acre site with 180 touring pitches.

🔌 🐾 ☉ 🗄 ❄ ⚡ 🔍 🖥 ✳ 🅰 🛢 🍃 ⬆ 🆃 🛒 🎠 ⛲ 🐕 ⛲

→ ∪ ▶ ◎ 🔺 ✂ ⚽ 🎵

💷

Credit Cards 🔳 🔳

Trevella Tourist Park (SW801599)
TR8 5EW ☎ 01637 830308
Signposted
Nearby town: Newquay
▶ ▶ ▶ ▶ ♣ ♦ ✦ Holiday Centre ★ 🏠 £5.95-£9.80
🏠 £5.40-£9 🅰 £5.95-£9.80
Open Etr-Oct (rs Nov-Etr) Booking advisable bank hols & Jul-Aug
A well established and very well run family site, with outstanding floral displays. Set in rural area close to Newquay between Crantock and A3075. A 15-acre site with 295 touring pitches and 50 statics.
Crazy golf, fishing & badminton.
See advertisement under NEWQUAY

🔌 🐾 ☉ 🗄 ❄ ⚡ 🔍 🖥 ✳ 🅰 🛢 🍃 ⬆ 🆃 ✖ 🍴 🐾 ➡ 🏸 ⛲

→ ∪ ▶ ◎ 🔺 ✂ ⚽ 🎵

💷

Credit Cards 🔳 🔳 🔳 🔳 🆂

QQQQQQQQQQ

Crantock Plains Touring Park (SW805589)
Crantock Plains Farm TR8 5PH
☎ 01637 830955 & 831273
Nearby town: Newquay
▶ ▶ ★ 🏠 fr £5.50 🏠 fr £5.50 🅰 fr £5.50
Open Etr-Sep Booking advisable Jul-Aug Last arrival 22.00hrs Last departure noon
A small rural site with level grassy touring pitches. From A3075 take 3rd turning right signed Crantock. Site on left along narrow lane. A 3-acre site with 40 touring pitches.

🔌 🐾 ☉ 🗄 ❄ ⚡ ✳ 🅰 🛢 🍃 ⬆ 🆃 🦮 ⛲

→ ∪ ▶ 🔺 ⚽ 🎵

Treago Farm Caravan Site (SW782601)
TR8 5QS ☎ 01637 830277 Signposted
Nearby town: Newquay
▶ ▶ ▶ 🏠 🏠 🅰
Open mid May-mid Sep (rs Apr-mid May & Oct no shop or bar) Booking advisable Jun-Aug Last arrival 22.00hrs Last departure 18.00hrs
Grass site in open farmland in a south-facing sheltered valley; direct access to Crantock and Polly Joke beaches, National Trust Land and many natural beauty spots. From A3075 W of Newquay turn right for Crantock. Site signed beyond village. A 4-acre site with 92 touring pitches and 7 statics.

🔌 🐾 ☉ 🗄 ❄ ⚡ 🖥 ❄ 🍴 🛢 🍃 ⬆ 🆃 ⛲

→ ∪ ▶ ✂ 🎵

DOWNDERRY

Carbeil Caravan & Camping Park (SX318544)
Treliddon Ln PL11 3LP ☎ 01503 250636 Signposted
Nearby town: Looe
▶ ▶ ★ 🏠 £4.50-£6.50 🏠 £4.50-£6.50 🅰 £4.50-£6.50
Open 31 Mar-Oct Booking advisable all year Last arrival

21.00hrs Last departure noon

A very small site in a steep valley. No level pitches except for small ridge tents, and basic facilities. Site at end of Downderry, up narrow lane and signed. A 1.25-acre site with 20 touring pitches and 6 statics.

See advertisement under LOOE

FALMOUTH

Tremorvah Tent Park (SW798313)
Swanpool TR11 5BA ☎ 01326 312103 Signposted
▶ ▶ ▶ ➌ £6-£6.60 ▲ £6.50-£7.10
Open mid May-Oct Booking advisable Jul-Aug Last arrival 22.00hrs Last departure 10.00hrs

A secluded tent park in a meadowland setting overlooking Swanpool Beach. No towed caravans. In Falmouth follow signs to 'Beaches', and on to Swanpool; site signed on right. A 3-acre site with 72 touring pitches.

Dishwashing sinks & electric cooking hob.

GOONHAVERN

Silverbow Park (SW782531)
Perranwell TR4 9NX
☎ 01872 572347 Signposted
▶ ▶ ▶ ▶ ♠ ♦♦ ★ ➌ £5.50-£12.30 ➌ £5.50-£12.30
▲ £5.50-£12.30
Open mid May-mid Sep (rs mid Sep-Oct & Etr-mid May swimming pool & shop closed) Booking advisable Jul-Aug Last arrival 22.00hrs Last departure noon

A very well kept park in a rural setting, thoughtfully laid out and screened by mature shrubs and trees. Adjacent to A3075 .5m S of village. A 14-acre site with 100 touring pitches and 15 statics.

Badminton courts, short mat bowls rink.

See advertisement under PERRANPORTH

Perran Springs Touring Park (SW796535)
Bodmin Rd TR4 9QG ☎ 01872 540568 Signposted
Nearby town: Newquay
▶ ▶ ▶ ➌➌ ▲
Open Etr or Apr-Oct Booking advisable Jul-Aug Last arrival anytime Last departure 10.00hrs

A brand new site with quality buildings and a good standard of facilities. Turn R off A30 on to B3285, signed Perranporth. Site on R in 1m. An 8-acre site with 120 touring pitches.

Rosehill Farm Tourist Park (SW787540)
TR4 9LA ☎ 01872 572448 Signposted
Nearby town: Perranporth
▶ ▶ ▶ ➌ £5-£8.50 ➌ £5-£8.50 ▲ £5-£8.50
Open Whit-Oct (rs Etr-Whit shop) Booking advisable Jul-Aug Last arrival 22.30hrs Last departure noon

A small, well-kept site set in hilly meadowland, .5m W of village on B3285. A 3-acre site with 65 touring pitches.

Off-licence in shop.

See advertisement under PERRANPORTH

GORRAN

Tregarton Farm Caravan & Camping Park (SW984437)
PL26 6NF ☎ 01726 843666 Signposted
Nearby town: St Austell
▶ ▶ ▶ ★ ➌ £7-£10 ➌ £7-£10 ▲ £7-£10
Open Apr-Oct (rs Apr & Oct pool closed) Booking advisable Jul-Aug Last arrival 22.00hrs Last departure noon

A fairly basic farm site, but a friendly one. The site lies 2m from the sea and off minor road to Gorran Haven. An 8-acre site with 150 touring pitches.

Camping equipment for sale, Off Licence.

See advertisement under MEVAGISSEY

Credit Cards

Trevor Farm Caravan & Camping Site (SW988418)
PL26 6LW ☎ 01726 842387 Signposted
Nearby town: St Austell
▶ ▶ ★ ➌ £5-£10 ➌ £5-£10 ▲ £5-£10
Open Apr-Oct Booking advisable Jan Last arrival 20.00hrs Last departure noon

A small family run camping park with good facilities, situated on a working farm. From St Austell bypass turn left onto B3273 for Mevagissey. On hilltop before descent to village turn right on unclass rd for Gorran; in 3.5m fork right, and site signed on right. A 4-acre site with 50 touring pitches.

Coarse fishing.

GORRAN HAVEN

Trelispen Caravan & Camping Park (SX008421)
PL26 6HT ☎ 01726 843501
▶ ➌➌ ▲
Open Etr & Apr-Oct Booking advisable Last arrival 22.00hrs Last departure noon

A very basic site in a beautiful, quiet location within easy reach of beaches. A 2-acre site with 40 touring pitches. A 30 acre nature reserve.

🂠 🂡 🂢 🂣 🂤 🂥 🂦 🂧 🂨 🂩 🂪 🂫

→ 🂬 🂭 🂮

HAYLE

St Ives Bay Holiday Park (SW577398)
73 Loggans Rd, Upton Towans TR27 5BH
☎ 01736 752274 Signposted
► ► ► ★ 🚐 £5-£14 🚍 £5-£14 ▲ £5-£14
Open 28 May-7 Sep (rs Etr-27 May & 7-30 Oct no entertainment, pool, food & bar service) Booking advisable Jan-Feb Last arrival 23.00hrs Last departure 09.00hrs
A site built on sand dunes adjacent to a three-mile long beach. The touring section forms a number of separate locations in amongst the statics. A 13-acre site with 240 touring pitches and 250 statics.
Crazy golf, video room.

🂠 🂡 🂢 🂣 🂤 🂥 🂦 🂧 🂨 🂩 🂪 🂫 🂬 🂭 🂮 🂯 🂰 🂱

🂲 🂳 🂴

→ 🂵 🂶 🂷 🂸

Credit Cards 🂹 🂺

HELSTON

Trelowarren Chateau Park (SW721238)
Mawgan TR12 6AF ☎ 01326 22637
(3m S off B3293 to St Keverne) Signposted
► ► ► 🂻 🚐 🚍 ▲
Open Apr-Sep Booking advisable bank hols & Jul-Aug Last arrival 21.00hrs Last departure noon
A very attractive setting in the extensive park of Trelowarren House. A 16-acre site with 225 touring pitches.

🂠 🂡 🂢 🂣 🂤 🂥 🂦 🂧 🂨 🂩 🂪 🂫 🂬 🂭 🂮 🂯 🂰 🂱

🂲 🂳

→ 🂵

HOLYWELL BAY

Trevornick Holiday Park (SW776586)
TR8 5PW ☎ 01637 830531 Signposted
Nearby town: Newquay
► ► ► ► ► 🂻 Holiday Centre ★ 🚐 £5-£15 🚍 £5-£15
▲ £5-£15
Open Etr & mid May-mid Sep Booking advisable Jul-Aug Last arrival anytime Last departure noon
A large seaside holiday complex with excellent facilities and amenities. From A3075 turn right near Rejerrah for Holywell Bay, and site on right. A 20-acre site with 435 touring pitches and 34 statics.
Fishing, pony trekking, entertainment.

🂠 🂡 🂢 🂣 🂤 🂥 🂦 🂧 🂨 🂩 🂪 🂫 🂬 🂭 🂮 🂯 🂰 🂱

🂲 🂳 🂴 🂵 🂶 🂷 🂸 🂹

→ 🂵 🂶 🂷 🂸 🂹 🂺 🂻

🂼

Credit Cards 🂽 🂾 🃟 🃏

See advertisement under Newquay

JACOBSTOW

Edmore Tourist Park (SX187955)
Wainhouse Corner EX23 0BJ ☎ 01840 230467
Signposted
Nearby town: Bude
► ► ★ 🚐 fr £4 🚍 fr £4 ▲ fr £4
Open Etr-Oct Booking advisable peak periods Last departure noon
Small, family run, rural campsite in good location, just off main A39. A 3-acre site with 28 touring pitches and 2 statics.

🂠 🂡 🂢 🂣 🂤 🂥 🂦 🂧 🂨 🂩 🂪

→ 🂫 🂬

KENNACK SANDS

Gwendreath Farm Caravan Park (SW738168)
TR12 7LZ ☎ 01326 290666
Nearby town: Helston
► ► ► ★ 🚐 £4.70-£5.99 🚍 £4.70-£5.99 ▲ £4.70-£5.99
Open Etr-Oct Booking advisable all times Last departure 10.00hrs
A compact cliff-top site, with spectacular sea-views. A 5-acre site with 10 touring pitches and 30 statics.

🂠 🂡 🂢 🂣 🂤 🂥 🂦 🂧 🂨 🂩 🂪 🂫 🂬 🂭 🂮 🂯 🂰

→ 🂱 🂲 🂳

🂴

Sea Acres Caravan Park (SW728162)
TR12 7LT ☎ 01326 290064 & 290665 Signposted
Nearby town: Helston
► ► ► ★ 🚐 £5.95-£10.50 🚍 £5.95-£10.50 ▲ £5.95-£10.50
Open Apr-Oct Booking advisable Jul-Aug Last arrival 23.00hrs Last departure 11.00hrs
A mainly static park with good touring facilities, set in meadowland and adjacent to sea and beach; 10m SE of Helston. A 10-acre site with 50 touring pitches and 100 statics.
Diving centre, creche, bowling, bike hire, golf.

🂠 🂡 🂢 🂣 🂤 🂥 🂦 🂧 🂨 🂩 🂪 🂫 🂬 🂭 🂮 🂯 🂰 🂱

🂲 🂳 🂴 🂵

→ 🂶 🂷 🂸 🂹 🂺 🂻

🂼

Credit Cards 🂽 🂾 🃟 🃏 🃐

Silver Sands Holiday Park (SW727166)
Gwendreath TR12 7LZ ☎ 01326 290631 Signposted
Nearby town: Helston
► ► ► 🚐 £4.80-£6 🚍 £4.80-£6 ▲ £4.80-£6
Open Apr-Sep (rs Etr (if in Mar) advance booking advisable) Booking advisable Jul-Aug Last arrival 22.00hrs Last departure noon
A small, remote site adjacent to a beach and well maintained. Take A3083 from Helston, at Culdrose naval

air station turn left on B3293 to Goonhilly earth station, and right at crossrds onto unclass rd. Site signed on left in 1m. A 4-acre site with 34 touring pitches and 16 statics.

KILKHAMPTON

East Thorne Caravan & Camping Park (SS260110)
EX23 9RY ☎ 01288 82618 Signposted
▶▶▶ 🚐🚐🛆

Open Apr-Oct Booking advisable Last arrival 22.00hrs Last departure 11.00hrs
Small rural campsite siutated adjacent to non-working farm, ideally positioned for touring Devon and Cornwall. In village centre follow B3254 Launceston road for approx .75m. A 2-acre site with 29 touring pitches and 1 static.

LANDRAKE

Dolbeare Caravan Park (SX363616)
St Ive Rd PL12 5AF ☎ 01752 851332 Signposted
Nearby town: Plymouth
▶▶▶ 🚐 £6.50-£7.50 🚐 £6.50-£7.50 🛆 £2.50-£7.50

Open all year Booking advisable peak periods only Last arrival 11.00hrs
A mainly level grass site with trees and bushes set in meadowland. Situated .75m N of Landrake off A38. A 4-acre site with 60 touring pitches.
Volley ball pitch, Boules pitch, Info Centre.

LAUNCELLS

Red Post Holiday Park (SS264052)
EX23 9NW ☎ 01288 81305 Signposted
▶▶ 🚐🚐🛆

Open 31 Mar-Oct Booking advisable Last arrival 23.00hrs
A simple site at rear of an inn and roadside cafe, midway between Bude and Holdsworthy on the A3072 at the junction with the B3254. A 3-acre site with 60 touring pitches.

Credit Cards 💳 💳

LEEDSTOWN (NEAR HAYLE)

Calloose Caravan & Camping Park (SW597352)
TR27 5ET ☎ 01736 850431
Signposted
Nearby town: St Ives
▶▶▶▶ 🏍😊★🚐 £5.75-£9 🚐 £5.75-£9 🛆 £5.75-£9

Open Apr-Sep (rs Apr-mid May & late Sep swimming pool) Booking advisable Etr, May bank hols & Jun-Aug Last arrival 22.00hrs Last departure 11.00hrs
A comprehensively equipped leisure park in a remote rural setting in a small river valley. Follow B3302 from 'Duke of Leeds' public house in town centre for .5m. A 7-acre site with 120 touring pitches and 17 statics.
Crazy golf, skittle alley & fishing
See advertisement under ST IVES

LOOE

'Treble B' Holiday Centre (SX228533)
Polperro Rd PL13 2JS ☎ 01503 262425 Signposted
▶▶▶▶ ▶ Holiday Centre ★ 🚐 £6.50-£9.50
🚐 £6.50-£9.50 🛆 £6.50-£9.50

Open Whit-mid Sep (rs May-Whit & mid-end Sep no entertainment in club) Booking advisable last wk Jul-1st 2 wks Aug Last arrival 23.00hrs Last departure noon
A typical holiday park, mainly for tourers and particularly popular for families with teenage children. Signed off A387. A 20-acre site with 500 touring pitches and 30 statics.
Dance hall/disco, crazy golf, off-licence, sinks.
See advertisement under Colour Section

Tencreek Caravan & Camping Park (SX233525)
PL13 2JR ☎ 01503 262447 & 01831 411843 Signposted
▶▶▶▶ ★ 🚐 £6.50-£10 🚐 £6.50-£10 🛆 £6.50-£10
Open all year Booking advisable Jul-Aug Last arrival 23.00hrs Last departure 10.00hrs
A mainly level grass site with good views. Signed off A387 W of Looe. A 14-acre site with 254 touring pitches and 45 statics.
Nightly entertainment & solarium.

Credit Cards 💳 💳 💳 💳 💳

Polborder House Caravan & Camping Park (SX283557)
Bucklawren Rd, St Martins PL13 1QR ☎ 01503 240265
Signposted
▶ ▶ ▶ ♦ ⊞ £6-£8 ⊞ £6-£8 ▲ £6-£8
Open Etr or Apr-Oct Booking advisable Jul-Aug Last
arrival 22.00hrs Last departure noon
*A very neat and well-kept small grassy site on high
ground above Looe in a peaceful rural setting. Friendly
and enthusiastic owners. Site signed from A387. A 3-
acre site with 36 touring pitches and 5 statics.*
Washing up & food preparation sinks.

🔧 🖎 ⊙ ▣ ⦿ ✳ 🍴 🖉 ⊞ 🅣 🕻 🕱 ♿
→ ∪ ↑ ◎ △ ⚓ 🎬 ♪
💷

LOSTWITHIEL

Powderham Castle Tourist Park (SX083593)
PL30 5BU ☎ 01208 872277 (1.5m E on A390) Signposted
Nearby town: Fowey
▶ ▶ ♦ ★ ⊞ £6.25-£8.35 ⊞ £6.25-£8.35 ▲ £6.25-£8.35
Open Apr-Oct Booking advisable peak periods Last
arrival 22.00hrs
*A very quiet and well-run site in a good touring location,
set in mature parkland and well screened. 1.5m SW of
Lostwithiel. A 12-acre site with 70 touring pitches and 38
statics.*
Badminton, soft tennis, boat hire & paddling pool.

🔧 🖎 ⊙ ▣ ⦿ ⚓ ▭ ✳ ⚙ 🍴 🖉 ⊞ 🕻 🐕 🎬
→ ∪ ↑ △ ⚓ 🎬 ♪ 🕱
💷

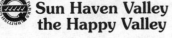
MAWGAN

See **Helston**

MAWGAN PORTH

Sun Haven Valley Caravan & Camping Site
(SW861669)

TR8 4BQ ☎ 01637 860373 Signposted

Nearby town: Newquay

▶▶▶ ♣ ♙♙ ★ ♨ £7-£8.50 ♨ £7-£8.50 ▲ £7-£8.50

Open May-Sep (rs Etr & mid Sep no laundry or disabled facilities) Booking advisable Jul-Aug Last arrival 22.00hrs Last departure 11.00hrs

An attractive site set on the side of a river valley with a camping area alongside the river. Exceptional floral landscape and very high quality facilities. Situated .75m from sea and fine sandy beach. Winner of the 1995 Campsite of the Year Award for the South West. A 5-acre site with 118 touring pitches and 36 statics.

Credit Cards 🔲 🔲

Trevarrian Holiday Park (SW853661)
TR8 4AQ ☎ 01637 860381 Signposted
Nearby town: Newquay
▶ ▶ ▶ ⊞ ⊞ Å

Open Etr-Sep Booking advisable Jun-Aug Last arrival
22.00hrs Last departure 11.00hrs
*A well-established and well-run holiday park
overlooking Mawgan Porth beach. From A39 at St
Columb rndbt turn right onto A3059 towards Newquay.
Fork left in approx 2m for St Mawgan to join B3276
coast road. Turn right and site on left. A 7-acre site with
185 touring pitches.*
Sports field & pitch n putt.

🏵 🐾 ⋒ ⊙ ⊟ ⊠ ⋜ ⋗ ⋒ ● ⊡ ✳ ♀ ⋀ ⋒ ⊘ ⊞ T
✕ ⋘ ⊑
→ U ⋗ ◎ ⊹ ♨ ✎

MEVAGISSEY
See **Gorran & Boswinger**

MULLION

Mullion Holiday Park (SW699182)
Lizard Peninsula, A3083 TR12 7LJ
☎ 01326 240428 & 240000 Signposted
Nearby town: Helston
▶ ▶ ▶ ▶ ⊕ ⊞ ⊞ Å

Open Etr & May-Sep Booking advisable Jul-Aug Last
arrival 21.00hrs Last departure noon
*A comprehensively equipped leisure park geared mainly
for self-catering holidays, set in rugged moorland on the
Lizard peninsula, adjacent to A3083 Helston road. A 10-
acre site with 150 touring pitches and 347 statics.*

Adventure playgrounds, sandpit, amusement & arcade.

🏵 ⋒ ⊙ ⊟ ⊠ ⋜ ⋗ ● ✳ ♀ ⋀ ⋒ ⊘ ✕ ⋘ ⋗ ♨ 🏛
🏛 ⋒ ⋔ ⊑ ⅋
→ U ⋗ ⊹ ✎
⊞

Credit Cards ▨ ▨ ▨ ▨ 🟐

'Franchis' Holiday Park (SW698203)
Cury Cross Lanes TR12 7AZ ☎ 01326 240301 Signposted
Nearby town: Helston
▶ ▶ ▶ ★ ⊞ £6-£7 ⊞ £6-£7 Å £6-£7

Open Wed before Etr-Sep (rs low season shop open on
request) Booking advisable end Jul-Aug Last arrival
22.00hrs Last departure noon
*This site is surrounded by hedges and coppices situated
on the A3083 between Helston and The Lizard, an ideal
position for exploring the Peninsula. A 4-acre site with
70 touring pitches and 12 statics.*
Dive air to 3500 P.S.I. Dishwashing facilities.

🏵 ⋒ ⊙ ⊠ ✳ ⋒ ⊘ ⊞ T ⋘ ⋔ ⊑
→ U ⋗ ✎ ⊟
⊞

Criggan Mill (SW670179)
Mullion Cove TR12 7EU ☎ 01326 240496
▶ ▶ ★ ⊞ £6.50-£10 ⊞ £6.50-£10 Å £6.50-£10

Open Apr-Oct Booking advisable Jul-Aug Last arrival
22.00hrs Last departure 10.00hrs ⌖
*A secluded site with level pitches in a combe near to
Mullion Cove. From the A3083 Helston road take B3296
to Mullion. A 1-acre site with 10 touring pitches and 30
statics.*

🏵 ⋒ ⊙ ⊟ ✳ ⋒ ✕ ⋘ ⊑
→ U ⋗ ✎

NEWQUAY

Hendra Holiday Park (SW833601)
TR8 4NY ☎ 01637 875778 (2m SE) Signposted
▶ ▶ ▶ ▶ ▶ ⊕ Holiday Centre ★ ⊞ £6-£9.70 ⊞ £6-£9.70
Å £6-£9.70

Open Etr or Apr-Oct (rs Apr-Spring bank hol) Booking
advisable Jul-Aug Last arrival dusk Last departure noon
*A large, long-established complex with mature trees
and bushes set in downland, with superb leisure
facilities. Situated 2m SE of Newquay, off Lane-Quintrel
Down road. A 31-acre site with 600 touring pitches and
160 statics.*
Solarium, fish bar, sauna & cycle hire.

🏵 ⋒ ⊙ ⊟ ⋜ ● ⊡ ✳ ♀ ⋀ ⋒ ⊘ ⊞ T ✕ ⋘ ⋗
🏛 🏛 ⋒ ⋔ ⊑ ⅋
→ U ⋗ ◎ △ ⊹ ♨ ✎
⊞

Credit Cards ▨ ▨ ▨ 🟐
See advertisement on page 64

Newquay Holiday Park (SW853626)
TR8 4HS ☎ 01637 871111 (on A3059) Signposted
▶ ▶ ▶ ▶ ⊕ Holiday Centre ★ ⚑ £6.35-£17.45
🚐 £6.35-£17.45 ▲ £6.35-£17.45
Open 13 May-15 Sep Booking advisable Jun-Aug Last
arrival 21.00hrs Last departure 10.00hrs ⊘
*A well-managed and maintained site with a wide range
of indoor and outdoor activities. A 14-acre site with 259
touring pitches and 12 statics.*
Pool tables, 9 hole pitch & putt, crazy golf.

🔟📻☉📺⚡☇🔆♀🏔🔋🌿⊞Ⓣ📞♿🛒🛆
➔⋃☉🛆⚓☎♨🎵

Credit Cards 🃏 💳

Rosecliston Park (SW815594)
Trevemper TR8 5JJ ☎ 01637 830326 (2m S on A3075)
Signposted
▶ ▶ ▶ ▶ ★ ⚑ £5.40-£9.20 🚐 £5.40-£9.20 ▲ £5.40-£9.20
Open Whit-Oct Booking advisable Jul-Aug Last arrival
22.00hrs Last departure 14.00hrs
*Small, well-organised site with attractively arranged
pitches. An 8-acre site with 130 touring pitches.*
Sauna & solarium.

🔟📻☉📺🍴⚡☇🔆♀🏔🔋🌿⊞Ⓣ📞
🛒🛆
➔⋃☉⚓☎♨🎵
💷

Credit Cards 🃏 💳 💳 🃏 🆂

Trencreek Holiday Park (SW828609)
Trencreek TR8 4NS ☎ 01637 874210 Signposted
► ► ► ► ★ ⊞ £5.20-£8.40 ⊞ £5.20-£8.40 ▲ £5.20-£8.40
Open Whit-mid Sep (rs Etr, Apr-May & late Sep
swimming pool, cafe & bar closed) Booking advisable
Jul-Aug Last arrival 22.00hrs Last departure noon ⌀
*Slightly sloping grassy site with excellent facilities, set
in meadowland in the village of Trencreek, 1.5m from
Newquay town centre. A 10-acre site with 194 touring
pitches and 6 statics.*
Coarse fishing on site.

🖫 🎗 ⊙ 🗗 🎗 ⚲ 🗖 ☀ ♇ ⚠ 🗋 ⌀ 🗈 ✕ 📞 ⏧ ⌗
🗛 🎗 &
→ ∪ Ρ ⊙ ⚙ ⚴ ⚏ ♪

Gwills Holiday Park (SW829592)
Ln TR8 4PE ☎ 01637 873617 (2m SE) Signposted
► ► ► ★ ⊞ £4.80-£8.20 ⊞ £4.20-£7.20 ▲ £4.80-£8.20
Open Etr-Oct (rs Etr-Whitsun takeaway closed) Booking
advisable Jul-Aug Last arrival 21.00hrs Last departure
11.00hrs
*A lightly wooded, riverside site with level and sloping
pitches. From A30 turn R at Indian Queens to A392 then
follow unclass road between Lane and Newlyn East. A
10-acre site with 150 touring pitches and 32 statics.*
Fishing.

🖫 🎗 ⊙ 🗗 🎗 🎐 ⚲ 🗖 ☀ ♇ ⚠ 🗋 ⌀ 🗈 📞 ⏧
🗛 🎗
→ ∪ Ρ ⚙ ⚴ ⚏ ♪

Credit Cards 🖭 🖭 🖭 🖭

Porth Beach Tourist Park (SW834629)
Porth TR7 3NH ☎ 01637 876531 (1m NE)
► ► ► ⊞ ⊞ ▲
Open Apr-Oct Booking advisable Jul-Aug Last arrival
22.00hrs Last departure 10.00hrs
*A well-run site set in meadowland adjacent to sea and a
fine sandy beach. Off B3276. A 6-acre site with 201
touring pitches and 12 statics.*

🖫 🎗 ⊙ 🗗 ☀ ⚠ 🗋 ⌀ 🗈 📞
→ ∪ Ρ ⊙ ⚙ ⚴ ⚏ ♪ 🎗

Treloy Tourist Park (SW858625)
TR8 4JN ☎ 01637 872063 & 876279 Signposted
► ► ► ★ ⊞ £5-£8 ⊞ £5-£8 ▲ £5-£8
Open Apr-Oct (rs Apr swimming pool & bar closed)
Booking advisable Jul-Aug Last arrival 24.00hrs Last
departure noon
*Attractive site with fine countryside views, within easy
reach of resorts and beaches. From A3058 take A3059, and
site signed on left. A 12-acre site with 119 touring pitches.*
Golf course & entertainment.Coarse fishing nearby.

🖫 🎗 ⊙ 🗗 🎗 🎐 ⚲ 🗖 ☀ ♇ ⚠ 🗋 ⌀ 🗈 ✕ 📞 ⏧
⏧ 🗛 🎗
→ ∪ Ρ ⚙ ⚴ ♪ ♪
£⊞
Credit Cards 🖭 🖭

Trenance Caravan & Chalet Park (SW818612)
Edgcumbe Av TR7 2JY ☎ 01637 873447 Signposted
▶ ▶ ▶ ★ ⚌ fr £5 ⚌ fr £5 ▲ fr £5
Open 26 May-Oct (rs Apr-25 May no showers or take-away restaurant) Booking advisable Jul-Aug Last arrival 22.00hrs Last departure 10.00hrs ✿
Principally a static park with a small, upgraded touring area on high ground, set within the urban confines of Newquay. A 2-acre site with 50 touring pitches and 190 statics.
Hairdressing salon, dishwashing facilities.

🖼⚌⊙🗗🖫⚌⊙⚌⊙⚌⊙⚌🖾🖴
→∪▶⊙⚌⚌⚌⚌
£

Credit Cards

Trethiggey Touring Park (SW846596)
Quintrell Downs TR8 4LG ☎ 01637 877672 (2m SE A392) Signposted
▶ ▶ ▶ ★ ⚌ £4.80-£7.40 ⚌ £4.20-£7.40 ▲ £4.20-£6.80
Open Mar-Dec Booking advisable Jul-Aug Last arrival 22.00hrs
A rather open field at Quintrell Downs on the Truro road. Considerably improved recently. On the A3058 3m from Newquay. A 6-acre site with 120 touring pitches and 12 statics.

½ mile from Watergate Bay's glorious sand and surf – on a coastline renowned for its beauty and beaches – only 4 miles from the premier resort of Newquay

Watergate Bay
HOLIDAY PARK

Proprietors
Gwen & Brian Jennings

● FOR A RELAXING HOLIDAY IN BEAUTIFUL....
COUNTRYSIDE NEAR the SEA

AA ▶ ▶ ▶

- Heated Pool
- Cafeteria
- Launderette
- Individual Pitches
- No Overcrowding
- Level site
- Free Evening Entertainment
- Licensed Club
- TV Video Games Room
- Self-Service Shop
- Electric hook-ups
- Site lighting
- Children's play area

Write or Tel for Colour Brochure

Watergate Bay
Holiday Park
Watergate Bay
Newquay
Cornwall TR8 4AD

Tel: St. Mawgan 01637 860387

Off licence & dishwashing sinks, recreation field.

🖼⚌⊙🗗🖫⚌⚌⚌⚌⚌⚌⚌⚌⚌⚌⚌
⚌⚌⚌⚌
→∪▶⊙⚌⚌⚌⚌
£

Credit Cards

NOTTER BRIDGE

Notter Bridge Caravan & Camping Park (SX384608)
PL12 4RW ☎ 01752 842318 Signposted
Nearby town: Plymouth
▶ ▶ ▶ ★ ⚌ £4.50-£6.50 ⚌ £4.50-£6.50 ▲ £4-£6.50
Open all year (rs Nov-Mar) Booking advisable peak periods Last arrival 23.00hrs Last departure 11.00hrs
Small, level grassy riverside site in wooded Lynner Valley, adjacent to A38, 2m W of Saltash. Fishing licences available. A 5-acre site with 55 touring pitches and 20 statics.
Salmon & trout fishing, canoeing.

🖼⚌⊙🗗🖫⚌⚌⚌⚌⚌⚌⚌⚌⚌⚌
→∪▶⚌⚌⚌⚌

PADSTOW

Trerethern Touring Park (SW913738)
PL28 8LE ☎ 01841 532061 Signposted
▶ ▶ ▶ ★ ⚌ £4.60-£7 ⚌ £4.60-£7 ▲ £4.60-£7
Open Apr-mid Oct Booking advisable Jul-Aug Last arrival 19.00hrs Last departure 16.00hrs
A rather open site situated 2m S of Padstow on eastern side of A389 Padstow-Wadebridge road. A 13.5-acre site with 90 touring pitches.
Motorvan hardstanding, electric & pumpout.

🖼⚌⊙🗗🖫⚌⚌⚌⚌⚌⚌⚌⚌⚌⚌
→∪▶⚌⚌⚌⚌

Dennis Cove Camping (SW918743)
Dennis Farm, Dennis Cove PL28 8DR ☎ 01841 532349 Signposted
▶ ▶ ★ ⚌ £6.85-£9.60 ⚌ £6.85-£9.60 ▲ £6.85-£9.60
Open Whitsun-Sep (rs Etr-Whitsun & Sep onwards swimming pool & club closed) Booking advisable before Jun Last arrival 23.00hrs Last departure noon
Level and slightly sloping site with mature trees set in meadowland, overlooking Padstow Bay with access to River Camel estuary and Padstow Bay beach. Approach Padstow on A389 and turn right into Sarah's Lane. A 4.5-acre site with 63 touring pitches.
Boating lake & windsurfing tuition.

⚌⊙⚌⚌⚌⚌⚌⚌⚌⚌⚌⚌⚌⚌
→∪▶⚌⚌⚌⚌⚌⚌

PELYNT

Camping Caradon (SX218539)
Trelawne PL15 2NA ☎ 01503 272388 Signposted
▶ ▶ ▶ ★ ⚌ £4.50-£8 ⚌ £4.50-£7.50 ▲ £4-£8
Open Etr-Oct Booking advisable Jul-Aug Last arrival 20.00hrs Last departure 11.00hrs
Established residential site with a level grass touring park. In rural setting. Off B3359, between Looe and ➡

Polperro. A 4-acre site with 85 touring pitches and 1 static.

🏢📻☉🔲🍳🔲☀♀🏔🛢🌙🚰🅣✗🔌♿🐾
→ ∪🌂☕🍴♨

PENTEWAN

Sun Valley Holiday Park (SX005486)
Pentewan Rd PL26 6DJ ☎ 01726 843266 Signposted
Nearby town: St Austell
►►►► 🏃‍♀️🚃 £6.50-£16 🚐 £6.50-£16 ▲ £6.50-£16
Open Apr (or Etr if earlier)-Oct (rs Apr & Oct shop & clubhouse not open) Booking advisable May-Sep Last arrival 23.00hrs Last departure 13.00hrs
A mainly static park in a woodland setting with a neat and well-maintained touring park. Sanitary facilities are outstanding. Situated 1m from sea, beach and river on B3273 St Austell-Mevagissey road. A 4-acre site with 22 touring pitches and 75 statics.

🏢📻☉🔲🍳🔶🔍🔍☀♀🏔🛢🌙🚰🅣✗🔌♿🐾🌙
→∪📍🔍☕🍴♨

Penhaven Touring Park (SX008481)
PL26 6DL ☎ 01726 843687 Signposted
Nearby town: Mevagissey
►►►🚃🚐▲
Open Etr or Apr-Oct Booking advisable public hols & end Jul-Aug Last arrival 22.00hrs Last departure 10.00hrs
Level, landscaped site in wooded valley, with river running by and 1m from sandy beach at Pentewan. Situated on B3273. A 13-acre site with 105 touring pitches.
Off-licence.

🏢📻☉🔲🍳🔶☀🏔🛢🌙🚰🅣🔌♿🐾
→∪📍🔍☕🍴♨

Credit Cards 💳 💳

Pentewan Sands Holiday Park (SX018468)
PL26 6BT ☎ 01726 843485 & 843448
Nearby town: Mevagissey
►►► 🚃 £5.50-£13.25 🚐 £5.50-£13.25 ▲ £5.50-£13.25
Open 30 Mar-Oct (rs 30 Mar-20 May & 16 Sep-Oct when shop, snack bar & pool may be closed) Booking advisable Jul-Aug Last arrival 23.00hrs Last departure 10.30hrs
A large camping site on the dunes adjacent to a private beach, well equipped for aquatic activities. 4m S of St Austell on B3273. A 32-acre site with 470 touring pitches and 123 statics.
Mini golf, cycle hire, boat launching.

🏢🍴📻☉🔲🍳🔶🔍🔍☀♀🏔🛢🌙🚰🅣✗🔌♿🐾♿
→∪📍🔍☕♨

Credit Cards 💳 💳 💳 💳 💳

PENZANCE

Bone Valley Caravan Park (SW472316)
Heamoor TR20 8UJ ☎ 01736 60313 Signposted
►► ★ 🚃 £7-£10 🚐 £6-£10 ▲ £6-£10
Open Mar-7 Jan (rs Oct-Dec & Mar shop closed)
Booking advisable Jul-Aug Last arrival 22.00hrs Last departure 11.00hrs
A compact grassy riverside site on the outskirts of Penzance, well maintained. A 1-acre site with 17 touring pitches and 1 static.

🏢📻☉🔲☀🛢🌙🚰🅣🌙
→∪🔍🔍☕🍴♨

PERRANARWORTHAL

Cosawes Caravan Park (SW768376)
TR3 7QS ☎ 01872 863724 & 863717 Signposted
►► ★ 🚃 £7 🚐 £6.50 ▲ £6
Open all year Booking advisable mid Jul-mid Aug
A mainly static and residential park with a neat and well-maintained camping annexe. 6m W of Truro on A39. A 2-acre site with 40 touring pitches and 100 statics.
Squash court.

🏢📻☉🔲🍳🛢🌙🚰🅣🔌📺
→∪📍♨♨

PERRANPORTH

Perran Sands Holiday Centre (SW766566)
TR6 0AQ ☎ 01872 573551
►►►►► Holiday Centre ★ 🚃 £8-£16 🚐 £8-£16 ▲ £8-£16
Open May-Oct Booking advisable Jul-Aug Last arrival 21.00hrs Last departure 10.00hrs
Large village complex, set amidst 500 acres of grassy dunes. Everything is provided for the family holiday with modern facilities. From A3078 turn left at Goonhavern on B3285 signed Perranporth; site entrance on right at top of descent into town. A 25-acre site with 450 touring pitches.
Crazy golf, pony trekking, amusement centre.

🏢📻☉🔲🍳🔶🔍🔍☀♀🏔🛢🌙🅣✗🔌♿🌙
→∪📍🔍♨

Perranporth Camping & Touring Site (SW768542)
Budnick Rd TR6 0DB ☎ 01872 572174 Signposted
►►►► 🚃🚐▲
Open Whit-Sep (rs Etr-Whitsun & mid Sep-end Sep shop & club facilities) Booking advisable Jul-Aug Last arrival 23.00hrs Last departure noon
A mainly tenting site with few level pitches but adjacent to a fine sandy beach. .5m E off B3285. A 6-acre site with 180 touring pitches and 8 statics.

🏢🍴📻☉🔲🍳🔶🔍🔲☀♀🏔🛢🌙🔌♿
🐾♿♿
→∪📍🔍☕♨

Credit Cards 💳

POLPERRO

Killigarth Manor Holiday Estate (SX214519)
PL13 2JQ ☎ 01503 72216 & 72409 Signposted
Nearby town: Looe
▶ ▶ ▶ ▶ ▶ ✿ Holiday Centre ★ ⚑ £8.80-£12
⚑ £8.80-£12 ▲ £8.80-£12
Open Etr-1st wk Oct (rs May-mid May & mid Sep-mid Oct entertainment restricted) Booking advisable 3rd wk Jul-Aug Last arrival 20.00hrs Last departure noon ✖
A well-ordered site on high ground on the approach to a historic fishing village on the A 387. A large touring and holiday complex with many amenities and facilities. A 7-acre site with 202 touring pitches and 147 statics. Amusement arcade, pool table & table tennis.

🛠🐾⊙🗑🍴🦐 🧺⚡🖵❄🎱🎡🍺⦿🚽🅣

✕🔌🧹🎟🐕🦽♿

➜∪🏴🛒🥄😷♪

Credit Cards 📇 💳 💳 📇

PORTHTOWAN

Porthtowan Tourist Park (SW693473)
Mile Hill TR4 8TY ☎ 01209 890256 Signposted
Nearby town: Redruth
▶ ▶ ▶ ✤ ★ ⚑ £5-£7.50 ⚑ £5-£7.50 ▲ £5-£7.50
Open Etr-Oct Booking advisable Jul-Aug Last departure noon
A neat, level grassy site on high ground above Porthtowan, with maturing landscape providing shelter

from winds. Leave A30 at Redruth onto unclass rd signed Portreath, and in 3m at T junc turn right for Porthtowan. Site on left. A 5-acre site with 31 touring pitches.

🛠🐾⊙🗑🍴🦐🍺❄🗏⦿♒⚡🅣🅣🔌🐕🦽♿

➜∪🏴⦿🛒😷♪

💷

Rose Hill Park (SW693466)
Rose Hill TR4 8AR ☎ 01209 890802
Nearby town: St Agnes
▶ ▶ ▶ ✤ ★ ⚑ £6-£8 ⚑ £6-£7 ▲ £6-£7
Open end Mar-end Oct Booking advisable Jun-Aug Last arrival 22.00hrs Last departure 11.00hrs
A small, well-kept park in an attractive position, set into the hillside and terraced. Site at bottom of descent to port. A 2.5-acre site with 40 touring pitches. Tourist information.

🛠🐾⊙🦐❄🍺⦿♒⚡🅣🔌🐕🦽♿

➜∪🏴🛒🥄😷♪

PRAA SANDS

Praa Sands Holiday Village (SW580284)
Pengersick TR20 9SH ☎ 01736 762201 Signposted
▶ ▶ ▶ ⚑ fr £2.70 ⚑ fr £2.70 ▲ fr £2.70
Open all year Booking advisable Jul-Aug Last arrival 22.00hrs Last departure 10.00hrs

An open site in a valley running down to a beach at the Hoe Point and Rinsey Head. Off A394 Helston-Penzance road. An 8-acre site with 200 touring pitches and 86 statics.
Video games room.

➡ ∪ ▶ △ ✦ ✈

£

REDRUTH

Cambrose Touring Park (SW684453)
Portreath Rd TR16 4HT ☎ 01209 890747 Signposted
Nearby town: Portreath
▶ ▶ ▶ ★ ⚐ £6.50-£8.50 ⚑ £6.50-£8.50 ▲ £6.50-£8.50
Open Apr-Oct Booking advisable Jul-Aug Last arrival 22.00hrs Last departure 11.30hrs
A mature park in a rural setting with trees and bushes. 2m from Redruth off B3300 (signposted 'Porthtowan and Portreath' from A30). A 3-acre site with 50 touring pitches.

➡ ∪ ▶ ◎ ☷ ✈

REJERRAH

Newperran Tourist Park (SW801555)
TR8 5QJ ☎ 01872 572407 in season & 01637 830308 Signposted
Nearby town: Newquay
▶ ▶ ▶ ▶ 👫 Holiday Centre ★ ⚐ £5.95-£9.20 ⚑ £5.40-£8.40 ▲ £5.95-£9.20
Open mid May-mid Sep Booking advisable Jul-Aug
A very good family site with excellent sanitary facilities, in an airy location, but with some screening from wind. 4m SE of Newquay and 1m S of Rejerrah on A3075. A 25-acre site with 270 touring pitches.
Crazy golf, adventure playground, pool & badminton.
See advertisement under NEWQUAY

➡ ∪ ▶ ◎ △ ✦ ☷ ✈

£

Credit Cards 🂠 🂡 🂢 🂣 🂤

Monkey Tree Touring Park (SW803545)
TR8 5QL ☎ 01872 572032 Signposted
Nearby town: Newquay
▶ ▶ ▶ ★ ⚐ £6-£11 ⚑ £6-£11 ▲ £6-£11
Open all year (rs Apr swimming pool weather permitting, shop) Booking advisable main season Last arrival 22.00hrs Last departure from 10.00
A quiet, open moorland setting, well-screened by mature hedges on high ground near the N Cornwall coast. Access from Rejerrah-Zelah road off A3075. A 12-acre site with 295 touring pitches and 6 statics.

Sauna, solarium, mountain bike hire & football pitch

➡ ∪ ▶ △ ✦ ☷ ✈

£

Credit Cards 🂠 🂡 🂢 🂣 🂤

RELUBBUS

AWARD

River Valley Caravan Park (SW565326)
TR20 9ER ☎ 01736 763398
Signposted
Nearby town: St Ives
▶ ▶ ▶ ✦ 👫 ⚑ £7.75-£8.70 ⚑ £7.75-£8.70 ▲ £7.75-£8.70
Open Mar-5 Jan (rs Nov-4 Jan hardstanding only, restricted facilities) Booking advisable Jul-Aug Last arrival 20.00hrs
A quiet, attractive, family-run site of quality in a picturesque river valley with direct access to shallow trout stream. Situated 4m from N and S coast sandy beaches, 3m from Marazion on B3280. An 18-acre site with 90 touring pitches.
Washing up sinks, fishing.

➡ ∪ ▶ ◎ ✈

£

Credit Cards 🂠 🂡 🂢

ROSUDGEON

Kenneggy Cove Holiday Park (SW562287)
Higher Kenneggy TR20 9AU ☎ 01736 763453 Signposted
Nearby town: Penzance
▶ ▶ ▶ ★ ⚐ £4-£7 ⚑ £4-£7 ▲ £4-£7
Open Apr-Nov Booking advisable Jul-Aug Last arrival 21.00hrs Last departure 11.00hrs
An attractive and neatly-kept site within a short walk of a sheltered, sandy beach and with lovely sea views. 6m W of Helston and 6m E of Penzance off A394, overlooking Mount's Bay. A 4-acre site with 60 touring pitches and 9 statics.

➡ ∪ ▶ △ ✦ ✈

RUTHERNBRIDGE

Ruthern Valley Holidays (SX014665)
PL30 5LU ☎ 01208 831395 Signposted
▶ ▶ ▶ ✦ ⚐ ⚑ ▲
Open Apr-Oct Booking advisable high season Last arrival 21.00hrs Last departure noon
An attractive woodland site in remote, small river valley S of Bodmin Moor. A 2-acre site with 29 touring pitches and 6 statics.
Off-licence.

➡ ∪ ✈

ST AGNES

Beacon Cottage Farm Touring Park (SW705502)
Beacon Dr TR5 0NU ☎ 01872 552347
Nearby town: Truro
▶ ▶ ▶ ★ 🚐 £5-£11 🚐 £5-£11 ▲ £5-£11
Open end May-Oct (rs Etr-Whitsun shop closed) Booking advisable Jul-Aug Last arrival 20.00hrs Last departure noon
A neat and compact site utilizing a cottage and outhouses, an old orchard and adjoining walled paddock. Unique location on a headland looking NE along the coast. From A30 at Threeburrows rndbt take B3277 to St Agnes, then Beacon Rd left. A 2-acre site with 50 touring pitches and 1 static.

🔲 🐾 ⊙ 🖥 🦐 ✳ ⚠ 🛈 𝓞 ⊞ 🕭 🐕 🐓 🐐
→ ∪ ▶ 🔺 ⤬ 🎵

ST AUSTELL

Trencreek Farm Holiday Park (SW966485)
Hewas Water PL26 7JG ☎ 01726 882540 Signposted
▶ ▶ ▶ ★ 🚐 £4-£8.50 🚐 £4-£8.50 ▲ £4-£8.50
Open Spring bank hol-13 Sep (rs Etr-Spring bank hol & 14 Sep-Oct restricted shop hours & pool closed) Booking advisable Jul-Aug Last arrival 21.00hrs Last departure noon
A working farm site with mature trees and bushes, close to river and lake. Off B3287, 1m from junction with A390. An 8-acre site with 140 touring pitches and 37 statics.
Fishing, fitness & agility course & mini golf.

🔲 🛵 🐾 ⊙ 🖥 🦐 ⤳ ☍ ◀ 🛒 ✳ ⚠ 🛈 𝓞 ⊞ 🔲
🕭 🧹 🐓 🐐 ♿
→ ∪ ▶ ⤬ 🎾 🎵

Credit Cards 🔲 ▬

ST BURYAN

Lower Treave Caravan Park (SW388272)
Crows-an-Wra TR19 6HZ ☎ 01736 810559 Signposted
▶ ▶ ▶ 🚐 🚐 ▲
Open Apr-Oct Booking advisable Jul-Aug Last arrival 22.30hrs Last departure noon
Terraced, grass site with trees and bushes, set in meadowland, 4m NE of Land's End off A30. A 5-acre site with 80 touring pitches and 5 statics.

🔲 🐾 ⊙ 🖥 🦐 ✳ 🛈 𝓞 ⊞ 🔲 🕭 🐐
→ ∪ ▶ 🎵

Tower Park Caravans & Camping (SW406263)
TR19 6BZ ☎ 01736 810286 Signposted
Nearby town: Penzance
▶ ▶ ▶ 🚐 🚐 ▲
Open Mar-Oct (rs Mar-Whitsun shop & cafe closed) Booking advisable Jul-Aug Last arrival 22.00hrs Last departure noon

A farm site near Land's End and 4m from Sennen Cove and Porthcurno. Off A30 and B3283. A 6-acre site with 102 touring pitches and 5 statics.

🔲 🛵 🐾 ⊙ 🖥 🦐 ◀ ☍ ✳ ⚠ 🛈 𝓞 ⊞ 🔲 ✕ 🕭
🧹 🏗 🏕 🐓 🐐 ♿
→ 🎵
💷

Treverven Touring Caravan & Camping Site (SW410237)
Treverven Farm TR19 6DL ☎ 01736 810221 Signposted
▶ ▶ ▶ 🚐 🚐 ▲
Open Etr-Oct Booking advisable Jul-Aug Last departure noon
An isolated but well-maintained farm site set off B3315 with panoramic views and in sight of the sea. A 6-acre site with 115 touring pitches.

🔲 🐾 ⊙ 🖥 🦐 ✳ 🛈 𝓞 🕭 🔲
→ 🎵

Camping & Caravanning Club Site (SW367279)
Higher Tregiffian Farm TR19 6JB
☎ 01736 871588 (in season) & 01203 694995 Signposted
Nearby town: Penzance
▶ ▶ ★ 🚐 £8.40-£9 🚐 £8.40-£9 ▲ £8.40-£9
Open end Mar-early Oct Booking advisable bank hols & Jul-Aug Last arrival 21.00hrs Last departure noon
A typical Club site with well-maintained facilities, situated just 2m from Land's End. Follow A30 from Penzance to Land's End, and site is signed off B3306 (St

Just Airport road). Please see the advertisement on page 27 for details of Club Members' benefits. A 4-acre site with 75 touring pitches.

🔌👥☉⚡🍴❄️🛒👜🐕🚉⛹️♿

→🏊

Credit Cards 💳💳

ST DAY

Tresaddern Holiday Park (SW733422)
TR16 5JR ☎ 01209 820459 Signposted
Nearby town: Redruth
▶▶▶ 🚐£4.75-£5.75 🚐£4.75-£5.75 ⛺£4.75-£5.75
Open Etr & Apr-Oct Booking advisable Jul-Aug
A rather basic 3-pennant site but in a good location. 2m NE of Redruth on B3298. A 2-acre site with 15 touring pitches and 17 statics.

🔌👥☉🔲❄️👜🌀📶🐕⛹️♿

→🚶🛒📞🏊

💷

ST GENNYS

Camping & Caravanning Club Site (SX176943)
Gillards Moor EX23 0BG ☎ 01840 230650 (in season) & 01203 694995 Signposted
Nearby town: Bude
▶▶▶★ 🚐£8.40-£10 🚐£8.40-£10 ⛺£8.40-£10
Open end Mar-early Oct Booking advisable bank hols & Jul-Aug Last arrival 21.00hrs Last departure noon
A well-kept, level grass site with good quality facilities. Signed off A39 1m S of Wainhouse Corner. Please see

---

the advertisement on page 27 for details of Club Members' benefits. A 6-acre site with 100 touring pitches.

🔌👥☉🔲🗄️❄️🍷🎢👜🌀📶🔌🛒🚉🐕⛹️

→🛒🛶🏊

Credit Cards 💳💳💳

ST IVES

Polmanter Tourist Park (SW510388)
Halsetown TR26 3LX ☎ 01736 795640 Signposted
▶▶▶▶ 🚐£6-£12 🚐£6-£12 ⛺£6-£12
Open Whit-10 Sep (rs Etr-Whit & 12 Sep-Oct shop, pool, bar & takeaway food closed) Booking advisable Jul-Aug
Last arrival 21.00hrs Last departure 10.00hrs
A well-developed touring park on high ground, with distant views of the sea in St Ives Bay. Signed off B3311 at Halestown. A 13-acre site with 240 touring pitches. Tennis courts, putting, & sports field.

🔌👥☉🔲🎾🔍🏊❄️🍷🎢👜🌀📶🔌📶✂️📞

🛒⛳🐕⛹️

→🚶🛒🛶🎣📶🏊

Credit Cards 💳💳💳💳💳

Ayr Holiday Park (SW509408)
TR26 1EJ ☎ 01736 795855 Signposted
▶▶▶ 🚐🚐⛺
Open Apr-Oct (rs Apr-mid May & Oct shop closed)
Booking advisable Jul-Aug Last arrival 22.00hrs Last departure 10.00hrs

A well-established park on a cliffside overlooking St Ives Bay. From town centre follow Penzance signs , turn right at 1st rndbt, and left at T junc. Signed ahead. A 2-acre site with 40 touring pitches and 43 statics.

🔌 📶 ⊙ 🗑 🔧 ✳ 🅰 🏠 ⊘ ⊞ 🅣 📞 🛒
→ 🚻 🅿 🍴 🍽 ♩

Trevalgan Family Camping Park (SW490402)

Trevalgan TR26 3BJ ☎ 01736 796433 Signposted
▶ ▶ ▶ ⚤ 🚐 £5-£9 🚐 £5-£9 🅰 £5-£9

Open May-Sep Booking advisable mid Jul-mid Aug Last arrival 23.30hrs Last departure noon
An open, level grass site on a working farm with very good facilities. From St Ives take B3306; site signed on right. A 4.75-acre site with 120 touring pitches.
Farm trail, pets corner.

🔌 📶 ⊙ 🗑 🔧 ⚡ 💻 ✳ 🅰 🏠 ⊘ ⊞ 🅣 ✖ 📞 🛒 🏛
🍴 🐕 🛒
→ 🚻 🅿 🍽 ♩
💷

ST JUST (NEAR LAND'S END)

Bosavern House Caravan Park (SW370305)

TR19 7RD ☎ 01736 788301
Nearby town: Penzance
▶ ▶ 🚐 🚐

Open Mar-Oct Booking advisable Jul-Aug Last arrival 22.00hrs Last departure 14.00hrs
A small, neat site in a walled garden behind a guest house. A 2-acre site with 12 touring pitches.

🔌 📶 ⊙ 🗑 ✳ 🏠 💻 ✖ 📞 🏛
→ 🚻 🅿 ⛵ ♩ 🛒

Kelynack Caravan & Camping Park (SW374301)

TR19 7RE ☎ 01736 787633 Signposted
Nearby town: Penzance
▶ ▶ 🚐 £4-£5 🚐 £4-£5 🅰 £4-£5

Open Apr-Oct Booking advisable Jul-Aug Last arrival 22.00hrs Last departure noon
A small, secluded site in the grounds of an old walled garden, surrounded by open countryside. 1m from town on B3306 Land's End road. A 2-acre site with 20 touring pitches and 13 statics.
Wash-up room.

🔌 📶 ⊙ 🗑 ⚡ ✳ 🅰 🏠 💻 ⊞ 🅣 📞 🏛 🍴 🐕 🛒
→ 🅿 ♩
💷

Roselands Caravan Park (SW387305)

Dowran TR19 7RS ☎ 01736 788571
(1.25m E on unclass rd, off A3071) Signposted
Nearby town: Penzance
▶ ▶ 🚐 🚐 🅰

Open May-Oct (rs Apr & Oct) Booking advisable Jun-Sep Last arrival 23.00hrs Last departure noon

A small site in an isolated rural setting with well-kept facilities and friendly owners. A 2-acre site with 12 touring pitches and 15 statics.

🔌 📶 ⊙ 🗑 ⚡ 🖥 ✳ 🍷 🅰 🏠 💻 ⊞ 📞 🏛 🐕 🛒
→ 🚻 🅿 ♩

ST JUST-IN-ROSELAND

Trethem Mill Touring Park (SW860365)

TR2 5JF ☎ 01872 580504 Signposted
▶ ▶ ▶ ★ 🚐 £5.50-£7.50 🚐 £5.50-£7.50 🅰 £5.50-£7.50

Open Apr-Oct Booking advisable Jul-Aug Last arrival 23.00hrs Last departure 11.00hrs
A carefully tended and sheltered park in a rural setting. Take A3078 for St Mawes, and site signed on right 3m N of St Mawes. A 4-acre site with 80 touring pitches.
Windsurf hire, mountain bike hire & info centre.

🔌 📶 ⊙ 🗑 🔧 ⚡ 🖥 ✳ 🅰 🏠 💻 ⊞ 🅣 📞 🐕 🍴
🛒
→ 🚻 ⛵ ♩ ♩

Credit Cards 💳 💳 💳 💳 💳

ST MERRYN (NEAR PADSTOW)

Carnevas Caravan & Camping Site (SW862728)

Carnevas Farm PL28 8PN ☎ 01841 520230 Signposted
Nearby town: Padstow
▶ ▶ ▶ ★ 🚐 £5-£8 🚐 £5-£8 🅰 £5-£8

Open Apr-Oct (rs Apr-Whit & mid Sep-Oct shop closed) Booking advisable Jul-Aug
A rather open site in a rural setting near the North coast. Off B3276 Padstow-Newquay road 2m SW of village. An 8-acre site with 195 touring pitches and 14 statics.

🔌 📶 ⊙ 🗑 🔧 ⚡ ✳ 🅰 🏠 💻 ⊞ 🅣 📞 🐕 🛒
→ 🚻 🅿 ⛵ ♩ 🍽 ♩

Tregavone Touring Park (SW898732)

Tregavone Farm ☎ 01841 520148 (2.5m off A389)
▶ ▶ 🚐 🚐 🅰

Open Mar-Oct
A working farm site with better than average facilities. The very well converted farm buildings look purpose built. Situated .5 mile off A389. A 3-acre site with 40 touring pitches.

🔌 📶 ⊙

Trevean Caravan & Camping Park (SW875724)

Trevean Ln PL28 8PR ☎ 01841 520772 Signposted
Nearby town: Padstow
▶ ▶ ★ 🚐 £4-£7 🚐 £4-£6 🅰 £4-£6

Open Apr-Oct Booking advisable mid Jul-Aug Last arrival 22.30hrs Last departure noon
A small working farm site with level grassy pitches in rather open countryside. Signed on left off B3276, 1.5m S of St Merryn. A 1.5-acre site with 36 touring pitches and 3 statics.

🔌 📶 ⊙ 🗑 ✳ 🅰 🏠 💻 ⊞ 📞 🛒
→ 🚻 🅿 ♩ 🍽 ♩
💷

ST MINVER

Gunvenna Touring Caravan & Camping Park (SW969782)

PL27 6QN ☎ 01208 862405

▶ ▶ ▶ ▶ ★ ⊕ £10-£12 ⊕ £10-£12 ▲ £8-£10

Open Apr-Oct Booking advisable Jul-Aug Last arrival mdnt Last departure 11.00hrs

Attractive site offering good facilities located 4m NE of Wadebridge on the B3314. Ideal position for touring North Cornwall. A 10-acre site with 75 touring pitches.

Swimming lessons.

🏠 📶 ☉ 🗄 🗨 🍃 ● ☀ ☂ ⚠ 🚽 ⊘ ✕ 🕻 🎠 🛒
&

→ ∪ ▶ 🛆 ⅄ 📽 ♪

St Minver Holiday Park (SW965772)

PL27 6RR ☎ 01208 862305 Signposted

▶ ▶ ▶ ★ ⊕ £7.50-£15 ⊕ £7.50-£15 ▲ £7.50-£15

Open 8 Apr-7 Oct Booking advisable Jul-Sep Last arrival mdnt Last departure 10.00hrs

A large, mainly static holiday park set around St Minver House in sylvan surroundings. From A39 N of Wadebridge take Port Isaac rd B3314; site signed on left in 3m. A 6-acre site with 120 touring pitches and 99 statics.

Craxy golf, free evening entertainment, amusements.

🏠 📶 ☉ 🗄 🗨 ● ☀ ☂ ⚠ 🚽 ⊘ 🖃 T ✕ 🕻 🛒 🛒
→ ▶

SCILLY, ISLES

(No map) No sites on the island hold AA classification.

TINTAGEL

See **Camelford**

TREGURRIAN

Camping & Caravanning Club Site (SW853654)

TR8 4AE ☎ 01637 860448 (in season) & 01203 694995

Nearby town: Newquay

▶ ▶ ★ ⊕ £8.40-£10 ⊕ £8.40-£10 ▲ £8.40-£10

Open end Mar-early Oct Booking advisable bank hols & Jul-Aug Last arrival 21.00hrs Last departure noon

A very well-kept older type club site with fairly basic essentials. From A3059 fork right for St Mawgan, then join B3276 coast road and turn left for Watergate Bay. Please see the advertisement on page 27 for details of Club Members' benefits. A 4-acre site with 106 touring pitches.

🏠 📶 ☉ ☀ ⚠ 🚽 ⊘ 🖃 T 🕻 🛒
→ ∪ ♪

Credit Cards 🏧 ▬▬ ▭

TRURO

(AWARD)

Leverton Place (SW774453)

Greenbottom,

Chacewater TR4 8QW ☎ 01872 560462 Signposted

▶ ▶ ▶ ▶ ♦♦ ☼ ★ ⊕ £7-£11 ⊕ £7-£11 ▲ £7-£11

Open all year (rs Oct-May not all facilities open all year round) Booking advisable Spring bank hol & Jun-early Sep Last arrival 22.00hrs Last departure noon

This attractive site is close to Truro yet in a pleasant

rural area 3.5m W of city, off A390 at Threemilestone Roundabout. A 9.75-acre site with 115 touring pitches and 15 statics.

Hairdrying room, childrens heated pool.

🏠 📶 ☉ 🗄 🗨 🍃 ● ✎ 🖵 ☀ ☂ ⚠ 🚽 ⊘ 🖃 ✕ 🕻 🛒
🛒 🛒 &

→ ∪ ▶ 📽 ♪

💷

Credit Cards 🏧 ▬▬ ▭ ▩ 🄢

Carnon Downs Caravan & Camping Park (SW805406)

Carnon Downs TR3 6JJ ☎ 01872 862283 (3m off A39)

Signposted

▶ ▶ ▶ ⊕ £6-£9 ⊕ £6-£9 ▲ £5-£8

Open Etr or Apr-Oct Booking advisable Jul-Aug Last arrival 23.00hrs Last departure 15.00hrs

A mature park with a high standard of landscaping set in meadowland and woodland just outside the urban area, adjacent to A39 Falmouth-Truro road. An 11-acre site with 150 touring pitches.

Baby & children bathroom.

🏠 🚐 📶 ☉ 🗄 🗨 🖵 ☀ ⚠ 🚽 ⊘ 🖃 T 🕻 🎠 🛒
→ ∪ ▶ 🛆 ⅄ 📽 ♪

💷 Credit Cards 🏧 ▬▬

Chacewater Park (SW740438)

Coxhill, Chacewater TR4 8LY ☎ 01209 820762

Signposted

▶ ▶ ▶ ⊕ £6-£8.50 ⊕ £6-£8.50 ▲ £6-£8.50

Open May-Sep Booking advisable Jul-Aug Last arrival 23.00hrs Last departure noon

A level grassy site with young trees set in meadowland. Along A30 towards Penzance, take A3047 to Scorrier, 400yds turn left at Crossroads Motel, continue to join B3298 for 1.25m, at next crossroads turn left to Chacewater & continue for 0.75m. A 4-acre site with 45 touring pitches and 12 statics.

Family shower rooms.

🏠 📶 ☉ 🗄 🗨 🖵 ☀ ⚠ 🚽 ⊘ 🖃 T 🕻 🎠 🛒
→ ∪ ▶

💷 Credit Cards 🏧 ▬▬ ▭ ▩

Liskey Touring Park (SW772452)

Greenbottom TR4 8QN ☎ 01872 560274 (3m W off A390)

Signposted

▶ ▶ ▶ ★ ♦♦ ⊕ £5.20-£8.50 ⊕ £5.20-£8.50 ▲ £5.20-£8.50

Open May-Sep (rs Apr-mid May shop & take away closed) Booking advisable Jul-Aug Last arrival 20.00hrs Last departure noon

Small, south facing park, neat and well-maintained with quality facilities, and enjoying panoramic views. A 4.5-acre site with 68 touring pitches.

Off-licence, dish washing, undercover playbarn.

🏠 🚐 📶 ☉ 🗄 🗨 🖵 ☀ ⚠ 🚽 ⊘ 🖃 T 🕻 🛒 🛒
🎠 🛒

→ ∪ ▶ 📽 ♪

Summer Valley (SW800479)
Shortlanesend TR4 9DW ☎ 01872 77878
(3m NW off B3284) Signposted
▶ ▶ ▶ ♣ ⊕ £6-£8 ⊕ £6-£8 ⚠ £6-£8
Open Apr-Oct Booking advisable Jul-Aug Last arrival
22.00hrs Last departure noon
*A very attractive and secluded site in a rural setting, and
very well-maintained. A 3-acre site with 60 touring
pitches and 1 static.*
Campers lounge.

🔊 📻 ⊙ 🗟 🖳 ✳ ⚠ 🌡 ⊘ ⊞ Ⓣ ⌱ 🐕 🐾
➔ ∪ ▶ 👟 ♪

Tretheak Manor Tourist Park
Veryan TR2 5PP ☎ 01872 501658 Signposted
▶ ▶ ▶ ⊕ £5-£7.50 ⊕ £5-£7.50 ⚠ £5-£7.50
Open Etr-or Apr-Oct Booking advisable Jul & Aug Last
arrival 21.00 hrs Last departure noon.
*A well-established, well run park in a secluded
countryside setting 2m S of Tregony on A3078, then
turn left after the Esso station and follow international
campsite signs. A 9 acre site with 175 touring pitches.
Fishing lake, all-service pitches for caravans and
motorhomes, tennis and bowls nearby.*

🔊 📻 ⊙ 🗟 🖳 ⚡ 🖳 ⚠ 🌡 ⊘ ⊞ Ⓣ ⌱ 🏛 ⌁ 🐕 🐾
➔ ∪ ⚐

Credit Cards ▨ ▤

WADEBRIDGE

Little Bodieve Holiday Park (SW995734)
Bodieve Rd PL27 6EG ☎ 01208 812323
▶ ▶ ▶ ★ ⊕ £8-£12 ⊕ £8-£12 ⚠ £8-£12
Open Mar-Oct (rs early & late season pool closed)
Booking advisable Jul-Aug Last arrival 22.00hrs Last
departure 11.00hrs
*An established and well-organised level grassy site 1m
from centre of Wadebridge in quiet rural area, with
good touring facilities. A 15-acre site with 195 touring
pitches and 75 statics.*
Crazy golf, water shute/splash pool & pets corner.

🔊 ⚑ 📻 ⊙ 🗟 🖳 ⚡ ✳ ⚐ ⚠ 🌡 ⊘ ⊞ Ⓣ ✗ ⌱
🏛 🐕 🐾 ⚐
➔ ∪ ▶ ⊙ ⚐ 👟 ♪
⊞ Credit Cards ▨ ▤ ▨ ⑤

WALL

Parbola Holiday Park (SW612366)
TR27 5LE ☎ 01209 831503 Signposted
Nearby town: St Ives
▶ ▶ ▶ ★ £5.75-£8.75 ⊕ £5.75-£8.75 ⚠ £5.75-£8.75
Open Etr-Oct (rs Etr-spring bank hol & Sep-Oct takeaway
closed) Booking advisable Jul-Aug Last arrival 22.00hrs
Last departure noon ⚗
*A level grassy site in Cornish downland. Follow old A30
to Connor Downs, turn left on unclass rd for Wall, and
site in village on right. A 17.5-acre site with 110 touring
pitches and 20 statics.*

Crazy golf & bike hire.

🔊 📻 ⊙ 🗟 🖳 ⚡ ⚑ 🖳 ✳ ⚠ 🌡 ⊘ ⊞ Ⓣ ⌱ ⚑ ⊞
🐾 ♿
➔ ∪ ▶ ♪
⊞
Credit Cards ▨ ▤ ᴮᴿᴵᵀᴵˢᴴ

WATERGATE BAY

Watergate Bay Tourist Park (SW850653)
Tregurrian TR8 4AD ☎ 01637 860387 Signposted
Nearby town: Newquay
▶ ▶ ▶ ★ ⊕ £7.25-£9.50 ⊕ £7.25-£9.50 ⚠ £7.25-£9.50
Open 22 May-12 Sep (rs Mar-21 May & 13 Sep-Nov
restricted bar, cafe, shop & swimming pool) Booking
advisable Jul-Aug Last arrival 22.00hrs Last departure
noon
*A well-established park on high ground above
Watergate Bay. Situated on B3276 .5m from Watergate
beach. A 9-acre site with 171 touring pitches.*
Entertainment, free minibus to beach.
See advertisement under NEWQUAY

🔊 ⚑ 📻 ⊙ 🗟 🖳 ⚡ 🖳 ✳ ⚐ ⚠ 🌡 ⊘ ⊞ Ⓣ ✗
⌱ 🏛 🐕 🐾 ♿
➔ ∪ ▶ ⊙ ⚐ ♪
⊞ Credit Cards ▨ ▤ ᴮᴿᴵᵀᴵˢᴴ ⑤

WHITECROSS

White Acres Holiday Park (SW890599)
TR8 4LW ☎ 01726 860220 Signposted
▶ ▶ ▶ ▶ ⊕ ⊕ £6-£8.40 ⊕ £6-£8.40 ⚠ £6-£8.40
Open Etr-Sep Booking advisable Jul-Aug
*A large holiday complex, partially terraced, in a rural
setting. From A30 at Indian Queen take A392 signed
Newquay. Site on right in 3m. An 11-acre site with 200
touring pitches and 100 statics.*
Entertainment, sauna, solarium, fishing lakes.

🗟 🖳 ⚡ ⚑ 🖳 ✳ ⚐ ⚠ 🌡 ⊘ ⊞ Ⓣ ✗ ⌱ ⚑ 🏛 🏛
⌁ 🐕 🐾
➔ ∪ ▶ 👟 ♪

Summer Lodge Holiday Park (SW890597)
TR8 4LW ☎ 01726 860415 & 861490 Signposted
Nearby town: Newquay
▶ ▶ ▶ ⊕ £2.95-£4.50 ⊕ £2.95-£4.50 ⚠ £2.95-£4.50
Open Whitsun-Oct (rs Etr-Whitsun & Sep-Oct shop cafe
& disco closed) Booking advisable Jul-Aug Last arrival
20.00hrs Last departure noon
*Small holiday complex offering use of good facilities.
From Indian Queens on A30 take A392 signed Newquay,
and site on left at Whitecross in 2.5m. A 2-acre site with
50 touring pitches and 126 statics.*

🔊 📻 ⊙ 🗟 🖳 ⚡ ⚑ ✳ ⚐ ⚠ 🌡 ⊘ ⊞ ✗ ⌱ 🏛 ⌁
🐾 ♿
➔ ∪ ♪
Credit Cards ▨ ▤ ᴮᴿᴵᵀᴵˢᴴ

CUMBRIA

AMBLESIDE

Skelwith Fold Caravan Park (NY355029)
LA22 0HX ☎ 015394 32277 Signposted
►►►►★ ♔ £8-£9 ♔ £7.50-£8.50
Open Mar-15 Nov Booking advisable public hols & Jul-Aug Last departure noon
In grounds of old mansion, this site is in a beautiful setting close to Lake Windermere. On the B5286, 2m from Ambleside. A 10-acre site with 150 touring pitches and 300 statics.
Family recreation area.
🔌🔥⊙📋🍳✳⚠🔥⬧✉🅣📞🛒🏕🐕🐎
♿
→∪ᴾ⊙⛵⚓⛳💈🎵

Low Wray National Trust Campsite (NY372013)
Low Wray LA22 0JA ☎ 015394 32810 Signposted
►►🛆

Open 1 wk before Etr-Oct Last arrival 23.00hrs no cars by tents
A site for tenters on banks of Lake Windermere, divided naturally into areas for families and for young people. 3m SW via A583 to Clappersgate, then B5286 and unclass road. A 10-acre site with 200 touring pitches and 6 statics.
Launching for sailing.
🔌⊙🔥🍳🛒♿
→⛵⚓⛳💈🎵🔳

APPLEBY-IN-WESTMORLAND

AWARD Q

Wild Rose Park (NY698165)
Ormside CA16 6EJ
☎ 017683 51077 Signposted
►►►► ♔ 🕯⊙🔥 £7.10-£10.70 ♔ £7.10-£10.70
🛆 £7.10-£10.70
Open all year (rs Nov-Mar shop, swimming pool & restaurant closed) Booking advisable bank & school hols Last arrival 22.00hrs Last departure noon
An excellent, well-maintained site with good views of surrounding countryside. Facilities are of a high standard. Site signed on unclass road to Great Ormside off B6260 from Appleby-in-Westmorland. A 12-acre site with 264 touring pitches and 240 statics. ➡

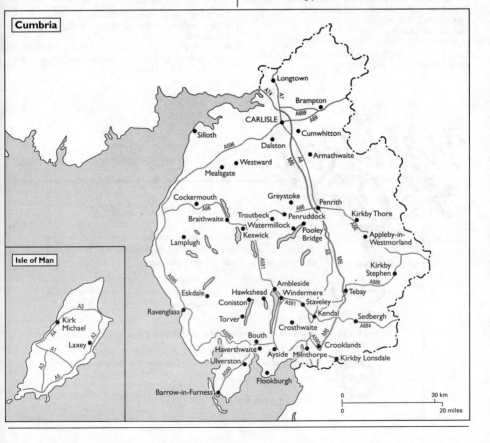

Cumbria

Longtown
Brampton
A7
A74
A689
CARLISLE
A689   A69
Silloth   Cumwhitton
A596   Dalston
Westward   Armathwaite
M6   A6
Mealsgate
Cockermouth   Greystoke
A66   Penrith
Braithwaite   Troutbeck   A66   Kirkby Thore
Watermillock   Penruddock
Lamplugh   Keswick   Pooley
Bridge   Appleby-in-
Westmorland
A595   A6   M6
A591   Kirkby
Stephen
Eskdale   Hawkshead   Ambleside   A685
Coniston   Windermere   Tebay
Ravenglass   A591   Staveley
Torver   Kendal   Sedbergh
Crosthwaite   A684
A5092   Bouth   M6
Haverthwaite   Crooklands
Ayside   Milnthorpe
Ulverston   Kirkby Lonsdale
A590
Flookburgh
Barrow-in-Furness

Isle of Man
A3
A1
Kirk
Michael   A2
Laxey
A3
A5

0   30 km
0   20 miles

Tourist Information, bike hire & pitch and putt.

🔌 🎣 ☉ 🖥 🚩 ⟨ ⚓ ⌷ ✳ ⚙ ▮ 🖊 ⊞ T ✗ 📞 ♨
🐾 🐖 ♿
➔ ▶ 🥾
💷

Credit Cards 🔲 🔲 🔲 🔲 ⑤

Hawkrigg Farm (NY659203)
Colby CA16 6BB ☎ 017683 51046 Signposted
▷ 🚐 🚐 Å
Open all year Booking advisable Jul-Aug Last arrival
23.30hrs
Attractive level farm site in a pleasant and quiet location on the edge of the small village of Colby. On entering village from Appleby turn left signed Kings Meadburn and Newby, and site on right in 800 yards. A 1-acre site with 15 touring pitches.

🔌 🎣 ☉ ✳
➔ ▶ 🥾 🖥

ARMATHWAITE
Englethwaite Hall Caravan Club Site (NY487504)
CA4 9SY ☎ 01228 560202
Nearby town: Carlisle
▷ 🚐 🚐
Open 26 Mar-11 Oct Booking advisable bank hols Last
arrival 20.00hrs Last departure noon

Tranquil site in the grounds of the old hall close to the Inglewood forest in the serene Eden Valley. Do not approach through Armathwaite. From junc 42 of M6 or A6 onto B6263 signed Wetherall, and in 1.75m at Cumwhitton turn R signed Wetherall Shield and Armathwaite. Site on R in 2.75m. A 5-acre site with 100 touring pitches.

🔌 ▮ 🖊 ⊞ T 📞 🐾 🐾
➔ 🥾 🐖

Credit Cards 🔲 🔲

AYSIDE
Oak Head Caravan Park (SD389839)
LA11 6JA ☎ 015395 31475 Signposted
▶ ▶ 🚐 🚐 Å
Open Mar-Oct Booking advisable bank hols Last
departure noon
A tiered grassy site with some hardstandings set in hilly country with woodland, close to A590. A 3-acre site with 60 touring pitches and 71 statics.

🔌 🎣 ☉ 🖥 🚩 ✳ ▮ 🖊 ⊞ 📞 🐾
➔ ∪ 🍴 🥾 🌙

BARROW-IN-FURNESS
South End Caravan Site (SD208628)
Walney Island LA14 3YQ ☎ 01229 472823 & 471556
Signposted
▶ ▶ ★ 🚐 £6.50-£8.50 🚐 £6.50-£8.50 Å £6.50-£8.50
Open Mar-Oct Booking advisable Jul-Aug Last arrival
22.00hrs Last departure noon

Mainly level grass site adjacent to sea, and close to a nature reserve, on southern end of Walney Island. From Barrow cross bridge onto island and turn L into council estate and L again just before new private estate. Signed. A 3-acre site with 60 touring pitches and 100 statics.

Bowling green.

🏢 📻 ⊙ 🗑 ⌇ ⬜ ✳ ♀ 🏔 🛈 🍃 🔀 📞 🛒 ♿
➜ ∪ ▶ 🍴 ⚓
£

BASSENTHWAITE LAKE

See map for locations of sites in the vicinity

BOUTH

Black Beck Caravan Park (SD335855)
LA12 8JN ☎ 01229 861274 Signposted
Nearby town: Newby Bridge
▶ ▶ ▶ ★ 🚐 £8-£11.50 🚐 £7-£8.50 ▲ £5.50-£8
Open Mar-Nov Booking advisable bank hols Last arrival 20.00hrs Last departure 13.00hrs
A quiet site surrounded by woods and fields close to S Cumbria and the Lake District. N of A590. A 2-acre site with 75 touring pitches and 235 statics.

🏢 📻 ⊙ 🗑 ⌇ ✳ 🏔 🛈 🍃 🔀 ❌ 📞 🛒 ♿
➜ ∪ 🎵

BOWNESS-ON-WINDERMERE

Sites are listed under **Windermere**

BRAITHWAITE

Scotgate Caravan Park (NY235235)
CA12 5TJ ☎ 017687 78343 Signposted
Nearby town: Keswick
▶ ▶ ★ 🚐 £11.50-£13.50 🚐 fr £6.50 ▲ fr £6.50
Open Mar-Oct Last arrival 22.00hrs Last departure 21.00hrs
A pleasant rural site with dramatic views towards Skiddaw. Situated at junction of A66 and B5292, 2m from Keswick. An 8-acre site with 165 touring pitches and 35 statics.

🏢 📻 ⊙ 🗑 ⌇ 🔦 ✳ 🏔 🛈 🍃 📞
➜ ∪ ◎ 🗲 🍴 🎵

BRAMPTON

Irthing Vale Holiday Park (NY522613)
Old Church Ln CA8 2AA ☎ 01697 73600 Signposted
▶ ▶ ▶ 🚐 🚐 ▲
Open Mar-Oct Booking advisable public hols & Jul-Aug Last arrival 23.30hrs Last departure noon
A grassy site on the outskirts of the market town on the A6071. A 3-acre site with 30 touring pitches and 26 statics.

🏢 📻 ⊙ 🗑 ✳ 🏔 🛈 🍃 🔀 🛒
➜ ∪ ▶ 🗲 🎵 🗑

CARLISLE

Orton Grange Caravan & Camping Park (NY355519)
Orton Grange, Wigton Rd CA5 6LA ☎ 01228 710252
Signposted
▶ ▶ ▶ ★ 🚐 £6.60-£8 🚐 £6.60-£8 ▲ £6.60-£8
Open all year Booking advisable bank hols & Jul-Aug Last arrival 22.00hrs Last departure noon
Mainly grassy site in rural surroundings close to A595, 4m from Carlisle. A 6-acre site with 50 touring pitches and 22 statics.
Cafe & Fast food facilities in Apr-Sep only.

🏢 📻 ⊙ 🗑 ⌇ ⌇ 🔦 ⬜ ✳ 🏔 🛈 🍃 🔀 T ❌ 📞 🛒
🚿 🏮 🛒 ♿
➜ ∪ ▶ 🍴 🎵
£

Credit Cards 🔲 💳

Dandy Dinmont Caravan & Camping Park (NY399620)
Blackford CA6 4EA ☎ 01228 74611 (4m N on A7)
Signposted
▶ ▶ 🚐 £6.50-£6.75 🚐 £6.50-£6.75 ▲ £4.25-£5.50
Open Etr-Oct (rs Mar showers not available) Booking advisable high season Last arrival anytime Last departure 15.00hrs
A level, sheltered site, screened on two sides by hedgerows. Situated alongside A7 about 1m N of junction 44 of M6. A 4-acre site with 47 touring pitches and 15 statics.

🏢 📻 ⊙ 🗑 ✳ 🛈 🍃 📞 🏮
➜ ∪ ▶ ◎ 🎵 🛒
£

COCKERMOUTH

Violet Bank Caravan Park (NY126295)
Simonscales Ln, Off Lorton Rd CA13 9TG
☎ 01900 822169 Signposted
▶ ▶ ▶ 🚐 🚐 ▲
Open Mar-15 Nov Booking advisable Spring bank hol & Jul-Aug Last arrival mdnt Last departure noon
Well-maintained site in a pleasant rural setting affording excellent views of Buttermere Hills. Approach by way of A5292 Lorton Road, via town centre. A 6.5-acre site with 30 touring pitches and 86 statics.

🏢 📻 ⊙ 🗑 ✳ 🏔 🛈 🍃 🔀 T 📞 🐴 🛒
➜ ∪ ▶ 🎵

CONISTON

Park Coppice Caravan Club Site (SD295955)
LA21 8LA ☎ 01539 441555 (1.25m SW) Signposted
▶ ▶ ▶ 🚐 🚐 ▲
Open Apr-Oct Booking advisable bank hols & mid Jul-Aug Last arrival 20.00hrs Last departure noon
Landscaped site in National Trust woodland with pitches grouped in open glades. Access from site across fields to Coniston Water. Where possible approach from

➡

South on A590. Final approach from N or S is narrow in places. A 20-acre site with 300 touring pitches.
Veg prep area.

🔌 📶 ⊙ 🔲 🎣 ※ 🅼 🛊 ⊞ T ℄ ➡ 🛒 ♿
→ ∪ ▶ 🛆 ⚓ 🚣

Credit Cards 🆑 💳

CROOKLANDS

Waters Edge Caravan Park (SD533838)
LA7 7NN ☎ 015395 67708
Nearby town: Kendal
▶ ▶ ▶ ★ 🚐 £9.75-£12.75 🚐 £9.75-£12.75 ▲ £6.75-£8.75
Open Mar-14 Nov Booking advisable bank hols
A small rural site, close to junc 36 of M6 yet in a very peaceful setting. From M6 follow signs for Kirkby Lonsdale A65, at second roundabout follow signs for Crooklands/Endmoor. Site 1m on right. A 2-acre site with 30 touring pitches and 10 statics.

🔌 📶 ⊙ 🎣 ⚓ 🛒 ※ 🛊 🅼 ⊘ T ℄ 🍴 🛒 ♿
→ ∪ 🚣
£

Credit Cards 🆑 💳 🔗

CROSTHWAITE

Lambhowe Caravan Park (SD422914)
LA8 8JE ☎ 015395 68483 Signposted
Nearby town: Kendal
▶ 🚐 🚐
Open Mar-Oct (rs Mar) Booking advisable Etr, Spring bank hol & Jul-Aug Last arrival 21.00hrs Last departure noon
A secluded wooded site on A5074 between Lancaster and Windermere, ideal for touring the Lake District National Park. No tents. A 1-acre site with 14 touring pitches and 112 statics.

🔌 📶 ⊙ 🔲 🛒 🛊 ℄
→ ▶

CUMWHITTON

Cairndale Caravan Park (NY518523)
CA4 9BZ ☎ 01768 896280
Nearby town: Carlisle
▶ ▶ ★ 🚐 £4.50-£5 🚐 £4.50-£5
Open Mar-Oct Booking advisable school & public hols Last arrival 22.00hrs
Lovely grass site set in tranquil Eden Valley with good views. Off A69 at Warwick Bridge on unclass road through Great Corby to Cumwhitton, turn left at village sign, then site in 1m. A 2-acre site with 5 touring pitches and 15 statics.

🔌 📶 ⊙ ※ 🛊 ⊞
→ ∪ ▶ ⚓ 🚣 🛒
£

DALSTON

Dalston Hall Caravan Park (NY378519)
Dalston Hall Estate CA5 7JX ☎ 01228 710165
Signposted
Nearby town: Carlisle
▶ ▶ ▶ ★ 🚐 fr £6.50 🚐 fr £6.50 ▲ fr £5.50
Open Mar-Oct Booking advisable Jul-Aug Last arrival 21.00hrs Last departure 13.00hrs
A neat, well-maintained site, on level grassy ground, situated in grounds of estate located between Carlisle and Dalston on B5299. Ideal position for touring northern Lake District, Carlisle and surrounding country. A 3-acre site with 60 touring pitches and 17 statics. 9 hole golf course & fly fishing.

🔌 📶 ⊙ 🔲 🎣 ※ 🛒 🅼 🛊 ⊘ ⊞ T ✗ ℄ 🏌 🛒 🐕
→ ▶ 🎦 🚣
£

ESKDALE

Fisherground Farm Campsite (NY152002)
Fisherground CA19 1TF ☎ 019467 23319
▶ ▶ ⚓ 🚐 £7 ▲ £7
Open 8 Mar-14 Nov
A mainly level grassy site on farmland amidst beautiful scenery, in Eskdale Valley below Hardknott Pass, between Eskdale and Boot. A 3-acre site with 30 touring pitches and 5 statics.
Adventure playground and miniature railway.

📶 ⊙ 🔲 🎣 ※ 🅼 ⊞ ℄
→ 🚣 🛒
£

FLOOKBURGH

Lakeland Leisure Park (SD372743)
Moor Ln LA11 7LT ☎ 015395 58235 & 58556
▶ ▶ ▶ ⊕ 🚐 🚐 ▲
Open Mar-14 Nov (rs 15 Nov-3 Jan open wknds only for static plots) Booking advisable May-Oct Last arrival 21.00hrs Last departure 11.00hrs
A complete leisure park with full range of activities and entertainments, making this flat, grassy site ideal for families. Approach on B5277 through Grange over Sands to Flookburgh, turn left at village square, and park is in 1 mile. A 10-acre site with 120 touring pitches and 670 statics.
Pony trekking & entertainment centre.

🔌 📶 ⊙ 🔲 🎣 🍸 🎣 ⚓ ⚓ ※ 🛒 🅼 🛊 ⊘ ⊞ T ✗ ℄ 🏌 🐕 🛒 ♿
→ ∪ ▶ 🚣

GREYSTOKE

Thanet Well Caravan Park (NY398349)
CA11 OXX ☎ 017684 84262 Signposted
Nearby town: Penrith
▶ ▶ ▶ ★ 🚐 fr £8 🚐 ▲
Open Mar-Oct Booking advisable bank hols & Jul-Aug Last arrival 21.30hrs

*A very isolated site in lovely rolling countryside.
Approach from M6 at junction 41 and follow B5305 for
6m towards Wigtown. Turn left at sign for Lamonby and
follow signs. A 3-acre site with 20 touring pitches and 60
statics.*

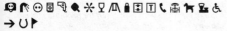

Whitbarrow Hall Caravan Park (NY405289)
Berrier CA11 OXB ☎ 01768 483456 Signposted
Nearby town: Penrith
► ► ► ⚬ £8-£10.80 ⚬ £8-£10.80 ⚬ £4-£8
Open Mar-Oct Booking advisable bank hols & for
electric hook up Last arrival 23.00hrs Last departure
23.00hrs
*A level grassy site, an ideal base for touring the Lake
District National Park. From Penrith towards Keswick
turn R off A66. An 8-acre site with 81 touring pitches and
167 statics.*
Table tennis, pool table & video games.

→ ∪ ►

HAVERTHWAITE

Bigland Hall Caravan Park (SD344833)
LA12 8PJ ☎ 01539 531702 Signposted
Nearby town: Grange-over-Sands
► ► ► ★ ⚬ £6-£7.25 ⚬ fr £6
Open Mar-Oct Booking advisable public hols Last arrival
22.30hrs Last departure 13.00hrs
*A wooded site in lovely countryside with direct access
from B5278. 3m from the southern end of Lake
Windermere and near the Haverthwaite Steam Railway.
A 30-acre site with 86 touring pitches and 29 statics.*
Off-licence on site.

→ ∪ ⚬ 🐾

HAWKSHEAD

Camping & Caravanning Club Site (SD337943)
Grizedale Hall LA22 0GL ☎ 01229 860257(in season) &
01203 694995
Nearby town: Ambleside
► ► ★ ⚬ £8.40-£10 ⚬ £8.40-£10
Open end Mar-early Oct Booking advisable Spring bank
hol & Jul-Aug Last arrival 21.00hrs Last departure noon
*A peaceful, sloping site with level pitches set in
Grizedale Forest, with lots of marked walks. Close to the
famous theatre in the forest with its live shows. Take
A590 from Newby Bridge via Greenodd, then minor
road to right at Penny Bridge. Please see the
advertisement on page 27 for details of Club Members'
benefits. A 3-acre site with 60 touring pitches.*

→ ⚬ 🐾

Credit Cards 💳 💳 💳

KENDAL

Camping & Caravanning Club Site (SD525948)
Millcrest, Skelsmergh, Shap Rd LA9 6NY ☎ 01539
741363 (in season) & 01203 694995 Signposted
► ► ► ★ ⚬ £9.30-£10 ⚬ £9.30-£10 ⚬ £9.30-£10
Open end Mar-early Nov Booking advisable bank hols &
high season Last arrival 21.00hrs Last departure 21.00hrs
*Sloping grass site, set in hilly wood and meadowland.
Situated on the A6, 1.5m N of Kendal. Please see
advertisement on page 27 for details of Club Members'
benefits. A 2-acre site with 55 touring pitches.*

→ ∪ ► ⚬

Credit Cards 💳 💳 💳

Low Park Wood Caravan Club Site (SD509878)
Sedgwick LA8 0JZ ☎ 015395 60186 (3m SW) Signposted
► ► ► ★ ⚬ £6-£12 ⚬ £6-£12
Open Apr-Oct Booking advisable bank hols & Jul-Aug
Last arrival 20.00hrs Last departure noon no cars by
tents
*Peaceful site with a stream at one end, and pitching
amongst glades of wild flowers at the other end. Follow
signs for Sedgwick off A590 down unclass rd for 150yds,
and site .5m along private rd. A 20-acre site with 180
touring pitches.*
Veg prep area.

→ ∪ ► 🍼 ⚬

Credit Cards 💳 💳 💳 💳

KESWICK

Camping & Caravanning Club Site (NY258234)
Derwentwater CA12 5EP ☎ 01768 772392 (in season) &
01203 694995 Signposted
► ► ► ★ ⚬ £9.40-£10.20 ⚬ £9.40-£10.20 ⚬ £9.40-£10.20
Open end Jan-end Nov Booking advisable all season
Last arrival 21.00hrs Last departure noon
*A well-situated lakeside site within walking distance of
the town centre. Please see advertisement on page 27
for details of Club Members' benefits. An 11-acre site
with 250 touring pitches.*

→ ∪ ⚬ 🍼 ⚬

Credit Cards 💳 💳 💳

Derwentwater Caravan Park (NX257234)
Crowe Park Rd CA12 5EN ☎ 017687 72579 Signposted
► ► ► ★ ⚬ £7.60-£8.40 ⚬ £7.60-£8.40
Open Mar-14 Nov Booking advisable at all times Last
arrival 22.00hrs Last departure noon
*A very well managed and maintained site which is
divided into two areas for tourers. Signed off B5289 in
town centre. A 4-acre site with 50 touring pitches and
160 statics.*

→ ∪ ► ⚬ ⚬ 🍼 ⚬ 🐾

Low Manesty Caravan Club Site (NY251187)
Manesty CA12 5UG ☎ 017687 77275
▷ ♠ 🚐 🚐
Open Apr-Oct Booking advisable bank hols, Jun-Sep &
late Oct Last arrival dusk Last departure noon
*A superbly peaceful site in lovely surroundings. Bypass
Keswick on A66 signed Cockermouth, turn L at rndbt
and follow signs to B5289. In 4.25m turn R over bridge
(check it is clear first) and site on R in 1m. When towing
do not travel along W side of Derwentwater. No arrivals
before noon or after dark. A 12-acre site with 60 touring
pitches.*

🏵 🎍 🖉 🚽 🇹 📞
➔ 🍴

Credit Cards

KIRKBY LONSDALE

Woodclose Caravan Park (SD618786)
Casterton LA6 2SE ☎ 01524 271597 Signposted
▶ ▶ ▶ ♠♠ ★ 🚐 £8-£13 🚐 £8-£11.50 ⚑ £5-£10
Open Mar-Oct Booking advisable bank hols, Jul-Aug &
Sep Last arrival 23.00hrs Last departure 16.00hrs
*A pleasant site in a quiet, rural area. Situated off the
A65, .5m SE of the town. A 9-acre site with 70 touring
pitches and 50 statics.*

🏵 📞 ⊙ 🗒 ✳ 🕭 🎍 🖉 🚽 📞 🐾 👌
➔ ▶ 🍴
💷

▶ ▶ ▶

Pennine View
Caravan & Camping Park

Cumbria Tourist Board
MEMBER

Station Road, Kirkby Stephen,
Cumbria CA17 4SZ. Tel: (017683) 71717

*Pennine View Caravan & Camping Park is a family
run site on the south side of the beautiful market town
of Kirkby Stephen, one mile from the town centre. An
ideal walking area, en route for the Coast to Coast
walk, within easy reach of the Yorkshire Dales and the
Lake District. Also within easy reach of the Settle to
Carlisle railway line. Kirkby Stephen station 1 mile.
Amenities: Modern toilet block with hot & cold
water, showers, hair dryers and razor points. Dish
washing area. Full laundry facilities. Chemical
disposal point. Calor & Camping Gas. Children's
play area. Milk & newspapers daily.*

Proprietors: Colin & Shiela Sim

KIRKBY STEPHEN

Pennine View Caravan & Camping Park (NY772076)
Pennine View, Station Rd CA17 4SZ ☎ 01768 371717
▶ ▶ ▶ ★ 🚐 fr £9.50 🚐 fr £9.50 ⚑ fr £7.75
Open Mar-Oct Booking advisable bank hols & Jul-Aug
Last arrival 22.00hrs Last departure 12.30hrs
*Once a railway goods yard on a now disused line, this is
an attractive, level, well-maintained site with river walks,
situated on the coast to coast path. 100 metres off A685
on the B6270. A 2.5-acre site with 43 touring pitches.*

🏵 📞 ⊙ 🗒 🕭 🎍 🖉 👌
➔ 🍴

KIRKBY THORE

Low Moor Caravan Site (NY624259)
CA10 1XQ ☎ 017683 61231
Nearby town: Appleby-in-Westmorland
▶ ▶ 🚐 🚐 ⚑
Open Apr-Oct Booking advisable high season Last
arrival 23.00hrs
*A small farm site with well cared for grounds and clean
sanitary facilities. 7m SE of Penrith on A66. A 2-acre site
with 25 touring pitches and 25 statics.*

🏵 📞 ⊙ 🗒 ✳ 🕭 🎍 🖉 🚽 📞 🐾 🎣 🐄 👌

LAMPLUGH

Inglenook Caravan Park (NY084206)
Fitzbridge CA14 4SH ☎ 01946 861240 Signposted
Nearby town: Cockermouth
▶ ▶ ▶ ♠ ★ 🚐 £7.35-£8.20 🚐 £7.35-£8.20 ⚑ £4-£8.20
Open all year Booking advisable bank hols Last arrival
20.00hrs Last departure noon
*An ideal touring site, well-maintained and situated in
beautiful surroundings just off A5086. A 3-acre site with
36 touring pitches and 22 statics.*

🏵 📞 ⊙ 🗒 ✳ 🕭 🎍 🖉 🚽 ✗ 📞 🐄 👌
➔ 🍴
💷

Dockray Meadow Caravan Club Site (NY085204)
CA14 4SH ☎ 01946 861357
▷ ♠ 🚐 🚐
Open 26 Mar-18 Oct Booking advisable bank hols
*A well-screened and sheltered site with a tumbling
stream running down one side and the fells behind. On
unclass rd past Lamplugh Tip pub signed Loweswater,
Lamplugh Green and Buttermere. Turn right in .75m and
site signed on right. A 4.5-acre site with 53 touring
pitches.*

🎍
➔ 🍴 🐄

LONGTOWN

Camelot Caravan Park (NY391666)
CA6 5SZ ☎ 01228 791248 Signposted
▶ ▶ ★ 🚐 fr £6.20 🚐 fr £6.20 ⚑ £3-£6.20
Open Mar-Oct Booking advisable Jul-Aug Last arrival
22.00hrs Last departure noon

Very pleasant level grassy site near junction 44 of M6. Ideal stopover site. A 1.5-acre site with 20 touring pitches and 1 static.

🏕🅿☉✳🔋🅰⏚🐕⛟
➜∪🅿♪
£

MEALSGATE

Larches Caravan Park (NY205415)
☎016973 71379 Signposted
▶▶▶▶ ♈♈ 🚐🚐 🅰

Open Mar-Oct (rs early & late season) Booking advisable Etr Spring bank hol & Jul-Aug Last arrival 21.30hrs Last departure noon
Set in wooded rural surroundings on the fringe of the Lake District National Park. Situated on A595 Carlisle-Cockermouth road. A 5-acre site with 73 touring pitches and 100 statics.
Ensuite units with toilets, shower, washbasin.

🏕🅿☉📷🍴🎣 ⬤🔲✳⋀🔋🅰⏚🔋🅣📞🐕
⛟♿
➜∪🅿♪

MILNTHORPE

Fell End Caravan Park (SD505780)
Slackhead Rd, Hale LA7 7BS
☎ 015395 62122 Signposted
▶▶▶▶ ♣♈♈ 🚐🚐 🅰

Open all year Booking advisable school & bank hols
Well-kept site, constantly improving and with high standards being continually maintained. Pleasantly situated in a very picturesque natural setting surrounded by woodland. Within easy reach of the lakes and South Cumbria. 4.75m from junction 35 of M6. An 8-acre site with 68 touring pitches and 215 statics.
Off-licence, TV aerial hook ups, kitchen facility.

🏕🅿☉📷🍴🔲✳⋀🔋🅰⏚🔋🅣📞🛒⛟♿
➜∪🅿🔺♪

PENRITH

Lowther Caravan Park (NY527265)
Eamont Bridge CA10 2JB ☎ 01768 863631 Signposted
▶▶▶▶ 🚐 £9-£10 🚐 £9-£10 🅰 £9-£10
Open mid Mar-mid Nov Booking advisable bank hols Last arrival 21.00hrs
A secluded natural woodland site with lovely on-site riverside walks and glorious surrounding countryside. From Penrith site is 3m S of Penrith on A6. A 10-acre site with 150 touring pitches and 407 statics.

🏕🅿☉📷🍴✳🍷⋀🔋🅰⏚🅣✖📞🛒🐕⛟♿
➜∪🅿♟♪
£

Thacka Lea Caravan Site (NY509310)
Thacka Ln CA11 9HX ☎ 01768 863319 Signposted
▶▶▶ 🚐 fr £6 🚐 fr £6
Open Mar-Oct Booking advisable public hols
A good, spotlessly clean site in urban area just off A6 and signed. A 2-acre site with 25 touring pitches.

🏕🅿☉✳🔋🅰⏚🔋
➜∪🅿♟♪⛟
£

PENRUDDOCK

Beckses Caravan Site (NY419278)
CA11 0RX ☎ 01768 483224 Signposted
▶▶▶ 🚐 fr £6 🚐 fr £6 🅰 £4.50-£6
Open Etr-Oct Booking advisable public hols Last arrival 20.00hrs Last departure 11.00hrs
A small site on sloping ground with level pitches and views of distant fells, on edge of National Park. From A66 towards Keswick turn right onto B5288. A 4-acre site with 23 touring pitches and 18 statics.

🏕🅿☉✳⋀🔋🅰⏚🔋🅣📞
➜∪♪⛟

POOLEY BRIDGE

Hillcroft Caravan & Camping Site (NY478241)
Roe Head Ln CA10 2LT ☎ 017684 86363 Signposted
Nearby town: Penrith
▶▶▶ 🚐🚐 🅰
Open Mar-14 Nov Booking advisable bank hols
A pleasant rural site close to the village and Ullswater; ➡

an ideal touring base. From A592 fork L just before Pooley Bridge, and site is signed on L. A 10-acre site with 125 touring pitches and 200 statics.

🔧 ⓡ 🌣 ⊡ 🏴 ※ 🅰 🅐 ⊕ ⊡ ① ✆ 🖳 ⚲
→ ∪ ⚠ ↯ ⤳ ◢

RAVENGLASS

Walls Caravan & Camping Park (SD087964)
CA18 1SR ☎ 01229 717250 Signposted
▶ ▶ ▶ ★ 🚐 £6.75 🚐 £6.50 🅰 £3.50-£6.75
Open Mar-15 Nov Booking advisable bank hols & summer Last arrival 22.00hrs Last departure noon
A well-maintained site in a woodland park with all hardstandings. Situated off A595 close to Ravenglass-Eskdale narrow railway service. A 5-acre site with 50 touring pitches.
Washing up sinks with free hot water.

🔧 ⓡ 🌣 ⊡ 🏴 ※ 🅐 ⊘ ⊡ ① 🏮 🖳
→ ◢ ⤳

SEDBERGH

Pinfold Caravan Park (SD665921)
Garsdale Rd LA10 5JL ☎ 01539 620576 Signposted
▶ ▶ ▶ 🚐 £8 🚐 £7.50 🅰 £7.50
Open Mar-Oct Booking advisable bank hols & Jul-Aug Last arrival 21.30hrs Last departure 13.30hrs
A mature site amongst beautiful scenery on a river bank; at edge of village on the Hawes road. A 4-acre site with 54 touring pitches and 56 statics.

🔧 ⓡ 🌣 ⊡ 🏴 ※ 🅐 ⊘ ⊡ ✆ 🖳
→ ∪ ▶ ⤳

SILLOTH

Stanwix Park Holiday Centre (NY108527)
Green Row CA5 4HH ☎ 016973 31671 (1m SW on B5300) Signposted
▶ ▶ ▶ ▶ ⊕ ★ 🚐 £7-£8.70 🚐 £7-£8.70 🅰 £7-£8.70
Open May-mid Sep (rs Apr & Oct no mid week entertainment or pool) Booking advisable Etr, Spring bank hol & Jul-Aug Last arrival 21.00hrs Last departure 11.00hrs
A large well-run family site within easy reach of the Lake District. Attractively laid-out, with lots of amenities to ensure a lively holiday. On outskirts of Silloth on B5300. A 4-acre site with 121 touring pitches and 212 statics.
Pony trekking & entertainment.

🔧 🛏 ⓡ 🌣 ⊡ 🏴 ⤳ 🔍 🔑 ◵ ⊡ ※ ♀ 🏴 🅐 ⊘ ① ✖
✆ 🏮 🖳
→ ∪ ▶ ◎ ⤳
💷

Credit Cards ▨ ▨ ▨ ▨ 🔵

Tanglewood Caravan Park (NY131534)
Causewayhead CA5 4PE ☎ 016973 31253 Signposted
▶ ▶ ▶ 🚐 £9 🚐 £9 🅰 £9
Open Mar-Oct Booking advisable Etr, Whit & Jul-Aug Last arrival 23.00hrs Last departure 10.00hrs

Mainly level grass site sheltered by a variety of trees and bushes, and set in meadowland adjacent to B5302 Wigton-Silloth road. A 2-acre site with 31 touring pitches and 58 statics.

🔧 ⓡ 🌣 ⊡ 🏴 🔍 🔑 ⊔ ※ ♀ 🏴 🅐 ⊡ ✆ 🐕 🐾
→ ∪ ▶ ⤳ 🖳
💷

STAVELEY

Ashes Lane Caravan & Camping Park (SD478962)
Ashes Ln LA8 9JS ☎ 01539 821119 Signposted
▶ ▶ ▶ ▶ 🚐 🚐 🅰
Open mid Mar-mid Jan Last departure noon
Large, well-equipped park in naturally secluded Lake District area. An 18-acre site with 200 touring pitches and 68 statics.

🔧 ⓡ 🌣 ⊡ 🏴 🔍 🔑 ⊔ ♀ 🏴 🅐 ✖ ✆ 🖳 🖳

TEBAY

Tebay Caravan Site (NY609060)
Orton CA10 3SB ☎ 015396 24511 Signposted
Nearby town: Kendal
▶ ▶ ▶ ★ 🚐 fr £6.50 🚐 fr £6.50
Open 14 Mar-Oct Booking advisable Jul-Aug Last departure noon
An ideal stopover site and good for touring the Lake District. Screened by high grass banks, bushes and trees. Site is adjacent to M6 at Tebay Service area .75m N of exit 38 for northbound traffic. Southbound traffic

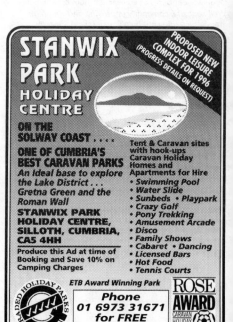

join northbound at junction 38, and can easily rejoin motorway with site warden's instructions. A 4-acre site with 70 touring pitches.

 🔌 ⊙ 🗄 🍳 ⚡ ⚐ 🔋 ✕ 🔦 🎣 🛖 🎪 ⛺ 🐕 🐴 🏪 ♿ ➜ ∪ ▶ 🏕 ♨ 🎵

⊞

TORVER

Hoathwaite Farm (SD296949)
LA21 8AX ☎ 015394 41349
Nearby town: Ulverston
▷ 🚐 🚗 🅰

Open all year Booking advisable all times Last arrival mdnt Last departure noon
A farm site with gently sloping fields on Coniston Lake edge, with superb views and tranquility. Turn E off A593 .5m N of Torver, 2.5m S of Coniston. A 20-acre site with 5 touring pitches and 29 statics.
Lake access for all associated sport.

✳ 🏪
➜ ∪ 🎣 🎵

TROUTBECK (NEAR KESWICK)

Troutbeck Head Caravan Park (NY383254)
CA11 0SS ☎ 017684 83521 Signposted
Nearby town: Keswick
▶ ▶ ▶ ★ 🚐 £5.75-£6.75 🚗 £5.75-£6.75
Open Mar-mid Jan Booking advisable bank & school hols Last arrival 21.00hrs Last departure 11.00hrs
A natural, unspoilt site surrounded by towering fells. Off A5091, 1m from A66. A 12-acre site with 54 touring pitches and 75 statics.

🔌 ⊙ 🗄 🍳 ⚡ ⚐ 🎣 🔋 🐕 🏪
➜ ∪ ▶ 🎣 🎵

ULVERSTON

Bardsea Leisure Park (SD292765)
Priory Rd LA12 9QE ☎ 01229 584712 Signposted
▶ ▶ ▶ ★ 🚐 £4.75-£12.95 🚗 £4.75-£12.95 🅰 £4.75-£10
Open Mar-Nov Booking advisable bank hols & Jul-Aug Last arrival 21.00hrs Last departure 18.00hrs
Attractively landscaped former quarry making a quiet and very sheltered site. On southern edge of town off the A5087, convenient for both the coast and the Lake District. A 5-acre site with 83 touring pitches and 73 statics.

🔌 ⊙ 🗄 🍳 ✳ 🎣 🔋 ⚐ ⊞ 🕐 🔦 🛖 🐕 🏪
➜ ∪ ▶ 🏕 🎵
⊞

WATERMILLOCK

Cove Caravan & Camping Park (NY431236)
Ullswater CA11 0LS
☎ 017684 86549 Signposted
Nearby town: Penrith
▶ ▶ ▶ ♠ 🏕 🚐 🚗 🅰
Open Etr-Oct Booking advisable bank & school hols Last arrival 21.00hrs Last departure noon

---

A family site in attractive rural setting amidst fells with views over the lake. Leave M6 at junction 40, turn W following signs for Ullswater (A592). Turn right at lake junction, then right at Brackenrigg Hotel. Site is 1.5m on left. A 3-acre site with 50 touring pitches and 38 statics.
Dishwashing area, drinks machine.

🔌 ⊙ 🗄 🍳 ✳ 🎣 ⚐ ⚡ ⊞ 🕐 🔦 🛖 🐕 🏪
➜ ∪ 🎣 🎵

The Quiet Site (NY431236)
Ullswater CA11 0LS ☎ 01768 486337 Signposted
▶ ▶ ▶ ♠ ★ 🚐 £7.50-£9 🚗 £6.50-£8 🅰 £6.50-£8
Open Mar-Oct Booking advisable bank hols & Jul-Aug Last arrival 22.00hrs Last departure noon
A well-maintained site in a lovely, peaceful location, with very good facilities, including a charming olde-worlde bar. Leave M6 at junction 40, turn W following signs for Ullswater (A592). Turn right at lake junction, then right at Brackenrigg Hotel. Site is 1.5m on right. A 6-acre site with 60 touring pitches and 23 statics.

🔌 ⊙ 🗄 🍳 🔦 🎣 ✳ 🎣 ⚐ ⚡ ⊞ 🕐 🔦 🐕 🏪
➜ ∪ 🎣 🎵

Ullswater Caravan Camping Site & Marine Park (NY438232)
CA11 0LR ☎ 01768 486666 Signposted
Nearby town: Ullswater
▶ ▶ ▶ ★ 🚐 fr £6.20 🚗 fr £4.65 🅰 fr £6.20
Open Mar-Nov Booking advisable public hols Last arrival 22.00hrs Last departure noon
A pleasant rural site with own nearby boat launching and marine storage facility. Leave M6 at junction 40, turn W following signs for Ullswater (A592) for 5 miles. Turn right alongside Ullswater for 2 miles, then turn right at telephone box signposted Longthwaite and Watermillock Church. Site .5 mile on right. A 9-acre site with 155 touring pitches and 55 statics.
Boat launching & moorings.

🔌 ⊙ 🔦 🎣 ✳ 🎣 ⚐ ⚡ ⊞ 🕐 ✕ 🔦 🐕 🏪 ♿
➜ ∪ ⛵ 🎣 🎵
⊞

WESTWARD

Clea Hall Holiday Park (NY279425)
CA7 8NQ ☎ 016973 42880 Signposted
Nearby town: Wigton
▶ ▶ ▶ ★ 🚐 £6-£7 🚗 £6-£7 🅰 £6-£7
Open Mar-Nov Booking advisable bank hols & Jul-Aug Last departure noon
A slightly sloping grassy site surrounded by woods, moorland and hills. 3.5m S of A595. A 10-acre site with 50 touring pitches and 83 statics.

🔌 ⊙ 🗄 🍳 🔦 🎣 ✳ 🎣 ⚐ ⚡ 🔋 🔦 🎣 🐕 🏪 ♿
➜ ∪ 🎣

See advertisement on page 88

WESTWARD : WIGTON : CUMBRIA : CA7 8NQ
Telephone: WIGTON (016973) 42880

Quiet, privately owned park situated
on the fringe of the Lake District
National Park.

Ideal base for visiting the
Lakes or Gretna Green.

Also caters for the country lovers who
can explore miles of footpaths.

Touring caravans and tents welcome.

WINDERMERE

Fallbarrow Park (SD401973)
Rayrigg Rd LA23 3DL ☎ 015394 44428 Signposted
▶ ▶ ▶ ▶ ♦♦ ⊕ £10.35-£15.55 ⊕ £10.35-£15.55
Open mid Mar-Oct Booking advisable bank hols & Jul-
Aug Last arrival 23.00hrs Last departure 13.00hrs
*A well-organised site with many facilities, a few
minutes' walk from Bowness on shore of Lake
Windermere. A 32-acre site with 83 touring pitches and
248 statics.*
Boat launching facilities.
See advertisement under Colour Section

🔌 🐾 ⊙ 🖥 🍴 ⚡ 🖵 🔆 ☂ 🏔 🔋 🖉 🛈 ✕ 📞 🚐 🏧
🗑 🐕 🛁
→ ∪ 🅿 ◎ 🔺 ☘ 🎯 🎣
💷

Credit Cards 🃏 🃏 🃏 🃏 🃏

**Limefitt Park
(NY416032)**
LA23 1PA ☎ 015394 32300
▶ ▶ ▶ ▶ ♦ ♦♦ ⊕ ⊕ £11.50-£14.50 ⊕ £11.50-£14.50
▲ £11-£13.50
Open 1 wk prior Etr-Oct Booking advisable bank hols &
Jun-Sep Last arrival 22.30hrs Last departure noon
*A lovely family site with superb facilities in a beautiful
location in the Lake District National Park. Direct access
off A592 approach from Windermere but do not enter*

Troutbeck village. A 12-acre site with 165 touring pitches and 45 statics.
Cycle hire & pony-trekking.
See advertisement under Colour Section

🔲 ⛽ ☉ 🔋 ⚡ 📞 ➕ ☀ ♀ ◭ 🎁 ⊘ 🆃 ✕ ☎ ⚕ ⛲

🎋 🐕 🐎

→ ∪ ▶ ⚓ 🔆 ♨ ♪

💷

Credit Cards ▨ ▰ ▰ ▨ ▨ 🅢

Park Cliffe Farm Camping & Caravan Estate (SD391912)
Birks Rd, Tower Wood LA23 3PG ☎ 01539 531344
Signposted
▶ ▶ ▶ ★ 🚐 £8-£13 🚐 £8.50-£10 ▲ £8-£10
Open Mar-Oct Booking advisable bank hols & Aug Last arrival 22.00hrs Last departure noon
A lovely hillside site on level and sloping ground with trees, bushes, rocks and mountain stream. 3m S of Windermere off A592. A 25-acre site with 250 touring pitches and 50 statics.
Off-licence.

🔲 ⛽ ☉ 🔋 ⚡ ☀ ◭ 🎁 ⊘ 🎁 ✕ ☎ ⚕ 🎋 🐕 🐎

→ ∪ ▶ ◎ ⚓ 🔆 ♪

💷

Credit Cards ▨ ▰ ▨

DERBYSHIRE

For the map of this county, see Staffordshire

ASHBOURNE

Sandybrook Hall Holiday Park (SK179481)
Buxton Rd DE6 2AQ ☎ 01335 342679 (1m N of Ashbourne on A515) Signposted
▶ ▶ 🚐 🚐 ▲
Open 26 Mar-Oct Booking advisable public hols & Jul-Aug
A well-equipped touring site on mostly sloping grass. Leave Ashbourne on A515 Buxton rd, and site on right in 2m opp sign for Thorpe and Dovedale. An 8-acre site with 70 touring pitches and 25 statics.
Bar meals, sand pit.

🔲 ⛽ ☉ ⚡ 📞 ☀ ♀ ◭ 🎁 ⊘ 🆃 ☎ ⚕ 🐕 🐎

→ ∪ ⚓ ♪

BAKEWELL

Greenhills Caravan Park (SK202693)
Crow Hill Ln DE45 1PX ☎ 01629 813467 & 813052
Signposted
▶ ▶ ▶ 🚐 🚐 ▲
Open all year (rs Oct-Apr bar & shop closed) Booking advisable school & bank hols Last arrival 23.00hrs Last departure noon
Nicely kept and run site. Tenting field well cut with path

of shorter grass to facilities block. NW of Bakewell on A6 for 1m, and site signed before Ashford in the Water, 50yds up unclass rd on right. An 8-acre site with 90 touring pitches and 60 statics.

🔲 ⛽ ☉ 🔋 ⚡ ☀ ♀ ◭ 🎁 ⊘ 🎁 🆃 ☎ 🐕 🐎

→ ▶ 🔲

Chatsworth Park Caravan Club Site (SK257712)
Chatsworth DE4 1PN ☎ 01246 582226 (4m NE)
▶ ▶ ♦ 🚐 🚐
Open Apr-Oct Booking advisable bank hols & wknds Last arrival 20.00hrs Last departure noon no cars by tents
Set in an old walled garden on the Chatsworth estate with views of the countryside, a beautiful rural site. Entrance is by private access along single track lane with passing places. No access through Chatsworth estate. A 6.5-acre site with 111 touring pitches.

🔲 ⛽ ☉ 🔋 ⚡ ⚡ ☀ ◭ 🎁 🎁 🆃 ☎ ⚕ ♿

→ ▶

Credit Cards ▨ ▰

BUXTON

Grin Low Caravan Club Site (SK046722)
Grin Low Rd, Ladmanlow SK17 6UJ ☎ 01298 77735 (2m SW) Signposted
▶ ▶ ★ 🚐 £10-£12.25 🚐 £10-£12.25 ▲ £11.80-£12.80
Open Apr-Oct Booking advisable bank hols & Jul-Aug Last arrival 20.00hrs Last departure noon
Former quarry imaginatively developed and landscaped. Well covered with grass and shrubs. A54 from ➡

Congleton too narrow and steep for towed caravans. An 11-acre site with 132 touring pitches.

🔧 📻 ☉ 🍴 🍳 ✳ ⚙ 🛁 🖉 🖃 🅣 📞
→ 🔌 ▶ 🍴 ♪

Credit Cards 🔳 🔲

Limetree Holiday Park (SK070725)
Dukes Dr SK17 9RP ☎ 01298 22988
▶ ▶ 🚐 🛆

Open Mar-Oct Booking advisable bank hols & Jul-Aug
Last arrival 21.00hrs Last departure noon
A most attractive and well-designed site, set on the side of a narrow valley in an elevated situation of gently sloping land with views. Leaving Buxton on A515 S, turn L after hospital and site is .25m on R. A 10.5-acre site with 35 touring pitches and 36 statics.

🔧 📻 ☉ 🍴 🍳 ✳ ⚙ 🛁 🖉 🖃 🅣 📞 🐕 🛒 ♿
→ 🔌 ▶ ◎ ⚠ 🌿 🍴

Credit Cards 🔳 🔲

Thornheyes Farm Campsite (SK084761)
Thornheyes Farm, Longridge Ln, Peak Dale SK17 8AD
☎ 01298 26421
▶ 🚐 fr £4.25 🚐 fr £3.25 🛆 fr £4

Open all year Booking advisable bank hols & high season Last arrival 22.30hrs Last departure evenings
A pleasant farm site run by a friendly family team, in the central Peak District. 1.5m N of Buxton on A6 turn east for Peak Dale, and after .5m south at crossroads, site is on right up Longridge Lane. A 2-acre site with 10 touring pitches.

🔧 📻 ✳ 🛁 🖃
→ 🔌 ▶ 🍴 📻 🛒

AWARD

Losehill Caravan Club Site (SK155834)
☎01433 620636 (0.5m NE)

▶ ▶ ▶ 🚿 👫 🚐 🚐 🛆

Open Apr-Oct Booking advisable bank hols & wknds
Last arrival 20.00hrs Last departure noon no cars by tents
A level site surrounded by trees, in the northern part of the Peak Park. A good base for many outdoor activities. A 6-acre site with 100 touring pitches.

🔧 📻 ☉ 🍴 🍳 ⚙ 🛁 🖃 🅣 📞 🐕 🛒 ♿

Credit Cards 🔳 🔲

Camping & Caravanning Club Site (SK072993)
SK14 7HZ ☎ 01457 866057 (in season) & 01203 694995 Signposted
Nearby town: Hyde
▶ ▶ 🚿 ★ 🛆 £6.60-£7.50

Open end Mar-end Oct Booking advisable bank hols & Jun-Aug Last arrival 21.00hrs Last departure noon
A beautifully located moorland site, overlooking the reservoirs and surrounded by hills. Tents only. Off the

---

A628. .5m from Glossop take B6105. Please see the advertisement on page 27 for details of Club Members' benefits. A 2-acre site with 45 touring pitches.

📻 ☉ 🍳 📞 🛒
→ ♪

Credit Cards 🔳 🔲 🔳

Coopers Caravan Site (SK121859)
Newfold Farm, Edale Village S30 2ZD ☎ 01433 670372
▶ ▶ 🚐 🚐 🛆

Open all year Booking advisable bank hols Last arrival 23.30hrs Last departure 15.00hrs
Rising grassland behind a working farm, divided by a wall into two fields, culminating in the 2062ft Edale Moor. Facilities converted from original farm buildings. Only 15 vans accepted. From A625 at Hope take minor rd for 4m to Edale, and site 800rds on the right. A 6-acre site with 135 touring pitches and 11 statics.

🔧 📻 ☉ 🍳 ✳ 🛁 🖉 🖃 ✖ 📞 🛒
→ 🔌

Caravan Club Site (SK412332)
Elvaston Castle Country Park, Borrowash Rd DE7 3EP
☎ 01332 573735
▶ ▶ 🚐 🚐 🛆

Open Apr-Oct Booking advisable bank hols & wknds
Last arrival 20.00hrs Last departure noon no cars by tents
Attractively laid out site in a lovely 200-acre country park. A 3-acre site with 55 touring pitches.

📻 ☉ 🍴 🍳 🛁 🖃 📞 🛒
→ 🔌

Credit Cards 🔳 🔲

Bank Top Farm (SK181498)
DE6 1LF ☎ 01335 350250
Nearby town: Ashbourne
▶ ▶ ▶ ★ 🚐 £4.25-£4.75 🚐 £4.25-£4.75 🛆 £4.25-£4.75

Open Etr-Sep Booking advisable peak periods Last arrival 22.00hrs Last departure 15.00hrs
Gently sloping grass site with some level pitches on working dairy farm, just off B5056. A 2-acre site with 36 touring pitches and 15 statics.
Working dairy farm with viewing gallery.

🔧 📻 ☉ 🍳 ✳ 🛒
→ ▶ ♪

Camping & Caravanning Club Site (SK049868)
Kinder Rd SK12 5LE ☎ 01663 745394 (in season) & 01203 694995 Signposted
Nearby town: Stockport
▶ ▶ ★ 🚐 £7.50-£8.20 🛆 £7.50-£8.20

Open end Mar-end Oct Booking advisable bank hols & peak periods Last arrival 21.00hrs Last departure noon
Pleasant site bordered by trees near the River Sett, off

A624. Please see advertisement on page 27 for details of Club Members' benefits. A 7-acre site with 90 touring pitches.
Drying room.

🏕☉🍴✳🅿🌿📞
➜🛒

Credit Cards 🔷 💳 💳

KIRK IRETON

Blackwall Plantation Caravan Club Site (SK250497)
Blackwall DE6 3JL ☎ 01335 370903
Nearby town: Ashbourne
▶▶🚐🚐

Open 26 Mar-3 Jan Booking advisable bank hols & Jun-Aug Last arrival 20.00hrs Last departure noon
A beautifully landscaped site on rising ground in a pine plantation. Pitches are in open clearings separated by trees, giving plenty of privacy. From Ashbourne on A417 for 3.5m, turn left at fork in 1.5m, and site on right in .5m. A 25-acre site with 150 touring pitches.
Veg prep area.

🏕🏕☉🔲🍴🅰🅿🛒
➜🔺✚🎵

Credit Cards 🔷 💳

MATLOCK

Darwin Forest Country Park (SK302649)
Darley Moor, Two Dales DE4 5LN
☎ 01629 732428 (3m NW off B5057) Signposted
▶▶▶🅿👫🚐 £11-£14.50 🚐 fr £11
Open all year Booking advisable bank hols & Jul-Aug Last arrival 21.00hrs Last departure 10.00hrs
A mostly level woodland site set amongst tall pines in the heart of the Derbyshire Dales. 3m NW off B5057. A 9-acre site with 57 touring pitches and 3 statics.

🏕🏕☉🔲🍴🔳 🍷🔲✳🍽🅰🅿✖📞🐕🛒
♿
➜∪🅿🎵🎵

£

Credit Cards 🔷 💳

@@@@@@@@@

Packhorse Farm (SK323617)
Tansley DE4 5LF ☎ 01629 582781
▶▶★🚐 £5.50-£8.50 🚐 £5.50-£7.50 🅰 £5.50-£7.50
Open all year Booking advisable bank hols Last arrival 22.30hrs Last departure noon
A pleasant, well-run farm site in quiet situation with good views. 2m NE of Matlock off A632 at the Tansley signpost. A 2-acre site with 30 touring pitches.

🏕🏕☉✳🔲🐕
➜∪🅿🎵🎵🎵🛒

Pinegroves Caravan Park (SK345585)
High Ln, Tansley DE4 5GS ☎ 01629 534815 & 534670
▶▶★🚐 fr £6 🚐 fr £6 🅰 fr £7.50
Open Apr or Etr-Oct Booking advisable bank hols & Jul-Aug Last arrival 22.00hrs Last departure 16.00hrs
A beautiful hilltop location overlooking Matlock and Riber Castle. Very secluded site in a former plant nursery. From Matlock take A615 for 3m, then 2nd right at crossroads and site 400yds on left. A 6-acre site with 100 touring pitches and 8 statics.
Area of woodland for walks.

🏕🏕☉✳🅰🔲📞🍽🔲🐕🛒♿
➜∪🅿✚🎵🎵
£

Sycamore Caravan & Camping Park (SK329615)
Lant Ln, Matlock Moor DE4 5LF ☎ 01629 55760
(2.5m NE off A632)
▶▶★🚐 £5-£7 🚐 £5-£7 🅰 £3-£7.50
Open 15 Mar-Oct Booking advisable bank hols Last arrival 22.00hrs
An open grassland site with mainly level touring pitches in two fields. 2.5m NE of Matlock off A632. A 6.5-acre site with 80 touring pitches and 35 statics.

🏕🏕☉✳🔲🅰🌿🔲📞
➜∪🅿🔺✚🎵🎵🔲🛒
£

Wayside Farm Caravan Park (SK361620)
Chesterfield Rd, Matlock Moor DE4 5LF ☎ 01629 582967
▶ ▶ ✿ fr £5 ✿ fr £5 ⚑ fr £5
Open all year (rs winter) Booking advisable Last arrival anytime Last departure flexible
A 1.5-acre site with 30 touring pitches.

🔥 📻 ⊙ 🇶 ✳ ⚠ 🔒 ⌀ ⊞ T 🔦 🏕 🐴 🐾 ♿
→ ∪ ▶ ◎ 🛆 ✦ 🐝 🜚 🗑

NEWHAVEN

Newhaven Holiday Camping & Caravan Park (SK167602)
SK17 0DT ☎ 01298 84300 Signposted
Nearby town: Buxton
▶ ▶ ▶ ✿ £6.50-£7.75 ✿ £6.50-£7.75 ⚑ £6.60-£7.75
Open Mar-Oct Booking advisable public hols Last arrival 23.00hrs Last departure anytime
Pleasantly situated within the Peak District National Park, between Ashbourne-Buxton on A515 at junction with A5012. Well-maintained and immaculate site. A 30-acre site with 95 touring pitches and 45 statics.

🔥 📻 ⊙ 🗋 🇶 ◑ ✳ ⚠ 🔒 ⌀ T 🔦 🐴 🐾
→ ∪
⊞

ROWSLEY

Grouse & Claret (SK258660)
Station Rd DE4 2EL ☎ 01629 733233 Signposted
▶ ▶ ★ ✿ £6-£9 ✿ £6-£9 ⚑ £5
Open all year Booking advisable wknds, bank hols & peak periods Last arrival 20.00hrs Last departure noon
A well-designed site behind an eating house on A6 between Bakewell and Chatsworth. A flat grassy area running down to the river. A 2.5-acre site with 29 touring pitches.

🔥 📻 ⊙ ◑ ✳ 🍴 ⚠ ✕ 🔦 🍺 🍽 ⌇
→ ∪ ▶ 🜚 🐾
⊞

Credit Cards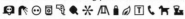

SHARDLOW

Shardlow Marina Caravan Park (SK444303)
London Rd DE72 2GL ☎ 01332 792832 Signposted
Nearby town: Derby
▶ ▶ ▶ ✿ £6.50-£9 ✿ £6.50-£9
Open Apr-Oct Booking advisable bank hols Last arrival 21.00hrs Last departure 14.00hrs
A steadily improving pleasant site with modern facilities, part of a large marina complex on the Trent/Mersey Canal. Situated near the A6 close to its junction with the M1. A 25-acre site with 67 touring pitches.

🔥 📻 ⊙ 🗋 🔒 ⌀ ⊞ T ✕ 🐾
→ ▶ ✦ 🐝 🜚

YOULGREAVE

Camping & Caravanning Club Site (SK206632)
c/o Hopping Farm DE45 1NA ☎ 01629 636555
(in season) & 01203 694995
Nearby town: Bakewell
▷ ★ ✿ £6.60-£7 ✿ £6.60-£7 ⚑ £6.60-£7
Open end Mar-end Sep Booking advisable bank hols & peak periods Last arrival 21.00hrs Last departure noon
Ideal for touring and walking in the Peak District National Park, this gently sloping grass site is accessed through narrow streets and along unadopted hardcore. Please see the advertisement on page 27 for details of Club Members' benefits. An 11.75-acre site with 100 touring pitches.

🔥 ✳ 🔒 🔦 🐾

Credit Cards

DEVON

ASHBURTON

Ashburton Caravan Park (SX753723)
Waterleat TQ13 7HU
☎ 01364 652552 Signposted
Nearby town: Newton Abbot
▶ ▶ ▶ ⚉ 👫 ✿ £7-£9 ⚑ £7-£9
Open Etr-Sep Booking advisable bank hols & Jul-Aug
Last arrival 22.30hrs Last departure noon

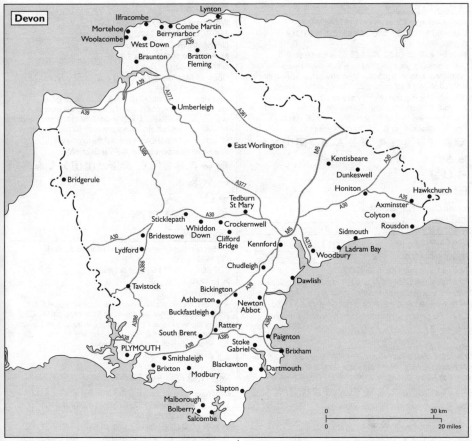

A secluded park set in an attractive location amongst the trees in Dartmoor National Park, offering quality facilities. From A38 in village centre turn right at T junc for Buckland on the Moor on unclass rd. Fork right at river bridge, and site 1.5m on left. A 2-acre site with 35 touring pitches and 40 statics.

🎯🏠🕭⊙🔲🧺❄🔌⌀📞🔋&

→∪▶🎵

Parkers Farm Holidays (SX779713)

Higher Mead Farm TQ13 7LJ ☎ 01364 652598
▶▶▶★🚽 £4-£7.50 🚐 £4-£7.50 ▲ £4-£7.50
Open Etr-end Oct Booking advisable Whitsun & school hols

A developing site terraced into rising ground, with maturing shrubs. Signed off A38, .75m E of Ashburton. An 8-acre site with 60 touring pitches and 25 statics.

🎯🕭⊙🔲🐾❄🏑🗼⌀📞🔋🗼🛒🏇🐕&
→∪▶◎🎵
🅿

River Dart Country Park (SX734700)

Holne Park TQ13 7NP ☎ 01364 652511 Signposted
▶▶▶🚽🏕★🚽 £7.30-£10.20 🚐 £7.30-£10.20
▲ £7.30-£10.20
Open May-Aug (rs Apr & Sep no evening facilities ie bar) Booking advisable Spring Bank Hol & Jul-Aug Last arrival 21.00hrs Last departure 10.00hrs

Mainly level site in a very attractive and quiet location in Holne Country Park just off the B3357. A 7-acre site with 117 touring pitches.

🎯🏠🕭⊙🔲🐾🔫🔍🛏❄🏑🗼⌀📞🔋🅣✖📞
🛏🐕🔋&
→∪▶🎵
🅿

Credit Cards 🔲▭▭▭

AXMINSTER

Andrewshayes Caravan Park (ST248988)
Dalwood EX13 7DY ☎ 01404 831225 & 831766
Signposted
▶ ▶ ▶ ★ ⊞ £8-£9.50 ⊞ £7-£9.50 ▲ £8-£9.50
Open Apr-Oct (rs Apr-21 May & Oct shop hours
restricted, pool closed) Booking advisable Spring bank
hol & Jul-Aug Last arrival 22.00hrs Last departure noon
*Slightly sloping site within easy reach of Lyme Regis,
Seaton, Branscombe and Sidmouth. Adjacent to A35. A
4-acre site with 90 touring pitches and 80 statics.*
Fast food/takeaway & cafe in high season.

🕎 🕅 ⊙ 🖥 🖳 ⊰ ◀ ▭ ✳ ⋀ 🔋 ⊘ 🗒 🅣 ✕ 🕻 🎺
🍺 ♿
→ ∪ ♪
💷

Credit Cards 🌑 �📇 🔃 🔊

BARNSTAPLE

See **Chivenor**

BERRYNARBOR

Napps Camping Site (SS561477)
Old Coast Rd EX34 9SW ☎ 01271 882557 Signposted
Nearby town: Combe Martin
▶ ▶ ▶ ★ ⊞ £4.50-£9 ⊞ £4.50-£7.50 ▲ £4.50-£7.50
Open Etr-Oct (rs Etr-Whitsun shop closed) Booking
advisable always for caravans Last arrival 22.00hrs Last
departure noon
*Seclusion is guaranteed at this cliff top site adjacent to
Combe Martin.Turn north off A399 W of Combe Martin
at bottom of hill. An 11-acre site with 250 touring
pitches and 2 statics.*

🕎 🕅 ⊙ 🖥 🖳 ⊰ ⊶ ◀ ✳ ⋀ 🔋 ⊘ 🗒 🅣 ✕ 🕻 🎺
🐕 🍺
→ ∪ ♪ ◉ ⚠ ✦ 🍽 ♪

Credit Cards 🌑 �📇

BICKINGTON (NEAR ASHBURTON)

Lemonford Caravan Park (SX793723)
TQ12 6JR ☎ 01626 821242 Signposted
Nearby town: Ashburton
▶ ▶ ▶ ★ ⊞ £6-£8 ⊞ £6-£8 ▲ £6-£8
Open Etr-Oct Booking advisable Whit & last wk Jul-1st
wk Aug Last arrival 22.30hrs Last departure 11.00hrs
*Small, secluded and well-maintained site. From Exeter
along A38 take A382 turnoff, take 3rd exit on
roundabout and follow site signs to Bickington. From
Plymouth take A383 signed Newton Abbot, then turn left
in 500m signed Bickington Camp on right hand turn. A
7-acre site with 70 touring pitches and 15 statics.*
Clothes drying area.
See advertisement under NEWTON ABBOT

🕎 🕅 ⊙ 🖥 🖳 ✳ ⋀ 🔋 ⊘ 🖥 🕻 🎺 🐕 🍺
→ ∪ ♪ 🍽 ♪
💷

BLACKAWTON

Woodland Leisure Park (SX813522)
TQ9 7DQ ☎ 01803 712598 Signposted
Nearby town: Dartmouth
▶ ▶ ▶ ▶ ⊹ ⊕ ⊞ £5.75-£9.90 ⊞ £5.75-£9.90
▲ £5.75-£9.90
Open 15 Mar-15 Nov Booking advisable anytime Last
departure 11.00hrs
*An extensive woodland park with a terraced grass
camping area, and facilities of a very high standard. A
wildlife park is attached, with entry free to campers. Signed
off A381 at Halwell. An 8-acre site with 80 touring pitches.
60 acre leisure park with animal farm complex.*
See advertisement under Colour Section

🕎 ⊶ 🕅 ⊙ 🖥 🖳 ✳ ⋀ 🔋 ⊘ 🖥 🅣 ✕ 🕻 🎺 🏬
🎴 🐕 🍺 ♿
→ ∪ ♪ ✦ ♪

Credit Cards 🌑 �📇 🔃

BOLBERRY

**Bolberry House Farm Caravan & Camping Park
(SX687395)**
TQ7 3DY ☎ 01548 561251 & 560926
▶ ▶ ⊞ ⊞ ▲
Open Mar-Oct
*A level park on high ground overlooking Hope Cove,
with wide countryside views. At Malborough on A381
turn R signed Hope Cove & Bolberry. Take L fork after
village signed Soar & Bolberry, and site signed in .5m. A
5.5-acre site with 70 touring pitches.*

🕎 🕅 ⊙ 🖳

BRATTON FLEMING

Greenacres Farm Touring Caravan Park (SS658414)
EX31 4SG ☎ 01598 763334 (2.5m N) Signposted
Nearby town: Barnstable
▶ ▶ ▶ ★ ⊞ £3.50-£6 ⊞ £3.50-£5.50
Open Apr-Oct Booking advisable all times Last arrival
23.00hrs Last departure noon
*New site with well-appointed facilities and enthusiastic
owners. On farmland, with good views over North
Devon. Site off A399 N of Stowford Cross. A 4-acre site
with 30 touring pitches.*

🕎 🕅 ⊙ 🖳 ⋀ 🔋 🕻 🎴 🐕 ♿
→ ∪ ♪ 🍺
💷

BRAUNTON

Lobb Fields Caravan & Camping Park (SS475378)
Saunton Rd EX33 1EB ☎ 01271 812090 Signposted
▶ ▶ ▶ ★ ⊞ £5-£7.50 ⊞ £3.50-£6 ▲ £3.50-£6
Open May-Sep Booking advisable Jul-Aug Last arrival
21.00hrs Last departure 11.30hrs
*Gently sloping grassy site on outskirts of Braunton, with
good wide entrance. A 14-acre site with 180 touring
pitches.*

🕎 🕅 ⊙ ✳ 🔋 ⊘ 🖥 🅣 🕻 🐕 🍺
→ ∪ ♪ ⚠ ♪ 🖥

BRIDESTOWE

Bridestowe Caravan Park (SX519893)
EX20 4ER ☎ 01837 861261 Signposted
Nearby town: Okehampton
▶▶▶ ★ ⊞ £6 ⊞ £6 ▲ £6
Open Mar-Dec Booking advisable Last arrival 22.30hrs
Last departure noon
*A small, well-established mainly static park in a rural
setting close to Dartmoor National Park. Leave A30 at
Sourton Down junc with A386, join old A30 (now B3278)
signed Bridestowe, and turn left in 5m. At village centre
turn left down unclass rd and site 1m on left. A 1-acre
site with 13 touring pitches and 40 statics.*

🖸🛈⊙📷🎇🔍✳⛰🚿🏧🅿🗑🎠🐎🦽
➔∪🍴
⬜

BRIDGERULE

Hedleywood Caravan & Camping Park (SS262013)
EX22 7ED ☎ 01288 381404 Signposted
Nearby town: Bude
▶▶▶ ★ ⊞ £5.50-£6.50 ⊞ £5.50-£6.50 ▲ £5.50-£6.50
Open all year Booking advisable public hols & Jul-Aug
Last arrival anytime Last departure anytime
*An isolated site in a good location, with a considerable
amount of landscaping work in progress. From B3254
take Widemouth road (unclass) at the Devon/Cornwall
boundary. An 8-acre site with 120 touring pitches and 12
statics.*
Dog kennels.

🖸🛈⊙📷🎇🔍✳🍸⛰🚿🏧🅿🗑🆃✂📞🚲🎠
🎢🐎🦽🏇
➔∪🅿☕🍴
⬜

BRIXHAM

Galmpton Touring Park (SX885558)
Greenway Rd TQ5 0EP ☎ 01803 842066 Signposted
▶▶▶ ⊞⊞▲
Open May-Sep (rs Apr & Oct shop closed) Booking
advisable Jul-Aug Last arrival 22.00hrs Last departure
11.00hrs
*An excellent location on high ground overlooking the
River Dart, with outstanding views of the river and
anchorage. Signed off A3022 Torbay/Brixham road at
Churston. A 10-acre site with 120 touring pitches.*

🖸🛈⊙📷🎇✳⛰🚿🏧🅿📞🚲🐎🦽♿
➔∪🅿◎⛱⚓☕🍴

Hillhead Holiday Camp (SX903535)
TQ5 0HH ☎ 01803 853204 (2.5m SW)
▶▶▶♦⊞⊞▲
Open Etr-Oct
*Attractive, well laid out site with screening and
landscaping to each pitch. Good views all around of
countryside and sea. Amenities block well screened
from touring park. On B3205 between Brixham and
Kingswear. A 12.5-acre site with 330 touring pitches.*

🛈📷⚡

BRIXTON

Brixton Camping Site (SX550520)
Venn Farm PL8 2AX ☎ 01752 880378 Signposted
Nearby town: Plymouth
▶⊞⊞▲
Open 15 Mar-14 Oct (rs 15 Mar-Jun & Sep-14 Oct no
warden) Booking advisable Jul-Aug Last arrival 23.00hrs
Last departure noon
*A small site adjacent to a farm within the urban confines
of Brixton on A379. A 2-acre site with 43 touring pitches.*

🖸🚜🛈⊙✳🖼
➔∪🅿⛏☕🍴🦽

BUCKFASTLEIGH

Beara Farm Campsite (SX751645)
Colston Rd TQ11 0LW ☎ 01364 642234 Signposted
▷ ★ ⊞ £5-£11 ⊞ fr £4 ▲ fr £4
Open all year Booking advisable peak periods Jul-Aug
Last arrival anytime Last departure anytime
*Level site, close to the River Dart and the Dart Valley
stream railway line, within easy reach of sea and moors.
Approach is narrow with passing places and needs care.
Leave A38 at Buckfast A384 junc, and take B3380 (old
A38) towards Buckfastleigh. Turn left on Old Totnes Rd
in .25m after passing under bridge. Turn right into
Colston Rd, and follow single track for 2m. A 4-acre site
with 30 touring pitches and 1 static.*

🛈⊙✳🖼🐎🏇
➔🍴
⬜

Ladram Bay Holiday Centre
OTTERTON · Nr BUDLEIGH SALTERTON
EX9 7BX ▶
Tel: Colaton Raleigh (01395) 568398

Devon at its spectacular best. A wide choice of
accommodation, in a superb setting. Pub with
free family entertainment 7 nights a week from
Spring Bank Holiday. Indoor heated swimming
pool. Safe private beach, shops and cafeteria.

Exit M5 at junction 30, A3052 (Sidmouth Road)
to Newton Poppleford, turn right on to B3178
(Budleigh Salterton Road) then follow signs to
Ladram Bay.

See gazetteer under Ladram Bay

BUDLEIGH SALTERTON

See **Ladram Bay**

CHUDLEIGH

Finlake Leisure Park (SX855786)
TQ13 0EJ ☎ 01626 853833 Signposted
Nearby town: Newton Abbot
▶ ▶ ▶ ▶ ▶ ♦ ⊛ **Holiday Centre** 🚐 🚗 Å

Open mid Feb-7 Jan Booking advisable bank hols & Jul-Aug Last arrival 22.00hrs Last departure 11.00hrs
A very well-appointed site situated in a wooded valley surrounded by 110 acres of wooded parkland. There are also a number of self-catering chalets. Signed off A38 at Chudleigh exit. A 110-acre site with 450 touring pitches. Fishing, horseriding & golf.

🔌 🛒 📻 ⊙ 🖥 🗟 ⚡ ♜ ✳ ♉ ⚙ ⓛ 🖉 🖅 Ⓣ ✂ 📞
🚿 🐴 🐾 ♿
→ ∪ ▶ ♩

Credit Cards 💳

Holmans Wood Tourist Park (SX881812)
Harcombe Cross TQ12 5TX ☎ 01626 853785 Signposted
▶ ▶ ▶ ♦ 🚐 🚗 Å

Open Mar-Nov Booking advisable bank hols & Jul-Aug Last arrival 22.00hrs Last departure 11.00hrs
Delightful small, personally-managed touring site, set back in secluded wooded area off A38. Convenient location for touring South Devon and Dartmoor National Park. An 11-acre site with 144 touring pitches.

Caravan storage facilities.

🔌 🛒 📻 ⊙ 🖥 🗟 ⚡ ♜ ✳ ♉ ⓛ 🖉 🖅 Ⓣ 📞 🛒 🚿 🐾
🐾 ♿
→ ∪ ▶ ⊁ ♩

Credit Cards 💳 💳

CLIFFORD BRIDGE

Clifford Bridge Park (SX780897)
EX6 6QE ☎ 01647 24226 Signposted
Nearby town: Moretonhampstead
▶ ▶ ▶ ★ 🚐 £6.85-£9.95 🚗 £5.95-£9.20 Å £6.85-£9.95

Open Etr-Sep Booking advisable school & bank hols Last arrival 22.00hrs Last departure 11.00hrs
A very attractive location in a deep wooded valley in the Dartmoor National Park. The approach roads are narrow and steep in parts, and care is needed in towing large units. Signed from Tedburn St Mary on unclass road. A 6-acre site with 65 touring pitches and 5 statics. Fly fishing on site.

🔌 📻 ⊙ 🖥 🗟 ⚡ ♜ ✳ ♉ ⓛ 🖉 🖅 Ⓣ 📞 🐴 🐾
→ ∪ ▶ ♩
💷

COLYTON

Leacroft Touring Park (SY217925)
Colyton Hill EX13 6HY ☎ 01297 552823
▶ ▶ ▶ 🚐 🚗 Å

Open 14 Mar-14 Nov Booking advisable Jul-Aug Last arrival 21.00hrs Last departure 13.00hrs
A mostly level site offering good sanitary facilities. A 10-

acre site with 138 touring pitches.
Off-licence.

🔌📶☀️🔲🔦🖵✳️🅰🛉⌀🖸↕️🆃🔌🎋🐎🐕🔋
♿
→⛽⛰️◎⚠️⚓🪝🎵

COMBE MARTIN

Stowford Farm Meadows (SS560427)
EX34 0PW ☎ 01271 882476 Signposted
▶▶▶▶♠★🚐💷 £3.20-£8.50 🚗 £3-£7.50 ▲ £3-£8.50
Open Etr-Oct (rs Etr-Spring bank hol & Oct some
amenities may not be available) Booking advisable bank
hols & Jul-Aug Last arrival 20.00hrs Last departure
10.00hrs
*Very gently sloping, grassy, sheltered and south-facing
site approached down a wide, well-kept driveway. From
A399 turn left signed Barnstaple. Site on left. A 50-acre
site with 570 touring pitches.*
Horse rides, fun golf, mini zoo, snooker room.
See advertisement under Colour Section

🔌📶☀️🔲🔦🦌 🔦🔲☀️🍴🅰🛉⌀↕️🆃✖️🔌
🛒🐎🔋
→⛽⛰️🎵
💷

Credit Cards 💳 ══ ═ 🔲 🅂

Sandaway Beach Holiday Park (SS568474)
Berrynarbor EX34 9ST ☎ 01271 866666
(towards Berrynarbor W on A399) Signposted
▶▶▶ 🚐🚗▲
Open Mar-Oct (rs before Spring bank hol & after 1 Oct
shop, club & reception limited opening) Booking
advisable before Apr for Jul-Aug Last arrival 20.00hrs
Last departure 10.00hrs
*Well-designed site, carefully screened and well laid out,
overlooking the sea. Situated on A399, .25m from
Combe Martin on coast side of road. A 2-acre site with
35 touring pitches and 86 statics.*
Amusement room.
See advertisement under ILFRACOMBE

🔌📶☀️🔲🔦🦌 ⚡🔲☀️🍴🅰🛉⌀🛒🔋
→⛽⛰️🪝😷🎵

CROCKERNWELL

Barley Meadow Caravan & Camping Park (SX757925)
EX6 6NR ☎ 01647 281629 Signposted
▶▶▶ 🚐🚗▲
Open 15 Mar-15 Nov Booking advisable bank hols & Jul-
Aug Last arrival mdnt Last departure noon
*A small, very well-maintained site set on high ground in
the National Park with easy access. Off the old A30, now
bypassed, and isolated. From M5 take A30, leave by exit
for Tedburn; turn left through Cheriton Bishop and
Crockernwell, and site on right. A 4-acre site with 40
touring pitches.*
Picnic tables.

🔌📶☀️🔦☀️🅰🛉⌀↕️🆃🪝🎋🔋
→🎵

DARTMOUTH

Deer Park Holiday Estate (SX864493)
Stoke Fleming TQ6 0RF ☎ 01803 770253
(Stoke Fleming 2m S A379) Signposted
▶▶▶ 🚐🚗▲
Open 15 Mar-Oct Booking advisable Jul-Aug Last arrival
anytime Last departure 10.00hrs
*A rather open, mainly level grass site on high ground
overlooking Start Bay. A 6-acre site with 160 touring
pitches and 48 statics.*

🔌📶☀️🔲🔦🦌⚡🛉☀️🍴🅰🛉⌀🖸↕️🆃✖️🔌🛒
🔋♿
→⛽⛰️🪝🎵

Little Cotton Caravan Park (SX858508)
Little Cotton TQ6 0LB ☎ 01803 832558
▶▶▶ 👫🚐🚗▲
Open 15 Mar-15 Nov Booking advisable Jul & Aug Last
arrival 22.00hrs Last departure noon
*A small, well-kept farm site on high ground above
Dartmouth. From Totnes take A381 signed Kingsbridge,
at Halwell take B3207 for Dartmouth, and site on right
before town. A 7.5-acre site with 95 touring pitches.*

🔌📶☀️🔲🛉⌀↕️🆃🔌🔋♿
→⛽🪝🎵

DAWLISH

Cofton Country Holiday Park (SX967801)
Starcross EX6 8RP ☎ 01626 890111
▶▶▶▶ 🚐💷 £5-£9.50 🚗 £5-£9.50 ▲ £5-£9.50
Open Etr-Oct (rs Etr-Spring bank hol & mid Sep-Oct
swimming pool closed) Booking advisable bank hols &
Jul-Aug Last arrival 20.00hrs Last departure noon
*A well-ordered grass site in a good holiday location 1m
S of Starcross on A379. A 16-acre site with 450 touring
pitches and 62 statics.*
Coarse fishing, pub with family room.

🔌📶☀️🔲🔦🦌⚡🔲☀️🍴🅰🛉⌀↕️🆃✖️🔌🛒
🐎🔋♿
→🪝🪝🎵

Credit Cards 💳 ══ ═

See advertisement on page 98

Lady's Mile Touring & Caravan Park (SX968784)
EX7 0LX ☎ 01626 863411
▶▶▶▶ 🚐🚗▲
Open 17 Mar-27 Oct (rs 17 Mar-21 May & 20 Sep-27 Oct
swimming pool closed) Booking advisable bank hols &
Jul-Aug Last arrival 20.00hrs Last departure 11.00hrs
*A well-ordered, clean and tidy site, with new sanitary
facilities. Fairly central for the surrounding beaches, and
1m N of Dawlish on A379. A 16-acre site with 286
touring pitches and 1 static.*
See advertisement under Colour Section

🔌🛒📶☀️🔲🔦🦌⚡🔦🔲☀️🅰🛉⌀↕️🆃🔌
🛒🐎🔋♿
→⛽⚠️🪝😷🎵

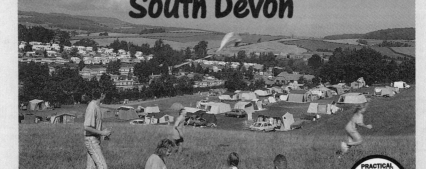

Golden Sands Holiday Park (SX968784)
Week Ln EX7 0LZ ☎ 01626 863099
► ► ► ★ ⊞ £5.50-£12 ⊞ £5.50-£12
Open Etr-Oct Booking advisable
A mainly static park with a small touring area set amongst trees. Signed off A379 Exeter/Dawlish road, 1m N of Dawlish. A 2.5-acre site with 60 touring pitches and 188 statics.

🔌 ⊙ 🗑 ♒ ⚡ 🍴 ⚠ 🅿 📞 🚻 ♨ 🛁 ⚒ ♿

Credit Cards 💳 💳 🆔

Peppermint Park (SX978788)
Warren Rd EX7 0PQ ☎ 01626 863436 & 862211
Signposted
► ► ► ★ ⊞ £5.50-£12 ⊞ £5.50-£12 Å £4.50-£12
Open Etr-Oct Booking advisable Spring bank hol & Jul-Aug Last arrival 20.00hrs Last departure 10.00hrs
Well-managed attractive site close to the coast with excellent facilities. From A379 at Dawlish follow signs for Dawlish Warren. Site on left in 1m. A 17-acre site with 250 touring pitches and 35 statics.
Licensed club & free entertainment.

🔌 🚿 ⊙ 🗑 ♒ ⚡ ⚓ ☀ 🍴 ⚠ 🅿 📞 ⊤ 🔌 🐴 ⚒ ♿
→ ► ⅃ ⅃

Credit Cards 💳 🆔

See advertisement on page 100

DUNKESWELL

Fishponds House Campsite (ST154074)
EX14 0SH ☎ 01404 891287
► ► ⊞ ⊞ Å

Open all year (rs Nov-Apr toilets in main house only)
Booking advisable school hols Last arrival 22.00hrs Last departure noon
A delightful site in lovely surroundings with the added luxury of the hotel facilities. A 2-acre site with 15 touring pitches.
Fishing.

🔌 🚿 ⊙ 🗑 ♒ ⚡ ⚓ ☀ 🍴 ⚠ 🅿 📞 ⊡ ✕ 🔌 🍴 🛒
♿
→ ∪ ⅃ ⅃

EAST WORLINGTON

Yeatheridge Farm Caravan Park (SS768110)
EX17 4TN ☎ 01884 860330
Nearby town: Witheridge
► ► ► ♿ ⊞ ⊞ Å
Open Etr-Sep Booking advisable Etr, Spring bank hol & school hols Last arrival 22.00hrs Last departure 22.00hrs
Gently sloping grass site with young trees set in meadowland in rural Devon. On B3042 1.5m W of Thelbridge Arms Inn. Site is NOT in East Worlington village which is unsuitable for caravans. A 9-acre site with 85 touring pitches and 2 statics.
Horse riding, fishing & pool table.
See advertisement under TIVERTON

🔌 🚿 ⊙ 🗑 ♒ ⚡ ♒ ⚓ 🔲 ☀ 🍴 ⚠ 🅿 📞 ⊡ ⊤ 🔌
🐴 🛒
→ ∪ ⅃

EXETER

See **Kennford**

HAWKCHURCH

Hunters Moon Touring Park (SY345988)
EX13 5UL ☎ 01297 678402 Signposted
▶ ▶ ▶ ♦ ★ ♨ £5.45-£8.30 ♨ £5.45-£8.30
▲ £5.45-£8.30
Open 15 Mar-Oct Booking advisable Whitsun & Jul-Aug
Last arrival 23.00hrs Last departure noon
An attractive site in wooded area with panoramic country views. An 11-acre site with 150 touring pitches.
All weather bowling green & putting green.

HONITON

See also **Kentisbeare**

Camping & Caravanning Club Site (SY176015)
Otter Valley Park, Northcote EX14 8SP
☎ 01404 44546 & 01203 694995
▶ ▶ ★ ♨ £8.60-£9.20 ♨ £8.60-£9.20 ▲ £8.60-£9.20
Open Mar-Oct Booking advisable bank hols & Jul-Aug
Last arrival 21.00hrs Last departure noon
A well run site just a short walk from the town. From Yeovil leave A30 at sign for A35 Dorchester, then turn left. Please see the advertisement on page 27 for details of Club Members' benefits. A 5-acre site with 90 touring pitches.

Credit Cards

MULLACOTT CROSS
CARAVAN PARK
▶▶▶

On North Devon's Heritage Coast. Lovely walks, clean beaches and on the edge of Exmoor. We offer touring sites, camping and self catering caravan accommodation. Bar and Restaurant.

For brochure write to:
Mullacott Cross Caravan Park,
Ilfracombe, Devon EX34 8NB.
or phone: **01271 862212 or 862200**

ILFRACOMBE

Mullacott Cross Caravan Park (SS511446)
Mullacott Cross EX34 8NB ☎ 01271 862212 & 862200 (Mullacott Cross 2.5m S A361) Signposted
▶▶▶ ★ ⊕ £6.50-£12 ⊕ £5.50-£10 ▲ £5.50-£10
Open Etr-Sep (rs Etr-Whit & Oct restaurant restricted) Booking advisable Whit & Jul-Aug Last arrival 21.00hrs Last departure noon
This meadowland site is on gentle grass slopes with views over the Atlantic coastline, 2m S of Ilfracombe and 3m E of the sandy beach at Woolacombe. Located adjacent to A361 Braunton-Ilfracombe road. An 8-acre site with 115 touring pitches and 160 statics.
Caravan accessory shop.

🧿🛞⊙🖥🍳🖵❊🏳🏔🛈🖉🔁🆃✂🌢🍴👗
→ ∪ ▶ 🛒 ⚽ ♩
£

Credit Cards 🟦 🟦 🟦 🟦 🟢

Watermouth Cove Holiday Park (SS558477)
Berrynarbor EX34 9SJ ☎ 01271 862504 (towards Berrynarbor 2.5m E A361)
▶▶▶▶ ⊕⊕▲
Open Etr-Oct (rs Etr-Whit & Sep-Nov pool, takeaway, club & shop) Booking advisable Whit & Jul-Aug Last arrival anytime Last departure 11.00hrs
Mainly level grass site amidst trees and bushes, set in meadowland with access to sea, beach and main road.
➡

A 6-acre site with 90 touring pitches.
Coastal headland fishing.

🔧📻☉◙🏳🍴🔌✳♀⚠🔊🍃📶🇹✕📞
♿🏮🎄🐾🛒
→⋃🏴⛽📽🎵

KENNFORD

Kennford International Caravan Park (SX912857)
EX6 7YN ☎ 01392 833046 Signposted
Nearby town: Exeter
▶ ▶ ▶ ▶ ★ 🚏 fr £8.50 🚐 fr £8.50 Å fr £8.50
Open all year Booking advisable public hols & Jul-Aug
Last arrival mdnt Last departure noon
*A well-kept touring site on the A38, with mature
landscaping. Mainly a transit site. An 8-acre site with
120 touring pitches.*

🔧🚐📻☉◙🏳🍴✳♀⚠🔊🍃📶🇹✕📞♿
🐾🛒♿
→⋃🏴⛽📽🎵
💷

Credit Cards 💳 💳 💳 💳

KENTISBEARE

Forest Glade Holiday Park (ST100075)
Cullompton EX15 2DT ☎ 01404 841381 Signposted
▶ ▶ ▶ ▶ ♦ ★ 🚏 £8.40-£13.40 🚐 £8.40-£13.40
Å £8.40-£13.40
Open 2 wks before Etr-Oct Booking advisable school
hols Last arrival 22.00hrs
*A quiet, attractive site in a forest clearing with well-kept
gardens and beech hedge screening, on top of the Black
Down Hills. Tent traffic from A373 signed at Keepers
Cottage Inn, 2.5m E of M5 junc 28. Touring caravans via
Honiton/Dunkeswell road. Please telephone for route
details. There is no need to visit Kentisbeare Village. A
5-acre site with 80 touring pitches and 57 statics.*
Adventure play area & childrens paddling pool.
See advertisement under HONITON

🔧📻☉◙🏳🍴♀⚠✳♀⚠🔊🍃📶🇹📞🚐
♿🐾🛒♿
→⋃🎵
💷

LADRAM BAY

Ladram Bay Holiday Centre (SY096853)
EX9 7BX ☎ 01395 568398 Signposted
Nearby town: Budleigh Salterton
▶ 🚏🚐Å
Open Spring bank hol-Sep (rs Etr-Spring Bank Hol pool
closed no boat hire & entertainment) Booking advisable
for caravans, school & Spring bank hols Last arrival
18.00hrs Last departure 10.00hrs
*A large caravan site with many static vans and a
separate camping area which is on terraced ground in
wooded surroundings. Overlooks rocky, shingle beach.
A 5-acre site with 255 touring pitches and 369 statics.*

Boat & canoe hire.
See advertisement on page 95

🔧📻☉◙🏳🍴✳♀⚠🔊🍃✕📞♿🏮🛒
→⋃🏴⛽📽🎵
Credit Cards 💳 💳

LYDFORD

Camping & Caravanning Club Site (SX512853)
EX20 4BE ☎ 01822 820275 (in season) &
01203 694995 Signposted
Nearby town: Okehampton
▶ ▶ ♦ ★ 🚏 £9.30-£10 🚐 £9.30-£10 Å £9.30-£10
Open end Mar-end Sep Booking advisable bank hols &
peak periods Last arrival 21.00hrs Last departure noon
*Site on mainly level ground looking towards the
western slopes of Dartmoor at the edge of the village,
near the spectacular gorge. Please see advertisement on
page 27 for details of Club Members' benefits. A 4-acre
site with 70 touring pitches.*

🔧📻☉◙🏳✳⚠🍃📶📞♿🛒
→⋃🏴⛽🎵
Credit Cards 💳 💳 💳

LYNTON

Camping & Caravanning Club Site (SS700484)
Caffyns Cross EX35 6JS ☎ 01598 752379 (in season) &
01203 694995 Signposted
▶ ▶ ▶ ★ 🚏 £9.30-£10 🚐 £9.30-£10 Å £9.30-£10
Open end Mar-end Oct Booking advisable bank hols &
peak periods Last arrival 21.00hrs Last departure noon
*A level grassy site, with bushes, set below hill in well-
wooded countryside. 2m SW of Lynton off A39
Barnstaple-Minehead road. Please see the
advertisement on page 27 for details of Club Members'
benefits. A 5-acre site with 105 touring pitches.*

🔧📻☉🏳✳⚠🍃📞
→⋃⚠📽🎵🛒
Credit Cards 💳 💳 💳

Channel View Caravan Park (SS724482)
Manor Farm EX35 6LD ☎ 01598 53349 Signposted
▶ ▶ ▶ 🚏🚐Å
Open Etr-mid Oct Booking advisable Jul-Aug Last arrival
22.00hrs Last departure 15.00hrs
*The site on the A39 has panoramic views over Lynton
and the Channel. A 6-acre site with 76 touring pitches
and 36 statics.*

🔧📻☉◙🏳✳♀⚠🔊🍃📶🇹📞♿🐾🛒
→⋃📽🎵
Credit Cards 💳 💳

Sunny Lyn Caravan Site (SS719486)
Lynbridge EX35 6NS ☎ 01598 53384 Signposted
▶ ▶ ▶ 🚏🚐
Open Jun-Aug (rs Etr-May & Sep-Oct shop & restaurant
restricted opening) Booking advisable Etr, spring bank
hol & mid Jul-Aug Last arrival 20.00hrs Last departure
noon

Part-level, part-sloping site, bordering trout stream, in a wooded combe within 1m of sea. On B3234. A 2-acre site with 37 touring pitches and 31 statics.
Pool table & table tennis, trout fishing on site.

🕹️📻☉🗄️🍽️🍴🗄️☼⛱️🏔️🚿🚮⚡🔲✗📞🏧👤

→🛒◉⚲🔩🎾♪

MALBOROUGH

Sun Park Caravan & Camping Site (SX707379)
Soar TQ7 3DS ☎ 01548 561378 Signposted
Nearby town: Salcombe
▶▶▶ 🚐 £4-£8 🛖 £3-£8
Open all year Booking advisable Jul-Aug Last arrival 22.00hrs Last departure 11.00hrs
A small country holiday park with a level camping site, approx .75m from a safe sandy beach at Soar Mill Cove. Take A381 from Kingsbridge, turn right at Malborough then take left fork to Soar Mill Cove. A 2.5-acre site with 65 touring pitches and 31 statics.

🕹️📻☉🗄️🍽️🍴🗄️☼🏔️🚿🚮⚡🔲📞🔲

→🛒◁⚲⚲♪🔲

Higher Rew (SX714383)
Higher Rew Farm TQ7 3DW ☎ 01548 842681 & 843681 Signposted
Nearby town: Salcombe
▶▶★ 🚐 fr £5 🚐 fr £5 🛖 fr £5
Open Mar-Nov Booking advisable Spring bank hol & mid Jul-Aug Last arrival 22.00hrs Last departure noon
A long-established park site in a remote location in sight of the sea. Take A387 Salcombe Rd from Kingsbridge to Malborough, turn right in village and then fork left along unclass rd with passing places signed Soar. A 5-acre site with 75 touring pitches.
Play Barn

🕹️📻☉🗄️🍽️☼🚿🚮⚡🔲📞🐕

→🛒⚲♪🔲

MODBURY

Southleigh Caravan & Camping Park (SX682515)
PL21 0SB ☎ 01548 830346 Signposted
▶▶▶▶ 🚐🚐🛖
Open 15 May-20 Sep (rs 19 Mar-14 May & 20 Sep-Oct limited facilities) Booking advisable mid Jul-Aug Last arrival 23.00hrs Last departure noon
A mainly static park, with a new and extensive clubhouse and restaurant adding to the amenities. From A38 at Wrangaton take B3210 signed Modbury, after California Cross take 2nd fork left signed Aveton Gifford and Bigbury. Site 2nd on right. A 4-acre site with 100 touring pitches and 100 statics.
Family room with shower & toilet, entertainment.

🕹️📻☉🗄️🍽️🍷🍴☼🍽️🏔️🚿🚮⚡🔲🔲✗📞🏧

🔲👤♿

→🛒▶♪

Camping & Caravanning Club Site (SX705530)
California Cross PL21 0SG ☎ 01548 821297 (in season) & 01203 694995 Signposted
Nearby town: Ivybridge
▶▶▶ 👫★ 🚐 £9.30-£10 🚐 £9.30-£10 🛖 £9.30-£10
Open end Mar-early Nov Booking advisable Spring bank hol & Jul-Aug Last arrival 21.00hrs Last departure noon
A well-ordered site sloping gently and partially terraced in rural surroundings, protected by high hedges. From A38 at Wrangaton turn left onto B3210 signed Modbury. At California Cross turn left signed Gara Bridge and site signed on right. Please see advertisement on page 27 for details of Club Members' benefits. A 4-acre site with 84 touring pitches.

🕹️📻☉🗄️🍽️☼🏔️🚿🚮⚡🔲🚮👤♿

→🛒

Credit Cards 🔲 🔲 🔲

Moor View Touring Park (SX705533)
California Cross PL21 0SG ☎ 01548 821485 Signposted
▶▶▶★ 🚐 £5-£8 🚐 £5-£8 🛖 £5-£8
Open Etr-Sep Booking advisable bank hols & mid Jul-Aug Last arrival 22.00hrs Last departure noon
A compact terraced site in picturesque South Hams, with wide views of Dartmoor and quality services. From A38 at Wrangaton take B3210 signed Modbury & site on L past service stn. A 4-acre site with 68 touring pitches.

🕹️📻☉🗄️🍽️🍴🗄️☼🏔️🚿🚮⚡🔲🔲📞🏧🏞️🐕

👤

→🛒▶♪

🔲

Credit Cards 🔲 🔲 🔲 🔲 🔲

Pennymoor Camping & Caravan Park (SX685516)
PL21 0SB ☎ 01548 830269 & 830542 Signposted
▶▶▶ 🚐🚐🛖
Open 15 Mar-15 Nov (rs 15 Mar-mid May 1 toilet & shower block only open) Booking advisable Jul-Aug Last arrival 22.30hrs Last departure noon
A well-established static park adjacent to a working farm set in rural surroundings. A good touring location. From A38 at Wrangaton take B3210 signed Modbury. After California cross take 2nd left signed Bigbury, and site 1st on right. A 6-acre site with 154 touring pitches and 70 statics.
Dishwashing facilities.

🕹️📻☉🗄️🍽️☼🏔️🚿🚮⚡🔲📞🐕👤♿

→🛒♪

See advertisement on page 104

MORTEHOE

Easewell Farm Coastal Holiday Park (SS465455)
EX34 7EH ☎ 01271 870225 Signposted
▶▶▶ 🚐🚐🛖
Open Etr-Sep (rs Etr no shop) Booking advisable Jul-Aug Last arrival 22.00hrs Last departure 10.00hrs
A clifftop site of varying terrain, well-run and ➥

maintained. A 17-acre site with 250 touring pitches. 9 hole golf on site.

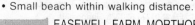

Twitchen Park (SS465447)
EX34 7ES ☎ 01271 870476 Signposted
Nearby town: Woolacombe
▶ ▶ ▶ ★ ⚏ £8.25-£16 ⚏ £8.25-£16 ▲ £7.25-£13.50
Open May-Sep (rs Apr & Oct outdoor pool closed, no entertainment) Booking advisable May bank hol & Jul-Aug Last arrival 23.00hrs Last departure 10.00hrs ⚘
A part-sloping grass site with trees and bushes, set in downland and wooded meadowland. From Mullacott follow signs to Mortehoe, and site in 2m on right. A 15-acre site with 132 touring pitches and 274 statics.
Table tennis, snooker, putting green, teenage disco.

Credit Cards 🖸 🖸 🖸 🖸

MULLACOTT CROSS
See **Ilfracombe**

Lemonford Caravan Park
▶▶▶

Undoubtedly one of the prettiest caravan and camping parks in South Devon. Situated only 10 miles from Torbay, 1 mile from Dartmoor and within 5 miles of eight major tourist attractions.

★ Excellent shower and toilet facilities
★ Private wash cubicles ★ Electric hook-ups
★ Children's play area ★ Shop ★ Village pub
★ 15 luxury caravans to hire
★ plus cottage

EXCELLENT

Bickington, Newton Abbot, South Devon, TQ12 6JR.

ROSE AWARD CARAVAN HOLIDAY PARK

For a Colour Brochure
Tel: Bickington (01626) 821242

NEWTON ABBOT

Dornafield
(SX838683)
Dornafield Farm, Two Mile Oak TQ12 6DD ☎ 01803 812732 Signposted
▶▶▶▶ ♣ ♀♀ ★ ☎ £6-£10.50 ☎ £6-£10.50 ▲ £6-£10.50
Open 20 Mar-Oct Booking advisable bank hols & Jul-Aug Last arrival 22.30hrs Last departure 11.00hrs
A quiet, very attractive and well-laid out site in a secluded wooded valley setting. Take A381 (Newton Abbot-Totnes) for 2m and at Two Mile Oak Inn turn right, then in .5m at cross roads turn left for site on right. A 12.5-acre site with 135 touring pitches. Wet weather room.

(symbols row)

Stover International Caravan Park (SX823745)
Lower Staple Hill TQ12 6JD ☎ 01626 821446 (A38 to junc A382 turn towards Newton Abbot) Signposted
▶▶▶▶ ✿ ☎ £7.15-£11.15 ☎ £7.15-£11.15 ▲ £7.15-£11.15
Open Etr & Spring Bank-mid Sep (rs mid Sep-Oct shop, cafe, bar & pool reduced hours) Booking advisable Jun-Aug Last arrival 21.00hrs Last departure noon
A very well-equipped site set in a good touring location. A 15-acre site with 200 touring pitches and 20 statics.

See advertisement on page 112.

(symbols rows)

Credit Cards 🔲 ▭

OKEHAMPTON

See **Whiddon Down**

PAIGNTON

Beverley Parks Caravan & Camping Park (SX886582)
Goodrington Rd TQ4 7JE ☎ 01803 843887 Signposted
▶▶▶▶▶ ✿ **Holiday Centre**
Open Etr-Oct Booking advisable Jun-Sep Last arrival 22.00hrs Last departure 10.00hrs ⚓
A well-ordered and well-established holiday park on raised ground adjacent to residential area south of town. A 12-acre site with 194 touring pitches and 205 statics. Table tennis, pool, spa bath, crazy golf, sauna.

(symbols rows)

Credit Cards 🔲 ▭ ▭ 🅖

Byslades Camping Park (SX853603)
Totnes Rd TQ4 7PY ☎ 01803 555072 (2m W on A385) Signposted
▶▶▶▶ ★ ☎ £5-£9.50 ☎ £4.50-£8.50 ▲ £4.50-£8.50

DARTMOOR VIEW CARAVAN PARK

01647 231545

A quiet, friendly, family Park on the edge of Dartmoor. The ideal centre for a touring holiday in Devon and Cornwall. Easy access from M5 with level pitches for tents, tourers and motorhomes. Rose Award caravans for hire. Excellent facilities including heated pool, shop, bar, takeaway, games room, play area. Fishing, walking and riding nearby. Colour brochure.
Dartmoor View Caravan Park, Whiddon Down, Okehampton, Devon, EX20 2QL

01647 231545

AA

Open Jun-Sep (rs Mar-May & Oct bar & swimming pool closed) Booking advisable Jul-Aug Last arrival 23.00hrs Last departure 10.00hrs

A well-kept terraced site on the outskirts of town. An 8-acre site with 170 touring pitches.
Ornamental lake, crazy golf.

Grange Court Holiday Centre (SX888588)
Grange Rd TQ4 7JP ☎ 01803 558010 Signposted
▶ ▶ ▶ ▶ ✿ ★ 🚐 £8.25-£17.50 🚐 £8.25-£17.50
Open 23 May-19 Sep (rs 15 Feb-22 May & 20 Sep-15 Jan club, entertainment & swimming pool) Booking advisable public hols & Jul-Aug Last arrival 22.00hrs Last departure 10.00hrs ⌀

Large grassy site situated amidst woodland near to sea, very well-equipped and maintained. 1.5m from Paignton on Brixham road. A 10-acre site with 157 touring pitches and 520 statics.
Crazy golf.

Credit Cards 🔲 🔲 🔲

Lower Yalberton Holiday Park (SX869584)
Long Rd TQ4 7PH ☎ 01803 558127 Signposted
► ► ► 🛋 🐕 Å

Open Whit & Jun-Sep Booking advisable Jul-Aug Last arrival 22.00hrs Last departure 10.00hrs

A large family-run touring and tenting site, well-kept and serviced. Signed off W end of Torbay ring road. A 25-acre site with 625 touring pitches and 8 statics. Entertainment in family lounge bar.

🖃 🖍 ⊙ 🗗 🗞 ⑂ ● ⛶ ✳ 🍸 ⚠ 🛈 🖉 🗓 ✗ 🍴 ♨
🐕 🐾 ⓚ
→ ∪ ▶ ◎ ⚓ ⚲ ☕ ♪

Credit Cards 🎴 💳

Widend Camping Park (SX852619)
Berry Pomeroy Rd, Marldon TQ3 1RT ☎ 01803 550116 Signposted
► ► ► ► ⚡ 🛋 🐕 Å

Open 15 Mar-15 Nov (rs 15 Mar-15 May & 15 Sep-15 Nov swimmimg pool, Club house May-Oct & Etr) Booking advisable Jul-Aug & Whit Last arrival 22.00hrs Last departure 11.00hrs

A terraced grass site paddocked and screened on high ground overlooking Torbay with views of Dartmoor. A well laid out and equipped site with high standards of maintenance. A 10-acre site with 165 touring pitches.

🖃 🖍 ⊙ 🗗 🗞 ● ✳ 🍸 ⚠ 🛈 🖉 🗓 T ☎ 🍴 🐕 🐾
ⓚ
→ ∪ ▶ ⚲ ☕ ♪

Credit Cards 🎴 💳

Marine Park Holiday Centre (SX886587)
Grange Rd TQ4 7JR ☎ 01803 843887 Signposted
► ► ► 🐕 £7-£11.50 🛋 £7-£11.50

Open Etr-Oct Booking advisable Jul-Aug Last arrival 22.00hrs Last departure 10.00hrs ⊘

A mainly static site catering for those who prefer peace and quiet. Next door to sister site Beverley Park whose amenities are available. Signed from ring road A3022 and B3198. A 2-acre site with 30 touring pitches and 66 statics.

🖃 🛒 🖍 ⊙ 🗗 🗞 ✳ ⚠ 🛈 🖉 🗓 ☎ 🚐 🐾
→ ∪ ▶ ◎ ⚓ ⚲ ☕ ♪
💷

Credit Cards 🎴 💳 💳

PLYMOUTH

Riverside Caravan Park (SX515575)
Longbridge Rd, Marsh Mills, Plympton PL6 8LD
☎ 01752 344122 (3m E off A38) Signposted
► ► ► ► ⚡ 🛋 🐕 Å

Open all year Booking advisable Jun-Aug Last arrival 22.00hrs Last departure 10.00hrs

A well-groomed site on the outskirts of Plymouth on the banks of the R Plym. Approach by way of Longbridge ➡

road, which is E of Marsh Mills roundabout. An 11-acre site with 293 touring pitches.

🔧 📻 ☉ 🗑 ⤳ ⚲ 🖵 ☀ 🅈 ⚠ 🛢 🖉 ⊞ 🆃 ✕ 🔌 ♿
🐕 ⚞
→ ∪ ⸙ ◎ ⚠ ⤚ 🏓 ♩
🖻

Credit Cards 🅰 ▦ ▭

RATTERY

Edeswell Farm Country Caravan Park (SX731606)
Edeswell Farm TQ10 9LN ☎ 01364 72177 Signposted
Nearby town: Totnes
▶ ▶ ▶ 🚐 £6.50-£8.50 🚐 £6.50-£8.50 ⚑ £6.50-£8.50
Open Etr-Sep Booking advisable school hols Last arrival 20.30hrs Last departure noon
Gently sloping, terraced grass site with mature trees, in hilly country and near river, off A385. A 3-acre site with 46 touring pitches and 18 statics.
Badminton, table tennis, adventure playground.

🔧 📻 ☉ 🗑 🖑 ⚲ ⚲ 🖵 ☀ 🅈 ⚠ 🛢 🖉 ⊞ 🆃 ✕ 🔌
♿ 🍴 🎾 🐕 ⚞ ♿
→ ∪ ⸙ ♩

ROUSDON

West Hayes International Caravan Park (SY298913)
DT7 3RD ☎ 01297 23456 Signposted
Nearby town: Lyme Regis
▶ ▶ ▶ ★ 🚐 £7.90-£10.35 🚐 £7.90-£10.35
Open all year (rs Nov-Mar showers, toilets, bar & shop) Booking advisable bank hols & Jul-Aug Last arrival 21.30hrs Last departure 11.00hrs
Level, grass site in downland overlooking the Axe Valley. On A3052 between Seaton and Lyme Regis. An 8-acre site with 148 touring pitches and 2 statics.

🔧 ⤳ 📻 ☉ 🗑 🖑 ⚲ ☀ 🅈 ⚠ 🛢 🖉 ⊞ 🆃 ✕ 🔌 ⚞
→ ∪ ⸙ ⚠ 🎾 ♩
🖻

Credit Cards 🅰 ▦

SALCOMBE

Alston Farm Camping & Caravanning Site (SX719419)
Malborough, Kingsbridge TO7 3BJ ☎ 01548 561260 (1.5m W of town off A381 towards Malborough) Signposted
▶ ▶ ▶ 🚐 🚐 ⚑
Open Etr-Sep (rs Oct no hot water to hand basins) Booking advisable mid Jul-Aug (touring caravans) Last arrival mdnt Last departure 11.00hrs
An established farm site in good rural location adjacent to the estuary. Facilities are fairly simple. A 10-acre site with 210 touring pitches and 42 statics.

🔧 📻 ☉ 🗑 🖑 ⚲ ☀ ⚠ 🛢 🖉 ⊞ 🔌 ♿ 🐕 ⚞
→ ∪ ⸙ ⤚ 🎾 ♩ 🖻

SEATON

See **Colyton**

SIDMOUTH

Kings Down Tail Caravan & Camping Park (SY173907)
Salcombe Regis EX10 0PD ☎ 01297 80313 (off A3052 3m E of junc with A375) Signposted
▶ ▶ ▶ ★ 🚐 £5.60-£7.70 🚐 £5.30-£6.65 ⚑ £5.60-£7.70
Open 15 Mar-15 Nov Booking advisable Whit, bank hols & mid Jul-Sep Last arrival 22.00hrs Last departure noon
A well-kept site on level ground on east side of Sid Valley in tree-sheltered position. Opposite Branscombe water tower on A3052. A 5-acre site with 100 touring pitches and 2 statics.
Off licence.

🔧 📻 ☉ 🗑 🖑 ⚲ ☀ ⚠ 🛢 🖉 ⊞ 🆃 🔌 🐕 ⚞
→ ∪ ⸙ ⤚ 🎾 ♩ 🖻
🖻

Oakdown Touring Park (SY168901)
Weston EX10 0PH ☎ 01297 680387 (off A3052,2.5m E of junc with A375) Signposted
▶ ▶ ▶ 🚐 £6.35-£9.65 🚐 £6.35-£9.65 ⚑ £6.35-£9.65
Open Apr-Oct Booking advisable Spring bank hol & Jul-Aug Last arrival 22.00hrs Last departure 11.00hrs
Friendly, well-maintained, level site with good landscaping. Reached by a short approach road off A3052, between Seaton and Sidmouth. A 9-acre site

with 120 touring pitches and 46 statics.
Dishwashing sinks.

Credit Cards ▨ ▨ ▨ ▨

Salcombe Regis Caravan & Camping Park (SY153892)
Salcombe Regis EX10 0JH ☎ 01395 514303
(off A3052 3m E of junc with A375) Signposted
▶▶▶ ★ ♨ £5.60-£8 ♨ £5.60-£8 ⚐ £5.60-£8
Open Etr-15 Oct Booking advisable bank hols & Jul-Aug
Last arrival 22.00hrs Last departure 10.00hrs
*Spacious level park 1.5m from Sidmouth and .5m from
the sea. A 16-acre site with 110 touring pitches and 10
statics.*
Off licence, bike hire, putting & barbecue hire.

Credit Cards ▨ ▨

SLAPTON

AWARD

Camping & Caravanning Club Site (SX825450)
Middle Grounds TQ7 1QW
☎ 01548 580538 (in season) & 01203 694995
Nearby town: Kingsbridge
▶▶ ♣ ♦♦ ★ ♨ £9.30-£10 ⚐ £9.30-£10

Open end Mar-end Oct Booking advisable bank hols &
Jul-Aug Last arrival 21.00hrs Last departure noon
*A very attractive location and well-run site open to non-
members. The site overlooks Start Bay within a few
minutes' walk of the beach. Take A379 coast road
signed Dartmouth, after Tor Cross village turn left at
American War Memorial for Slapton. Site on right.
Please see the advertisement on page 27 for details of
Club Members' benefits. A 6-acre site with 115 touring
pitches.*

🔊 ᛚ ☉ ◵ ☀ ⚠ 🏺 🖋 🔋 ⟲ 🖢 ★ 🐕 🐾 ᘯ
➔ ∪ 🎣

Credit Cards 🔲 🔲 🔲

◷◷◷◷◷◷◷◷◷◷

SMITHALEIGH

Smithaleigh Caravan & Camping Park (SX585554)
PL7 5AX ☎ 01752 893194 Signposted
▶ ▶ ▶ 🚐 🚐 Ⓐ
Open all year Booking advisable Jun-Aug Last arrival
22.00hrs Last departure 11.00hrs
*A well-located touring site with level grassy pitches. A 7-
acre site with 125 touring pitches.*
9-hole crazy golf.

🔊 ᛚ ☉ 📷 ◵ ◵ 🔎 ☀ ⚠ 🏺 🖋 ⬚ Ⓣ ✕ 🔋 ⟲
🛗 🎏 ⟆ 🐕 🐾 ᘯ
➔ ∪ 🅿 🜄 ⚡ 🎣 🎣

SOUTH BRENT

Webland Farm Holiday Park (SX715594)
Avonwick TQ10 9EX ☎ 01364 73273 (1m S of A38)
Signposted
Nearby town: Totnes
▶ ▶ ★ 🚐 £5-£6 🚐 £5-£6 Ⓐ £5-£6
Open Etr-15 Nov (rs 15 Mar-Etr shop closed) Booking
advisable school hols Last arrival 22.00hrs Last
departure noon
*A park surrounded by farmland, with sloping pitches
mainly for tents. For towed caravans, access can be
awkward. 1m S off A38. A 5-acre site with 35 touring
pitches and 50 statics.*

🔊 ᛚ ☉ 📷 🔎 ☀ ⚠ ⬚ 🔋 🐕 ᘯ
➔ ∪ 🅿

STARCROSS

See **Dawlish**

STICKLEPATH

Olditch Caravan & Camping Park (SX645935)
EX20 2NT ☎ 01837 840734 Signposted
Nearby town: Okehampton
▶ ▶ 🚐 fr £6 🚐 fr £6 Ⓐ fr £5
Open 14 Mar-14 Nov Booking advisable bank hols & Jul-
Aug Last arrival 22.00hrs Last departure 16.00hrs
*A basic farm site with trees and bushes set in Dartmoor
National Park. Some pitches are now tiered. .5m E of
village on A30, and 3m from Okehampton. A 3-acre site*

with 32 touring pitches and 20 statics.
Small tourist information area

🔊 ᛚ ☉ ◵ 🔎 ☀ ⚠ 🏺 🖋 ✕ 🔋 🛗 ᘯ
➔ ∪ 🅿 ⚰ 🎣
🔁

STOKE GABRIEL

**Ramslade Touring Park
(SX861592)**
Stoke Rd TQ9 6QB ☎ 01803 782575
Signposted
Nearby town: Paignton
▶ ▶ ▶ ▶ ✦ ⚶ ★ 🚐 £7.50-£10 🚐 £7.50-£10 Ⓐ £7.50-£10
Open mid Mar-Oct Booking advisable Jul-Aug also Etr &
Spring bank hol Last arrival 20.00hrs Last departure
11.00hrs
*A high quality park in a rural setting next to the Dart
Valley. Situated between Paignton and the picturesque
village of Stoke Gabriel on the River Dart, .75 miles from
Stoke Gabriel. An 8-acre site with 135 touring pitches.*
Paddling pool and dishwashing room.

🔊 ⟲ ᛚ ☉ 📷 ◵ 🔎 ☀ ⚠ 🏺 🖋 ⬚ Ⓣ 🔋 ⟲
🛗 ⟆ 🐕 🐾 ᘯ
➔ ∪ 🅿 ⚰ 🜄 ⚡ ⚰ 🎣

◷◷◷◷◷◷◷◷◷◷

TAVISTOCK

Harford Bridge Holiday Park (SX504768)
PL19 9LS ☎ 01822 810349 Signposted
▶ ▶ ▶ ★ 🚐 £5.80-£8.75 🚐 £5.80-£8.75 Ⓐ £5.80-£8.75
Open 22 Mar-4 Nov Booking advisable Aug Last arrival
21.00hrs Last departure noon
*Level, grassy site with mature trees, set in Dartmoor
National Park, beside the River Tavy. 2m N of Tavistock
on A386. A 10-acre site with 120 touring pitches and 80
statics. The park is our 1996 cover photograph.*
Fishing.

🔊 ᛚ ☉ 📷 ◵ 🔎 🔎 ☀ ⚠ 🏺 🖋 ⬚ 🔋 🛗 ⟆
🐕 ᘯ
➔ ∪ 🅿 ⚰ 🎣
🔁

Higher Longford Farm Caravan Site (SX520747)
Moorshop PL19 9LQ ☎ 01822 613360 Signposted
▶ ▶ ▶ 🚐 £7-£9 🚐 £7-£9 Ⓐ £7-£9
Open all year Booking advisable Jun-Aug Last arrival
22.30hrs Last departure noon
*A very pleasant small park on an isolated working farm
in a moorland location. On the B3357 between
Ashburton and Tavistock in the Dartmoor National Park.
A 6-acre site with 52 touring pitches and 24 statics.*
Farm animals.

🔊 ᛚ ☉ 📷 ◵ ☀ ☀ ⚠ 🏺 🖋 ⬚ Ⓣ ✕ 🔋 🛗 🐕 🐾
ᘯ
➔ ∪ 🅿 🎣
🔁

Langstone Manor Camping & Caravan Park (SX524738)
Moortown PL19 9JZ ☎ 01822 613371 (2.5m W off B3357)
Signposted
▶▶▶ ★ 🚐 £6-£7 ▲ £6-£7
Open 15 Mar-15 Nov Booking advisable bank hols & Jul-Aug Last arrival 23.00hrs Last departure 11.00hrs
A secluded site within the National Park. Signed off B3357 Tavistock to Princetown road. A 3-acre site with 40 touring pitches and 25 statics.

🔌🏠⊙📻🍳🐕🔍☀♀⚠🛈🌿⊞✕📞🎪🐴
→ ∪ ▶ ♪ 🛒

Woodovis Holiday Park (SX432744)
PL19 8NY ☎ 01822 832968 Signposted
▶▶▶ ♦ ★ 🚐 £7-£8 🚐 £7-£8 ▲ £7-£8
Open Mar-Jan Booking advisable Jul-Aug Last arrival 22.00hrs Last departure noon
A well-kept small park in a remote woodland setting. Take A390 Tavistock-Liskeard road, after 2m at Gulworthy crossroads turn right, for site in 1.5m. A 14.5-acre site with 54 touring pitches and 23 statics.
Mini-golf & boules court.

🔌🏠⊙📻🍳🐕 🔍☀⚠🛈🌿⊞🅃📞🎪🔚
🐴🛒
→ ∪ ▶ ⊚ ⚲ ♪

Credit Cards 🔷

**SPRINGFIELD
HOLIDAY PARK**
▶▶▶
**Tedburn Road, Tedburn St Mary, Exeter,
Devon EX6 6EW
Telephone: 01647 24242**

A small, quiet, family owned park for the discerning, set in 9 acres of beautiful countryside.

Situated 8 miles west of Exeter, close to Dartmoor National Park, central for beaches.

Heated swimming pool, immaculate facilities, shop with off-licence, laundry, kitchen with microwaves, games room, children's play area. Extra facilities planned for 1996.

*88 pitches for caravans/motor homes/tents.
Electric hook ups.*

**AA Campsite of the year 1994
– Southwest region**

TEDBURN ST MARY

Springfield Holiday Park (SX788935)
Tedburn Rd EX6 6EW ☎ 01647 24242
(1.5m E of village off A30) Signposted
Nearby town: Exeter
▶▶▶ 🚐 £7-£8.50 🚐 £7-£10 ▲ £5-£7.50
Open 15 Mar-15 Nov Booking advisable Jul-Aug Last arrival 22.00hrs Last departure 14.00hrs
This terraced site offers panoramic views of the surrounding countryside, a tranquil atmosphere and useful facilities. A 9-acre site with 88 touring pitches and 12 statics.
Licensed shop & kitchen with microwaves.

🔌🏠⊙📻🍳🐕⚲🔍☀⚠🛈🌿⊞🅃📞🎪🔚
🐴🛒
→ ∪ ▶ ♪

TIVERTON
See **East Worlington**

TORQUAY
See **Newton Abbot**

UMBERLEIGH

Camping & Caravanning Club Site (SS606242)
Over Weir EX37 9DU ☎ 01769 560009 (in season) &
01203 694995 Signposted
▶▶▶ ★ 🚐 £9.40-£10.20 🚐 £9.40-£10.20 ▲ £9.40-£10.20
Open end Mar-end Oct Booking advisable bank hols &
Jul-Aug Last arrival 21.00hrs Last departure noon ➡

YEATHERIDGE FARM
(Touring) Caravan Park
E. WORLINGTON, CREDITON, DEVON EX17 4TN
Telephone Tiverton (01884) 860 330
AA ▶▶▶
OFF THE A377 AND B3137 (OLD.A373) ON THE B3042

WHY ARE WE DIFFERENT? We are a small Central Park with panoramic views on a genuine working farm with plenty of animals to see and some to touch! We also offer peace and space with freedom to roam the farm with its 2½ miles of woodland and river bank walks, coarse fishing lakes, 2 indoor heated swimming pools with 200 ft water flume, TV lounge, children's play area, hot and cold showers, wash cubicles – ALL FREE. Other amenities include horse riding from the park, electric hook-up points, campers' dish washing, laundry room, shop with frozen foods, fresh dairy products, ice pack service, a welcome for dogs ★ Summer parking in our storage area to save towing ★ Ideally situated for touring coast, Exmoor and Dartmoor. Golf and Tennis locally.
*ALSO 2 CARAVANS TO LET –
PROPRIETORS/OWNERS – ALAN & ANN HOSEGOOD
WRITE OR PHONE FOR FREE COLOUR BROCHURE*

A compact site on high ground with fine country views adjacent to wooded area. Approached by metalled road, with wide entrance. Situated on the B3227, 200yds from the A377 at Umberleigh. Please see the advertisement on page 27 for details of Club Members' benefits. A 4-acre site with 60 touring pitches.

Fishing, tennis & skittles.

🏧 📻 ☺ 🖥 🗞 🔍 🔌 ⌷ ☀ 🏔 🛢 🖉 🏕 📞 🏕 🛒
➜ 🏳 🦪

Credit Cards

WEST DOWN

Hidden Valley Coast & Country Park (SS499408)
EX34 8NU ☎ 01271 813837 (1m SW off A361)
Signposted
Nearby town: Ilfracombe
▶ ▶ ▶ ♠ ★ 🚐 £3.50-£9 🚗 £3.50-£8 🛆 £3.50-£9
Open 15 Mar-15 Nov Booking advisable high season
Last departure 10.00hrs
A delightful, well-appointed family site set in a wooded valley. A completely new site with great potential. 1m SW of Ilfracombe off A361. A 25-acre site with 135 touring pitches.
Lounge/bar.
See advertisement under ILFRACOMBE

🏧 📻 ☺ 🖥 🗞 ☀ 🏔 🛢 🖉 🏕 🔲 📞 🛒 🎣 🏕
🛒 ♿
➜ ∪ 🏳 ✈ 📹 🦪

WHIDDON DOWN

Dartmoor View Caravan & Camping Park (SX685928)
EX20 2QL ☎ 01647 231545 Signposted
Nearby town: Okehampton
▶ ▶ ▶ ♠ ★ 🚐 £5.75-£8 🚗 £5.75-£8 🛆 £4.25-£8
Open Mar-15 Nov Booking advisable Etr, Whitsun & Jul-Aug Last arrival 22.30hrs Last departure noon
A pleasant, informal site with modern facilities on high ground within the National Park. In rural location yet near to the main A30 West Country road, .5m from Whiddon Down. A 5-acre site with 75 touring pitches and 40 statics.
Off licence, hire service, games room & putting.

🏧 📻 ☺ 🖥 🗞 ⚡ 🔌 ⌷ 🐟 🛡 🏔 🛢 🖉 🔲 📞 🐕
🛒
∪ 🦪 🖥
See advertisement under DEERHAMPTON

WOODBURY

Webbers Farm Caravan Park (SY029878)
Castle Ln EX5 1EA ☎ 01395 232276 Signposted
Nearby town: Exmouth
▶ ▶ ▶ 🚐 🚗 🛆
Open Etr-Sep Booking advisable all times Last arrival 22.00hrs Last departure 11.00hrs
Unspoilt farm site in two parts, with a fine view over River Exe towards Dartmoor. 4m from junction 30 of M5. Take the A376, then the B3179 to Woodbury Village, site is 500yds E of village. An 8-acre site with 85 touring pitches.
Pets corner, caravan storage facilities.

🏧 🎣 📻 ☺ 🖥 🗞 ☀ 🏔 🛢 🖉 🔲 📞 🛒 🐕 🛒 ♿
➜ ∪ 🏳 🦪

WOOLACOMBE

Golden Coast Holiday Village (SS482436)
Station Rd EX43 7HW ☎ 01271 870221 & 870343
Signposted
Nearby town: Barnstaple
▶ ▶ ▶ ▶ ▶ **Holiday Centre** ★ ⊞ £9-£20 ⊞ £9-£20 Å £3-
£6.50

Open Etr-Oct Booking advisable mid Jul-end Aug Last
arrival 23.30hrs Last departure 10.00hrs
This holiday village includes villas and static caravans
as well as the camping site. Woolacombe is surrounded
by National Trust land. Follow road to Woolacombe Bay
from Mullacott, and site in 1.5m on left. A 10-acre site
with 231 touring pitches.
Sauna, solarium, jacuzzi, pool table, entertainment.

🔂 🛴 ⊙ 🖳 🖳 🛝 🔦 🔦 🞐 ❉ ⛱ ⚠ 🛢 ⌀ 🖃

🕾 ✕ 🗶 🏕 📮 🛒 🐕 🐎

→ ∪ ⓟ ◎ △ ↯ ☺ 🎵

⊞

Credit Cards 🂡 ⚌ ▨ 🂱 🔊

Woolacombe Sands Holiday Park (SS471434)
Beach Rd EX34 7AF ☎ 01271 870569 Signposted
▶ ▶ ▶ ★ ⊞ £6.50-£13.50 ⊞ £6.50-£13.50 Å £5.50-£12.50
Open Apr-Sep Booking advisable 20 Jul-Aug Last arrival
22.00hrs Last departure 10.00hrs
A terraced site with level pitches and good facilities.
From Woolacombe Bay go uphill towards Mullacott, and
site in .25m on right. A 20-acre site with 150 touring

pitches and 63 statics.

🔂 🛴 ⊙ 🖳 🖳 🛝 🔦 ❉ ⛱ ⚠ 🛢 ⌀ 🖃 🔦 🏕 🐕 🐎 🛒

→ ∪ ⓟ 🎵

Credit Cards 🂡 ⚌ 🔊

DORSET

BERE REGIS

Rowlands Wait Touring Park
(SY842933)
Rye Hill BH20 7HL ☎ 01929 471958
Signposted
Nearby town: Dorchester
▶ ▶ ▶ ♠ ♠♠ ★ ⊞ £5.30-£8.30 ⊞ £5.30-£8.30
Å £5.30-£8.30
Open Mar-Oct Booking advisable bank hols & Jul-Aug
Last arrival 21.30hrs Last departure noon
This park lies in a really attractive setting overlooking
Bere and the Dorset countryside, set amongst
undulating areas of trees and shrubs. At the A35
roundabout E of village exit left for village. At the next
roundabout exit left for Bovington Camp. Do not enter
village. Site signed on right approx 1.5m. An 8-acre site
with 71 touring pitches.

🔂 🛴 ⊙ 🖳 🖳 🔦 ❉ ⚠ 🛢 ⌀ 🖃 🕾 🔦 🏕 🐕 🐎 🛒

→ ∪ ⓟ 🎵

⊞

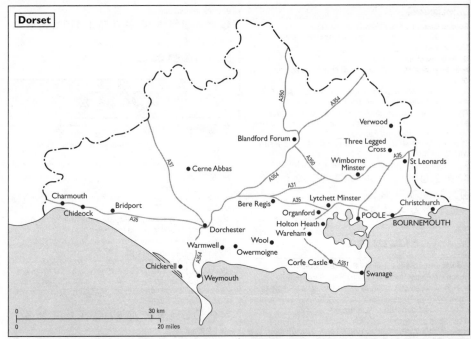

Dorset

BLANDFORD FORUM

The Inside Park (ST869046)
Down House Estate DT11 0HG ☎ 01258 453719 Signposted
▶ ▶ ▶ ♠ ⊞ £7-£10 ⊞ £7-£10 ⚠ £7-£10
Open Etr-Oct Booking advisable bank hols & Jul-Aug
Last arrival 22.00hrs Last departure noon
*An attractive, well-sheltered and quiet site with some
level pitches, in an isolated valley of woods and
pasturelands. From town cross R Stour and follow signs
to site in 1.5m. A 12-acre site with 125 touring pitches.*
Farm trips (main season). Kennels for hire.

🏮 📻 ☉ 🖥 🔧 🔍 ✳ 🏔 🛢 ⊘ 🎴 🚽 ⊤ 📞 ↩ 🐕 🐾 ♿
→ ∪ ▶ 🏌
⊞

Credit Cards 🔳 🔳 🔳

BOURNEMOUTH

Chesildene Touring Caravan Park (SZ107951)
2 Chesildene Av BH8 0DS ☎ 01202 513238 Signposted
▶ ▶ ▶ ⊞ ⊞
Open Apr-Oct Booking advisable Spring BH & Jul-Aug
*A well-maintained, level site in a quiet residential area
close to the town centre and convenient for Poole. From
Ringwood direction: 1m SW leave A31 and A338
signposted Bournemouth. In 7m at roundabout turn
right onto A3060 then in 1m turn right at signpost. A 3-
acre site with 70 touring pitches.*

🏮 📻 ☉ 🖥 🔧 🔍 ✳ 🏔 🛢 ⊘ 🎴 ⊤ 📞 🐾
→ ∪ ▶ ⌦ 📹 🏌

BRIDPORT

Binghams Farm Touring Caravan Park (SY478963)
Melplash DT6 3TT ☎ 01308 488234
▶ ▶ ▶ ♠ ⊞ £8-£11 ⊞ £8-£11 ⚠ £8-£11
Open all year Booking advisable bank hols Last arrival
22.00hrs Last departure 11.00hrs
*A very good site with good quality buildings, fittings
and services, in a lovely rural setting. Take A3066 signed
Beaminster, then left into farm road after 1.5m. A 3-acre
site with 40 touring pitches.*
Washing-up facilities.

🏮 📻 ☉ 🖥 🔧 🔍 ✳ 🏔 🛢 ⊘ 🎴 📞 🏛 ⧰ 🐕 🐾
♿
→ ∪ ▶ ◎ 🎣 📹 🏌
⊞

Freshwater Beach Holiday Park (SY493892)
Burton Bradstock DT6 4PT ☎ 01308 897317
▶ ▶ ▶ ⊞ £6.50-£13 ⊞ £6.50-£13 ⚠ £6.50-£13
Open 15 Mar-Oct Booking advisable Jul-Aug Last arrival
23.30hrs Last departure 10.00hrs
*A well-maintained, typical holiday site with newly-built
toilet block. On B3157, 1.5m E of Bridport. A 13-acre site
with 175 touring pitches and 250 statics.*

🏮 📻 ☉ 🖥 🔧 🔍 ✳ 🍴 🏔 🛢 ⊘ 🎴 ⊤ ✗ 📞 🎪
🐾
→ ∪ ▶ ◎ 🔺 🎣 📹 🏌
Credit Cards 🔳 🔳 🔳 🔳

Highlands End Farm Caravan Park (SY454913)
Eype DT6 6AR ☎ 01308 422139 (Eype, 1m W of A35)
Signposted

▶▶▶♣★ ⊞ £7.50-£10.75 ⊞ £7.50-£10.75 ▲ £7.50-£10.75
Open mid Mar-early Nov Booking advisable public hols
& Jul-Aug Last arrival 22.00hrs Last departure 11.00hrs
*A well-screened site with clifftop views over Channel
and Dorset coast. Adjacent to National Trust land and
overlooking Lyme Bay. A 9-acre site with 195 touring
pitches and 160 statics.*
Solarium, Gym & snooker room.

🔌 ⋒ ⊙ ⓑ ⚲ ⛾ ⚲ ⚫ ☼ ⦵ ⚞ 🔋 🔆 ⊞ ⊤ ✕ ✆
♨ 🐾 ⚞ ⚞
➜ ∪ ▮ ⤙ ⛾ ♪
Credit Cards 🔲 💲

CERNE ABBAS

Giant's Head Caravan & Camping Park (ST675029)
Giants Head Farm, Old Sherborne Rd DT2 7TR ☎ 01300
341242 Signposted
Nearby town: Dorchester

▶▶ ⊞ £5-£6.50 ⊞ £5-£6.50 ▲ £5-£6.50
Open Etr-Oct (rs Etr bar & shop closed) Booking
advisable Aug Last arrival anytime Last departure
13.00hrs
*Part-level, part-sloping, grassy site set in Dorset
downland near Cerne Giant (a figure cut into the chalk).
A good stopover site ideal for tenters and back-packers
on the Ridgeway route. Go into Dorchester avoiding bypass. Take Sherborne road at town roundabout, after*

*500 yards take right fork at garage. A 4-acre site with 50
touring pitches.*
Two holiday chalets.

🔌 ⋒ ⊙ ⓑ ⚲ ⟁ ⛾ ⚲ ⦵ 🔋 ⊞ ♨ 🐾 ⚞
➜ ∪ ▮ ⊙ ♪
🆔

CHARMOUTH

Wood Farm Caravan & Camping Park (SY356940)
Axminster Rd DT6 6BT ☎ 01297 560697 Signposted
Nearby town: Lyme Regis

▶▶▶▶★ ⊞ £7-£11 ⊞ £7-£11 ▲ £7-£11
Open Etr-Oct Booking advisable school hols Last arrival
19.00hrs Last departure noon
*A pleasant, well-maintained terraced site adjoining the
A35. A 13-acre site with 216 touring pitches and 83
statics.*
Coarse fishing lake open 16 Jun-15 Mar.

🔌 ⋒ ⊙ ⓑ ⚲ ⟁ ⚲ ⚫ ☼ ⦵ 🔋 ⊘ ⊤ ✆ ➜ ♨
🐾 ⚞
➜ ∪ ▮ ⊙ ⟁ ⛾ ♪
🆔

Monkton Wylde Farm Caravan Park (SY336964)
DT6 6DB ☎ 01297 34525 Signposted
Nearby town: Lyme Regis

▶▶▶ ⚬⚬ ★ ⊞ £5.50-£7.50 ⊞ £5.50-£7.50 ▲ £5.50-£7.50
Open Etr-Oct (rs low & mid season site gate will be
locked at 22.30hrs) Booking advisable after Xmas Last

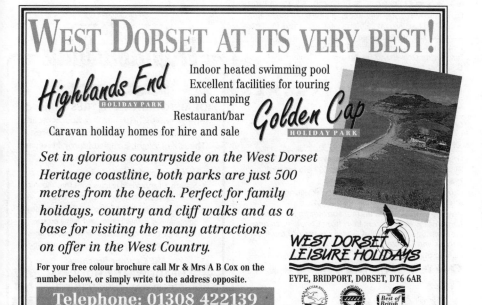

arrival 22.00hrs Last departure 11.00hrs

A pleasant family site in a secluded location yet central for Charmouth, Lyme and the coast. Situated on a 200 acre sheep and cereals farm. Leave A35 3m NW of Charmouth, and take B3165 signposted Marshwood. Site .24m on left. A 6-acre site with 60 touring pitches. Family shower room.

🔲🏕️☉🅿️🗑️🔧✳️🏚️🔌⭕️🎋🍴♨️⛺️
➔∪🕈△🎿♨️🎵

CHICKERELL (NEAR WEYMOUTH)

Bagwell Farm Touring Park (SY627816)
DT3 4EA ☎ 01305 782575 Signposted
Nearby town: Weymouth
▶ ▶ ▶ ♣ ★ 🚐 £5-£8.75 🚐 £5-£8.75 ▲ £4-£7.75
Open 16 Mar-Oct Booking advisable Jul-Aug Last arrival 21.30hrs Last departure 11.00hrs

Attractive terraced site set in hillside and valley leading to sea, with good views of Dorset downland. Situated 4m W of Weymouth on the B3157 Abbotsbury-Bridport road, 500yds past the 'Victoria Inn' public house. A 14-acre site with 320 touring pitches.
Wet suit shower on site.

🔲🚲🏕️☉🅿️🗑️🔧🔍✳️🏚️🔌⭕️🎋🔲📞⛺️🐎🍴
♨️♿
➔∪🕈🎿♨️🎵
💷

CHIDEOCK

Golden Cap Caravan Park (SY422919)
Seatown DT6 6JX ☎ 01297 489341 Signposted
▶ ▶ ▶ ★ 🚐 £7.50-£10.75 🚐 £7.50-£10.75 ▲ £7.50-£10.75
Open mid Mar-early Nov Booking advisable public hols & Jul-Aug Last arrival 22.00hrs Last departure 11.00hrs

A grassy site, well-situated overlooking sea and beach and surrounded by National Trust parkland. Ideal base for touring Dorset and Devon. From A35 centre of Chideock follow signs. An 11-acre site with 150 touring pitches and 194 statics.

🔲🏕️☉🅿️🗑️🔧✳️🏚️🔌⭕️🎋🔲📞🍴🐎♨️♿
➔∪🕈🎿♨️🎵
Credit Cards 🔲

CHRISTCHURCH

Grove Farm Meadow Holiday Caravan Park (SZ136946)
Stour Way BH23 2PQ ☎ 01202 483597 Signposted
▶ ▶ ▶ ★ 🚐 £5.50-£10 🚐 £5.50-£10
Open Mar-Oct Booking advisable peak periods Last arrival 21.00hrs Last departure noon ⌛

A well-maintained site in rural surroundings on the banks of the River Stour, 1.5m from Christchurch and 3m from Bournemouth. A 2-acre site with 48 touring pitches and 180 statics.
Fishing on site.

🔲🚲🏕️☉🅿️🗑️🔧🔍🏚️🔌⭕️🎋🔲📞🍴♨️
🎋♨️♿
➔∪🕈◎△🎿♨️🎵
Credit Cards 🔲

CORFE CASTLE

Woodland Camping and Caravan Park (SY953818)
Glebe Farm, Bucknowle BH20 5NS ☎ 01929 480280 Signposted
Nearby town: Swanage
▶ 🕈♣ 🚐 £7 🚐 £7 ▲ £7
Open Etr-Oct (weather permitting) Last arrival 21.00hrs Last departure 11.00hrs

A gently sloping grass site set in the Purbeck Hills with natural landscaping and lovely views. No short stays. Adjacent to main A351 Swanage road. A 7-acre site with 65 touring pitches.
Pony rides on site.

🏕️☉🔧✳️🏚️🔌⭕️📞🔲♨️
➔∪🕈🎵

DORCHESTER

Crossways Caravan Club Site (SY778889)
Crossways DT2 8BE ☎ 01305 852032 (5.5m E)
▶ ▶ ▶ 🚐🚐
Open 31 Mar-25 Oct Booking advisable bank hols & Jul-Aug

An imaginatively landscaped site in an old quarry in attractive forest setting. From Affpuddle follow B3390 across level crossing and turn left into site. A 10-acre site with 150 touring pitches.

🏕️🔧🏚️🔌
➔♨️
Credit Cards 🔲

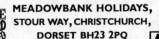

HOLTON HEATH

Sandford Holiday Park (SY939916)
BH16 6JZ ☎ 01202 622513 Signposted
▶ ▶ ▶ ▶ ⚑ ⚑ ▲
Open May-Oct (rs Nov-Apr) Booking advisable Jul-Aug
& bank hols Last arrival 22.00hrs Last departure
11.00hrs ⚘
*Good family site for those wanting entertainment, set in
wooded meadowland with direct access to A351 Poole-
Wareham road. A 20-acre site with 525 touring pitches
and 304 statics.*
Hairdressers, entertainment, dancing, crazy golf.
🕹 🛒 🎣 ⊙ 🗄 🗒 ⚡ ⚲ ⚫ ⌷ ☼ ⛾ 🗚 🔒 ⊘ Ⓣ ✗
📞 🏪 🏛 🎠 🛒 ♿
→ ∪ ⴵ ⊙ ⚘ 🕿 ♫
Credit Cards 💳 💳

LYME REGIS

See **Hawkchurch & Charmouth**

LYTCHETT MINSTER

South Lytchett Manor Caravan Park (SY954926)
BH16 6JB ☎ 01202 622577 Signposted
Nearby town: Poole
▶ ▶ ▶ ⚑ £7.80-£10 ⚑ £7.80-£10 ▲ £7.80-£10
Open Apr-15 Oct Booking advisable end May-end Aug
Last arrival 22.00hrs Last departure 11.00hrs
*A small, well-maintained site with mature trees set in
meadowland. On B3067, off A35, 1m E of Lytchett
Minster. A 10-acre site with 50 touring pitches.*
🕹 🎣 ⊙ 🗄 🗒 ⌷ ☼ 🗚 🔒 ⊘ 🗄 Ⓣ 📞 🐕 🛒 ♿
→ ∪ ⴵ 🕿 ♫
Credit Cards 💳 💳 💳 💳

ORGANFORD

Pear Tree Farm Caravan & Camping Park (SY938922)
BH16 6LA ☎ 01202 622434 Signposted
Nearby town: Poole
▶ ▶ ▶ ⚑ £6.50-£8.50 ⚑ £6.50-£8.50 ▲ £6.50-£8.50
Open Etr & Apr-Oct Booking advisable Etr, Spring bank hol
& end Jul-Aug Last arrival 21.00hrs Last departure 11.00hrs
*An attractive hilly site on fairly level grass. 6m W of
Poole off A351 at Holton Heath. A 7.5-acre site with 105
touring pitches.*
🕹 🎣 ⊙ 🗄 🗒 ☼ 🗚 🔒 ⊘ 🗄 Ⓣ 📞 🎠 🐕 🛒 ♿
→ ∪ ⴵ △ ⚘ 🕿 ♫
💷

Organford Manor (SY943926)
BH16 6ES ☎ 01202 622202 & 623278 Signposted
Nearby town: Poole
▶ ▶ ★ ⚑ £6.50-£8 ⚑ £5.50-£7 ▲ £6.50-£8
Open 15 Mar-Oct Booking advisable peak periods Last
arrival 22.00hrs Last departure noon
*A quiet, secluded site in the grounds of the manor
house, with level grassy areas with trees and shrubs.
Take the first turning on left off A35 after the Lytchett
roundabout at the junction of A35/A351, site entrance is* ➡

BEACON HILL TOURING PARK

Set in 30 acres of lovely English woodland with open grassy spaces and nature rambles, but only minutes from the South's most beautiful beaches; Beacon Hill offers some of the best facilities available at Touring Parks today plus the delights of Poole, Bournemouth and Dorset's endless tourist attractions.

Overnight stops for Poole-Cherbourg, Poole-St. Malo. Brittany Ferries. Only 3 miles from ferry terminal.

Heated Swimming Pool ★ Games Rooms ★ Children's Adventure Playground ★ Tennis Court ★ Fishing ★ Take-away food ★ Full licensed Bar ★ Well stocked shop with Off licence ★ Best beaches for windsurfing ★ Riding nearby

Free showers – disabled facilities ★ Laundry Rooms ★ Hair Driers and Razor Points ★ Dishwashing facilities with free hot water ★ Calor Gas ★ Public Telephone ★ Caravan Rallies welcome ★ Electric Hook-ups

Beacon Hill Touring Park, Blandford Road North, near Poole, Dorset. Tel. (01202) 631631

DIRECTIONS: Situated a ¼ of a mile north from the junction of the A35 and A350 towards Blandford, approximately 3 miles north of Poole.

---

a short distance on the right. An 8-acre site with 75 touring pitches and 45 statics.

🔌 📶 ⊙ 🗑 🔧 ✳ 🏔 🚰 🖊 ⊞ 📞 🛟
→ ∪ ▶
£

OWERMOIGNE

Sandyholme Caravan Park (SY768863)
Moreton Rd DT2 8HZ ☎ 01305 852677 Signposted
Nearby town: Dorchester
▶ ▶ ▶ ★ 🚲 £5-£9.50 🚐 £5-£9.50 ▲ £5-£9.50
Open Etr-Oct Booking advisable peak periods Last arrival 21.30hrs Last departure noon
Level, grass site with trees and bushes set in woodland near the coast at Lulworth Cove, about a mile outside the village of Owermoigne. A 5-acre site with 65 touring pitches and 40 statics.
Restaurant/takeaway in peak season.

🔌 📶 ⊙ 🗑 🔧 🔍 ✳ 🍷 🏔 🚰 🖊 ⊞ 🇹 ✕ 📞 🚮 🛟
→ 🎣
£

Credit Cards 🟦 💳

POOLE

Beacon Hill Touring Park (SY977945)
Blandford Rd North BH16 6AB ☎ 01202 631631
(off A350, NW of junc A35) Signposted
▶ ▶ ▶ 🚲 🚐 ▲
Open Etr-Sep (rs low & mid season bar, take-away food, swimming pool) Booking advisable Etr, Whit & Jul-Aug

---

Camping International

The New Forest with its quaint villages set in unspoilt open country and full of wild life. Bournemouth with its shops and entertainments. Dorset & Hants coast and country. 60+ places of interest to visit in good or bad weather.

STATISTICALLY THE BEST WEATHER IN THE U.K.

Enjoy all this whilst staying at one of the most popular parks in the area. Designed for the more discerning camper/caravanner who demands superior continental standards along with all of the facilities.

CAMPING INTERNATIONAL HOLIDAY PARK
229 Ringwood Rd, St. Leonard's, Ringwood, Hants BH24 2SD
Telephone (01202) 872817   Fax: (01202) 861292

ANWB
Recommended

Last arrival 23.00hrs Last departure 11.00hrs
Set in attractive, wooded area with conservation very much in mind. Two large ponds are within the grounds and the terraced pitches offer some fine views. A 30-acre site with 170 touring pitches.
Fishing & view point.
See advertisement under Colour Section

🛡 🕮 ☉ 🗎 🗐 ⟨ ⟩ ♦ ✳ ⬭ 🏔 🛡 ⟿ 🖾 Ⓣ 📞 🖃
🏕 🛒 ♿
→ ∪ �🏳 ◬ ⛖ ☕ ↗

ST LEONARDS
Camping International Holiday Park (SU104024)
Athol Lodge, 229 Ringwood Rd BH24 2SD
☎ 01202 872817 Signposted
Nearby town: Ringwood
▶ ▶ ▶ ▶ ★ 🚐 £7-£10.40 🚐 £7-£10.40 🅰 £7-£10.40
Open Mar-Oct (rs Mar-May & Sep-Oct (ex bank hols) restaurant/take-away food not available) Booking advisable school & bank hols Last arrival 22.30hrs Last departure 10.30hrs
Small, well-equipped, level camping site surrounded by trees adjacent to A31. An 8-acre site with 200 touring pitches.
Football/basketball park.

🛡 🕮 ☉ 🗎 🗐 ⟨ ♦ ⬛ ✳ ⬭ 🏔 🛡 ⟿ 🖾 Ⓣ ✗ 📞
⟿ 🏕 🎪 🐕 🛒
→ ∪ 🏳 ↗
🖃

Credit Cards 🃏 🟦 🟫 🃏 🆂

Shamba Holiday Park (SU105029)
230 Ringwood Rd BH24 2SB ☎ 01202 873302
Signposted
Nearby town: Ringwood
▶ ▶ ▶ ★ 🚐 £6-£10 🚐 £6-£10 🅰 £6-£10
Open Mar-Oct Booking advisable bank hols & Jul-Aug
Last arrival 23.30hrs Last departure 11.00hrs
Level grassy site in hilly wooded country. 3m W of Ringwood off A31. A 7-acre site with 150 touring pitches.

🛡 🕮 ☉ 🗎 🗐 ♦ ✳ ⬭ 🏔 🛡 ⟿ 🖾 Ⓣ ✗ 📞 🏕 🛒
→ ∪ 🏳 ↗

SWANAGE
Ulwell Cottage Caravan Park (SZ019809)
Ulwell Cottage, Ulwell BH19 3DG
☎ 01929 422823 & 424931 Signposted
▶ ▶ ▶ ★ 🚐 £9.50-£16 🚐 £9.50-£16 🅰 £9.50-£16
Open Mar-7 Jan (rs Mar-spring bank hol & mid Sep-early Jan takeaway closed, shop open variable hours) Booking advisable bank hols & Jul-Aug Last arrival 23.00hrs Last departure 11.00hrs
Nestling under the Purbeck Hills surrounded by scenic walks and only 2m away from the beach. A 3-acre site with 77 touring pitches and 140 statics.
See advertisement under Colour Section

🛡 🕮 ☉ 🗎 🗐 ✳ ⬭ 🏔 🛡 ⟿ 🖾 ✗ 📞 🏕 🛒 ♿
→ ∪ 🏳 ◎ ◬ ⛖ ☕ ↗
🖃

Credit Cards 🃏 🟦 🟫

THREE LEGGED CROSS
Woolsbridge Manor Farm Caravan Park (SZ103050)
Three Legged Cross BH21 6RA ☎ 01202 826369 (2m off A31,3m W of Ringwood)
Nearby town: Ringwood
▶ ▶ ▶ ★ 🚐 £5-£10 🚐 £5-£10 🅰 £5-£10
Open Etr-Oct Booking advisable bank hols & Aug Last arrival 22.00hrs Last departure 13.00hrs
A flat quiet site with a very low density and clean, well-maintained toilets. Situated 2m off A31, 3m W of Ringwood. A 6.75-acre site with 60 touring pitches.
See advertisement under RINGWOOD

🛡 🕮 ☉ 🗐 ✳ 🏔 🛡 ⟿ 🖾 Ⓣ 📞 🚲 🏕 🐕 🛒 ♿
→ ∪ 🏳 ↗

VERWOOD
Camping & Caravanning Club Site (SU068097)
Sutton Hill, Woodlands BH21 6LF ☎ 01202 822763 & 01203 694995
▶ ▶ ▶ 🚐 🚐 🅰
Open end Mar-early Nov
A popular site with pleasant wardens and staff. 7m from Ringwood on B3081, 1.5m past Verwood on R. Please see the advertisement on page 27 for details of Club Members' benefits. A 12.75-acre site with 150 touring pitches.

🛡 🕮 ☉ 🗎 🗐 🏔 📞

Credit Cards 🃏 🟦 🟫

WAREHAM

Birchwood Tourist Park (SY917883)
North Trigon BH20 4DD ☎ 01929 554763 & 01202 745442 Signposted

▶ ▶ ▶ ★ ⚑ £3.50-£5 ⚑ £3.50-£5 ⚑ £3.50-£5

Open Mar-Oct Booking advisable bank hols & Jul-Aug Last arrival 22.00hrs Last departure noon

A well-maintained new site which should mature into a very attractive site. Situated 3m N of Wareham on road linking A351 at Wareham and Bere Regis. A 25-acre site with 175 touring pitches.

Riding stables, bike hire, pitch & putt, table tennis

See advertisement under Colour Section

⚐ 📷 ☉ 🗂 ⛏ 🔍 ✦ ✳ 🏔 🛈 ⊘ ⊡ Ⓣ ✕ 丶 ⚓ 🎏
🐕 🦳 ♿
→ ∪ ▷ ⤴ 🍴 🥤
💶

Lookout Holiday Park (SY927858)
Stoborough BH20 5AZ ☎ 01929 552546 Signposted

▶ ▶ ▶ ★ ⚑ £7.50-£9 ⚑ £7.50-£9 ⚑ £7.50-£9

Open Mar-Dec Booking advisable bank hols & Jul-Aug Last arrival 22.00hrs Last departure noon ⚘

Ideal family touring site on main road to Swanage 2m from Wareham. The touring pitches are set well back from the road. A 7-acre site with 150 touring pitches and 90 statics.

9 hole crazy golf.

⚐ 📷 ☉ 🗂 ⛏ ✦ ✳ 🏔 🛈 ⊘ ⊡ Ⓣ 丶 ⚓ 🦳
→ ∪ ▷ ⤴ 🍴 🥤

Manor Farm Caravan Park (SY872866)
1 Manor Farm Cottage, East Stoke BH20 6AW ☎ 01929 462870

▶ ▶ ▶ ⚑ £5.50-£7 ⚑ £5.50-£7 ⚑ £5.50-£7

Open Etr-Sep Booking advisable school hols Last arrival 22.00hrs Last departure 11.00hrs

An attractive, mainly touring site in a quiet rural setting. From Wareham follow Dorchester road (A352) for 2m then turn left onto B3070, at first crossroads turn right, then next crossroads turn right; site is on the left. From Wool take B3071 and follow Bindon Lane unclass, in 1.75m turn left. A 2.5-acre site with 40 touring pitches.

⚐ 📷 ☉ ⛏ ✳ 🏔 🛈 ⊘ ⊡ 丶 🎏 🐕 🦳
→ ∪ ▷ ⤴ 🍴 ♪ 🗂
💶

WARMWELL

Warmwell Country Touring Park (SY764878)
DT2 8JD ☎ 01305 852313 Signposted

Nearby town: Dorchester

▶ ▶ ▶ ▶ ★ ⚑ £6.50-£14 ⚑ £6.50-£14 ⚑ £6.50-£14

Open mid Mar-Jan Booking advisable Etr-Sep & Xmas Last arrival dusk Last departure 11.00hrs

A landscaped terraced site 5m from the Lulworth beaches. Take B3390 1m N. A 15-acre site with 190 touring pitches.

⚐ 📷 ☉ 🗂 ⛏ ✳ ♀ 🏔 🛈 ⊘ ⊡ Ⓣ 丶 ⚓ 🐕 🦳 ♿
→ ∪ ▷ ☉ ⚠ ⤴ ♪
💶

Credit Cards

WILKSWORTH FARM CARAVAN PARK
Cranborne Road, ▶▶▶
Wimborne BH21 4HW ♣♣
Telephone: (01202) 885467

AA Best Campsite for South of England 1994

A family run site for families. A high standard
awaits you at our peaceful secluded park,
close to Kingston Lacy, Poole and
Bournemouth. An attractively laid out
touring and camping park, with heated
outdoor swimming pool and tennis court.
Luxury six berth caravans for hire.

WEYMOUTH

Pebble Bank Caravan Park (SY659775)
Camp Rd, Wyke Regis DT4 9HF ☎ 01305 774844
▶▶ ★ ⊞ £7.50-£10 ⊞ £7-£9 Å £6-£9
Open Etr- mid Oct bar open high season & wknds only
Booking advisable peak times Last arrival 21.00hrs Last
departure 11.00hrs
*A sloping, mainly static site overlooking Lyme Bay and
Chesil Beach. A 4-acre site with 40 touring pitches and
80 statics.*

🔌 ⬛ ⊙ 🗄 🖳 ☀ 🛒 Ⓜ 🔋 ∅ 🔲 📱 🗑 🐕
→ ∪ ▶ ◉ △ ⚓ ☕ 🎵
💷

WIMBORNE MINSTER

Merley Court Touring Park (SZ008984)
Merley BH21 3AA ☎ 01202 881488 (1m S A349) Signposted
Nearby town: Wimborne
▶▶▶▶ ★ ⊞ £5.90-£11.20 ⊞ £5.90-£11.20
Å £5.90-£11.20
Open Mar-7 Jan (rs low season pool closed & bar/shop
open limited hrs) Booking advisable bank hols & Jun-
Sep Last arrival 22.00hrs Last departure 11.00hrs
*A superb site in a quiet, rural position on the edge of
Wimborne, with woodland on two sides and good
access roads. An 11-acre site with 160 touring pitches.*
Badminton, mini football, table tennis, crazy golf.

🔌 ⬛ ⊙ 🗄 🖳 ⟟ ⚲ 🔍 🛒 ☀ 🛒 Ⓜ 🔋 ∅ 🔲 🗑 ✗
🗑 ⬛ 🎋 🦮 🐕 🛒 ♿
→ ∪ ▶ ⚓ ☕ 🎵

Wilksworth Farm Caravan Park (SU004018)
Cranborne Rd BH21 4HW ☎ 01202 883769 & 885467
Signposted
Nearby town: Wimborne
▶▶▶▶ ♣ ★ ⊞ £6-£9 ⊞ £6-£9 Å £6-£9
Open Mar-30 Oct (rs Mar no shop) Booking advisable
Spring bank hol & Jul-Aug Last arrival 22.30hrs Last
departure 11.30hrs
*This popular and attractive site lies in the heart of
Dorset, 1m N of the town on the B3078. It is well-
maintained with good facilities and was Winner of the
1994 Best Campsite of the Year Award for the South of
England. An 8-acre site with 85 touring pitches and 77
statics.*
Paddling pool, volley ball & mini football pitch.

🔌 ⬛ ⊙ 🗄 🖳 ⟟ ⚲ 🔍 ☀ Ⓜ 🔋 ∅ 🔲 T 🗑 🎋 🐕
🛒 ♿
→ ∪ ▶ ◉ 🎵

Charris Camping & Caravan Park (SY991988)
Candy's Lane, Corfe Mullen BH21 3EF
☎ 01202 885970 (2m W off A31) Signposted
▶▶▶ ★ ⊞ £4.75-£5.75 ⊞ £4.75-£5.75 Å £4.75-£5.75
Open Mar-Oct Booking advisable bank hols & Jul-Aug
Last arrival 22.30hrs Last departure 13.00hrs
*A neat, clean, simple site enjoying a rural situation, with
views of surrounding countryside. Located off the A31
Dorchester road, just a few minutes' drive from
Wimborne. A 3-acre site with 45 touring pitches.*

🔌 ⬛ ⊙ 🗄 ☀ 🔋 ∅ 🔲 🗑 🐕 🛒
→ ∪ ▶ 🎵

Springfield Touring Park (SY987989)
Candys Ln, Corfe Mullen BH21 3EF ☎ 01202 881719
Nearby town: Wimborne
▶▶▶ ★ ⊞ £5-£7 ⊞ £5-£7 Å £4-£7
Open mid Mar-Oct Booking advisable bank hols & Jul-
Aug Last arrival 22.00hrs Last departure 11.00hrs
*A small touring site with good facilities and
hardworking owners. A quiet site overlooking the Stour
Valley. Turn left off A31 at rndbt at W end of Wimborne
bypass signed Corfe Mullen. Within .25m turn right into
Candys Lane, and entrance 300yds past farm. A 3.5-acre
site with 45 touring pitches.*

🔌 ⬛ ⊙ 🖳 ☀ Ⓜ 🔋 ∅ 🔲 🗑 🛒 ♿
→ ∪ ▶ 🎵
💷

WOOL

Whitemead Caravan Park (SY841869)
East Burton Rd BH20 6HG ☎ 01929 462241 Signposted
Nearby town: Wareham
▶▶▶ ★ ⊞ £5-£8 ⊞ £5-£8 Å £5-£8
Open Apr-Oct Booking advisable public hols & mid Jul-
Aug Last departure noon
*Well laid-out level site in valley of River Frome, 300yds
W off A352. A 5-acre site with 95 touring pitches.*

🔌 ⬛ ⊙ 🗄 🖳 ☀ Ⓜ 🔋 ∅ 🔲 T 🗑 🎋 🐕 🛒 ♿
→ ∪ ▶

CO DURHAM

For the map of this county, see Northumberland

BEAMISH

Bobby Shafto Caravan Park (NZ218541)
Cranberry Plantation DH9 0RY ☎ 0191 370 1776
Signposted
▶▶▶ ⊞ ⊞ ⚲

Open Mar-Oct Booking advisable school hols Last
arrival 11.00hrs Last departure 11.00hrs
A tranquil rural site surrounded by mature trees. A 9-acre site with 20 touring pitches and 35 statics.

🔲 📞 ☉ 🔲 🔌 ⊟ ✳ 🍴 ⚠ 🅹 ⊘ ⊞ Ⓣ 📞 🅻
→ ∪ ▶ ⌇ 🎮 ♪ 🔳

CASTLESIDE

Allensford Caravan & Camping Park (NZ083505)
DH8 9BA ☎ 01207 591043 Signposted
▶▶▶ ⊞ ⊞ ⚲

Open Mar-Oct Booking advisable Whit wknd Last arrival
22.00hrs Last departure noon
*Level parkland with mature trees, in hilly moor and
woodland country near the urban area adjacent to River
Derwent and A68. Situated approx 2m SW of Consett, N
on A68 for 1 mile then right at Allensford Bridge. A 2-acre site with 40 touring pitches and 46 statics.*

DISCOVER DERWENTSIDE
at ALLENSFORD PARK ▶▶▶

A secluded riverside site in the beautiful Derwent
Valley, where Northumberland and Durham merge,
Allensford offers an ideal base from which to discover
Derwentside.
Only yards from the A68 holiday route to Scotland, the
site is set amid extensive woodland and riverside walks.
There is an on site shop and tourist information centre
to cater for all visitors' needs. Within a few minutes
drive lies the rugged beauty of the North Pennines,
Beamish Museum, Durham Cathedral and Hadrian's
Wall.

Brochure/prices — contact:
Allensford Caravan Park, Castleside,
Consett, Co. Durham DH8 9BA.
Tel: (01207) 591043

DERWENTSIDE
district council
The District That
Leads in Leisure

Tourist information centre.
🔲 📞 ☉ 🔲 🔌 ✳ ⚠ 🅹 ⊘ Ⓣ 📞 🅻
→ ∪ ▶ 🎮 ♪

WYCLIFFE (NEAR BARNARD CASTLE)

Thorpe Hall (NZ105141)
DL12 9TW ☎ 01833 627230 (off unclass between
Wycliffe & Greta Bridge) Signposted
Nearby town: Barnard Castle
▶▶ ✦ ★ ⊞ £7.50-£8 ⊞ £7-£7.50

Open Apr-Oct (rs Mar no showers restricted parking)
Booking advisable bank hols & Jul-Aug Last arrival
21.00hrs Last departure 13.00hrs
*A very pleasant site with good facilities in the grounds
of a large country house. Lies S of River Tees and 5m
from Barnard Castle. A 2-acre site with 12 touring
pitches and 16 statics.*

🔲 📞 ☉ 🅹 🅻 📞 🐎
→ ♪ 🅻
£

ESSEX

BRADFIELD

Strangers Home Inn (TM143308)
The Street CO11 2US ☎ 01255 870304 Signposted
Nearby town: Harwich
▶ ⊞ ⊞ ⚲

Open Mar-Oct Booking advisable Jul-Aug Last arrival
23.00hrs
*A quiet field behind the pub on the edge of the village.
Surrounded by farmland and close to the Stour estuary.
A 2-acre site with 65 touring pitches.*

🔲 📞 ☉ 🔲 ✳ 🍴 ⚠ 🅹 ⊘ ✕ 📞 🏛
→ ∪ 🔺 ♪ 🔳 🅻

CANEWDON

Riverside Village Holiday Park (TQ929951)
Creeksea Ferry Rd, Wallasea Island SS4 2EY ☎ 01702
258297 & 258484 Signposted
Nearby town: Southend-on-Sea
▶▶▶ ★ ⊞ £8-£12.50 ⊞ £8-£12.50 ⚲ £5-£12.50

Open Mar-Oct Booking advisable public hols Last arrival
22.00hrs Last departure noon
*A pleasant and popular riverside site, well laid out and
very neat. An 8-acre site with 60 touring pitches and 180
statics.*
Boule pitch.

🔲 📞 ☉ 🔲 🔌 ✳ 🍴 ⚠ 🅹 ⊟ ✕ 📞 🏛 🐎 📺
→ ∪ ▶ 🔺 ♪

COLCHESTER

Colchester Camping Caravan Park (TL971252)
Cymbeline Way, Lexden CO3 4AG ☎ 01206 45551
Signposted
▶▶▶▶ 🚿 ★ ⊞ £6-£10 ⊞ £6-£10 ⚲ £6-£10

Open all year Booking advisable public hols Last arrival

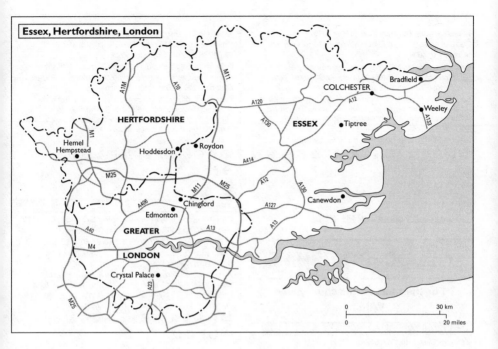

20.00hrs Last departure noon

A well-designed campsite on level grassland, on the west side of Colchester near the town centre. Close to main routes to London (A12) and east coast. A 12-acre site with 251 touring pitches.
Badminton court & putting green on site.

🔌📶☉🗑🍳✂️🏔🚰🌿🖲🚻🔦🛖🐕🐾♿
→ ∪ ⛵ ⚓ 🎯 🎣

Credit Cards ▨ ▨ ▨

Waldegraves Farm Holiday Park (TM033133)

Mersea Island, West Mersea CO5 8SE ☎ 01206 382898 Signposted
▶ ▶ ▶ 🚐🚙🛖
Open Mar-Oct Booking advisable bank hols Last arrival 22.00hrs

A spacious and pleasant site, located between farmland and its own private beach on the Thames Estuary. Facilities include two fresh water fishing lakes. Signed from Colchester. Follow signs through town to Mersey and military barracks. A 15-acre site with 60 touring pitches and 205 statics.
Boating and fishing on site.

🔌📶☉🗑🛒🛏️✂️🏔🚰🌿🖲✖️🔦🛖🍴
🐾🐕
→ ∪ ⚓ 🎣 🖲

Credit Cards ▨ ▨

Roydon Mill Leisure Park (TL403104)

CM19 5EJ ☎ 01279 792777 Signposted
▶ ▶ ▶ 🚐🚙🛖
Open all year Booking advisable bank hols Last arrival 23.00hrs Last departure 23.00hrs 🐾

A busy complex with caravan sales and water sports. Facilities have recently been upgraded. Signed from A414 between A10 and Harlow. An 11-acre site with 120 touring pitches and 149 statics.
Large lake, clay pigeon shooting, waterski school.

🔌📶☉🗑🛒✂️🏔🚰🌿🖲🚻✖️🔦🛖🍴
🛒
→ ∪ ⚓ 🔱 🎯 🎣

Credit Cards ▨ ▨

TIPTREE

Villa Farm (TL881155)

West End Rd CO5 0QN ☎ 01621 815217
Nearby town: Colchester
▷ 🚐🚙🛖
Open Apr-Sep Booking advisable mid Jun-mid Jul Last arrival 23.00hrs Last departure anytime

Grassland site on fruit farm, quiet except mid-June to mid-July which is picking season (when booking is advisable). From Tiptree follow B1022, at pub fork right into West End Road. A 7-acre site with 5 touring pitches.

→ ∪ 🎯 🎣 🛒

WEELEY

Weeley Bridge Caravan Park (TM145219)
CO16 9DH ☎ 01255 830403 (off A133) Signposted
▶ ⚏ fr £10 ⚏ fr £10
Open Mar-Oct (rs Nov-Feb open wknds only & 10 days
Xmas) Booking advisable Last arrival 22.00hrs Last
departure 10.00hrs no cars by caravans
*Level grass touring area at far end of large static park
beside Weeley Station and freight depot. Signed from
A133 to Clacton. A 16-acre site with 26 touring pitches
and 290 statics.*
Private fishing lake, live entertainment wknds.

🖭 🐾 ⊙ 🖬 ⚫ ♀ ⚠ 🅸 ⊘ 🆃 ✕ ✆ 🛒 🕮 🗚 🛪 🐕 🐾
🦽
➔ ∪ ♪
🔠

Credit Cards ▣ ▤ ▦ ⑩ ▨ ▧ 🄢

GLOUCESTERSHIRE

**For the map of this county, see
Wiltshire**

CHELTENHAM

Caravan Club Site (SO954245)
Cheltenham Racecourse GL50 4SH ☎ 01242 523102
Signposted
▶ ▶ ⚏ ⚏
Open 2 Apr-mid Oct Booking advisable bank hols & for
awning pitches Last arrival 20.00hrs Last departure
noon
*A mainly level site on Cheltenham Racecourse in hilly
country with nearby downland 1.5m N of town on A435
Evesham road. A 4-acre site with 84 touring pitches.*
Two sinks for veg prep & dish washing.

🖭 🐾 ⊙ 🅸 ⊘ 🆃 🆃 ✆
➔ ∪ ♪ ◎ 🍴 ♪ 🖬 🐾
Credit Cards ▣ ▤

Longwillows Caravan & Camping Park (SP967278)
Station Rd, Woodmancote GL52 4HN
☎ 01242 674113 (3.5m N) Signposted
▶ ▶ ⚏ £5.50-£6 ⚏ £5.50-£6 ▲ £2.75-£6
Open Mar-Oct Booking advisable bank hols & Jul-Aug
Last arrival 23.00hrs Last departure 18.00hrs
*Mostly level site with good quality, clean toilet facilities.
A 4-acre site with 80 touring pitches and 87 statics.*
Seperate games area

🖭 🐾 ⊙ 🖬 🥤 ✳ ♀ ⚠ 🅸 ⊘ 🆃 ✕ ✆ 🕮 🐕 🦽
➔ ∪ ♪ ⅄ 🍴 🐾

CIRENCESTER

Mayfield Touring Park (SP020055)
Cheltenham Rd, Perrott's Brook GL7 7BH
☎ 01285 831301 Signposted
▶ ▶ ▶ ⚏ £4.75-£7.50 ⚏ £3.75-£7.25 ▲ £3.75-£6.75
Open Mar-Oct Booking advisable public hols & Jun-Aug
Last arrival 22.30hrs Last departure noon ⊗
*Part-level, part-sloping grass site, in hilly meadowland
in the Cotswolds, an area of outstanding natural beauty.
Situated off A435, 2m from Cirencester. A 4-acre site
with 72 touring pitches and 26 statics.*
Dishwashing area.

🖭 🐾 ⊙ 🖬 🥤 ✳ 🅸 ⊘ 🆃 🆃 ✆ 🗚 🐾
➔ ▶
🔠

COLEFORD

Christchurch Forest Park Camping Ground (SO568129)
GL16 8BA ☎ 01594 833376 (site) Signposted
▶ ▶ ▶ ★ ⚏ £2.40-£7.40 ⚏ £2.40-£7.40 ▲ £2.40-£7.40
Open Mar-Oct Booking advisable bank hols Last
departure noon ⊗
*A well-appointed site in open forest with good
amenities. A good base for walking. From Coleford
follow signs for Symonds Yat to Berry Hill where site is
signed. A 20-acre site with 350 touring pitches.*

🖭 🐾 ⊙ 🖬 ⚫ ✳ ⚠ 🅸 ⊘ 🆃 ✆ 🐾 🦽
➔ ∪ ▶ 🍴 ♪
Credit Cards ▣ ▤ ▦ 🄢

GLOUCESTER

Red Lion Camping & Caravan Park (SO849258)
Wainlode Hill, Norton GL2 9LW ☎ 01452 730251
Signposted
▶ ▶ ▶ ⚏ fr £6 ⚏ fr £6 ▲ fr £6
Open all year Booking advisable spring bank hol Last
arrival 22.00hrs Last departure noon
*An attractive meadowland site opposite River Severn.
Ideal fishing centre and touring base. Turn off A38 at
Norton and follow road to river. A 13-acre site with 60
touring pitches and 20 statics.*
Bar snacks, hot & cold food.

🖭 🐾 ⊙ 🥤 ✳ ♀ 🅸 ⊘ ✆ 🗚 🛪 🐾
➔ ∪ ▶ ♪

SLIMBRIDGE

Tudor Caravan & Camping (SO728040)
Shepherds Patch GL2 7BP ☎ 01453 890483 Signposted
Nearby town: Dursley
▶ ▶ ▶ ★ ⚏ £6.40-£6.65 ⚏ £6.40-£6.65 ▲ £5.30-£6.65
Open all year Booking advisable bank & school hols Last
arrival 22.30hrs Last departure 22.30hrs
*Level grass and gravel site with trees and bushes, set in
meadow by canal, off A38. Nearby is the Wildlife Trust.
Access through pub car park. An 8-acre site with 85
touring pitches.*

🖭 🐾 ⊙ 🥤 ✳ ♀ 🅸 ⊘ 🆃 🆃 ✕ ✆ 🕮 🗚 🐾
➔ ∪ ♪ 🖬
🔠

SOUTH CERNEY

Cotswold Hoburne (SU055958)
Broadway Ln GL7 5UQ ☎ 01285 860216 Signposted
Nearby town: Cirencester
►►►► **Holiday Centre** ★ ⚏ £7.75-£16 ⚏ £7.75-£16
🛆 £5.50-£12.75
Open Good Fri-Oct Booking advisable public hols & high season Last arrival 21.00hrs Last departure 10.00hrs ⚘
A large holiday centre on flat grassy ground and adjoining the Cotswold Water Park. A 70-acre site with 302 touring pitches and 211 statics.
Crazy golf, fishing & pedal-boat hire.

Credit Cards

HAMPSHIRE

NEW FOREST

The New Forest covers 144 square miles and is composed of broadleaf and coniferous woodland, open commonland and heath. This unique area was originally a royal hunting forest and there are long established rights of access. It is not a 'Forest Park' but similar facilities for visitors are maintained by the Forestry Commission; these include caravan and camp sites, picnic sites, car parks, way-marked walks and an ornamental drive. The camp sites are open from the Friday before Easter until the end of September (two sites remain open in October). Information and camping leaflet available from the Forestry Commission, Queens's House, Lyndhurst, Hants SO43 7NH. Telephone Lyndhurst (01703) 283771. Information also available from the Tourist Information Centre at Lyndhurst Car Park. Telephone Lyndhurst (01703) 282269. See Ashurst, Brokenhurst, Fritham and Bransgore for AA pennant classified sites. AA 'Venture' sites are listed under the following locations: Brokenhurst, Lyndhurst and Sway.

ASHURST

Ashurst Campsite (SU332099)
Lyndhurst Rd SO4 2AA ☎ 01703 283771 & 282269
(tourist inf) Signposted
►►► ★ ⚏ £6-£9.50 ⚏ £6-£9.50 🛆 £6-£9.50
Open Etr-Oct Booking advisable Spring bank hol & peak season Last arrival 23.30hrs Last departure noon ⚘
Situated just off the A35 Southampton-Bournemouth road, this quiet, secluded Forestry Commission site is set amongst woodlands and heathland on the fringe of the New Forest. See under 'Forestry Commission' for further information. A 23-acre site with 280 touring pitches.
Lightweight camping area.

Credit Cards

Hampshire and the Isle of Wight

BRANSGORE

Harrow Wood Farm Caravan Park (SZ194978)
Harrow Wood Farm, Poplar Ln BH23 8JE
☎ 01425 672487
Nearby town: Christchurch
▶ ▶ ▶ ♦♦ ⊞ £7.50-£10 ⊞ £7.50-£10
Open Mar-6 Jan Booking advisable bank & school hols
Last arrival 22.00hrs Last departure noon ⚅
A very well laid out site in a pleasant rural position with adjoining woodland and fields. Leave village from S, and take last turning on left past shops. Site at top of lane. A 6-acre site with 60 touring pitches.
Washing up facilities.

🔌 🌣 ⊙ 🔲 🏮 ✳ 🅰 ⊘ ⊞ 📞
➔ 🎣 💺

Holmsley Campsite (SZ215991)
Forest Rd, Holmsley BH23 7EQ
☎ 01703 283771 & 282269 (tourist inf) Signposted
▶ ▶ ▶ ★ ⊞ £6-£9.50 ⊞ £6-£9.50 🅰 £6-£9.50

Open Etr-Sep Booking advisable Spring bank hol & peak periods Last departure noon
A large Forestry Commission site, in rural surroundings on the fringe of the New Forest. See under Forestry Commission for further information. From A35 S take Bransgore turn on right, and right again in 1m. Site signed. An 89-acre site with 700 touring pitches.

🔌 🌣 ⊙ 🔲 ✳ 🅰 🅿 ⊘ 🆃 📞 🖐 🍴 ♿
➔ ∪ ▶

Credit Cards 🔲 🔲

BROCKENHURST

Hollands Wood Campsite (SU303038)
Lyndhurst Rd SO42 7QH
☎ 01703 283771 & 282269 (tourist inf) Signposted
▶ ▶ ▶ ♦ ★ ⊞ £7-£9.50 ⊞ £7-£9.50 🅰 £7-£9.50
Open Etr-Sep Booking advisable Spring bank hol & peak season Last arrival 23.30hrs Last departure noon
Large and very popular secluded site, set amongst oak and woodland, within the New Forest adjoining Balmer

Next stop
The New Forest

Perfect for families, with wonderful facilities AND a 50% price reduction for out of season mid-week breaks!

- Free centrally heated showers.
- Indoor and outdoor heated swimming pools, jacuzzi, sauna, steam room and solarium.
- Licensed restaurant and family pub.
- Shops, takeaway, launderette.
- Play Area, fishing/swimming, riding. Fitness Suite, Toning Tables, Dance Studio/Aerobics.

OPEN ALL YEAR

SEND FOR A FREE COLOUR BROCHURE

WINNER OF CALOR GAS 1995 'BEST PARK IN BRITAIN'

Sandy Balls Estate, Godshill,
Fordingbridge, Hants. SP6 2JY.
Tel: (01425) 653042.
Fax: (01425) 653067.

...awn. See under 'Forestry Commission' for further information. A 168-acre site with 600 touring pitches.

Credit Cards

Roundhill Campsite (SU332021)
Beaulieu Rd SO42 7QL ☎ 01703 283771 & 282269 (tourist inf) Signposted
£5.60-£8 £5.60-£8 £5.60-£8
Open Etr-Sep Booking advisable Spring bank hol Last departure noon
Large secluded site amongst gorse and birch within the New Forest. There is a separate area for motorcyclists and also a lightweight camping area. A 156-acre site with 500 touring pitches.
Motorcyclists camp, Rally site. Dishwashing rooms.

Credit Cards

Aldridge Hill Campsite (SU282034)
SO42 7QD ☎ 01703 283771 & 282269 (tourist inf) Signposted
£6 £6 £6
Open mid May-early Jun & end Jun-early Sep Booking advisable Spring bank hol Last departure noon
A beautiful site in a forest glade bordered by Ober Water stream with many secluded pitches. From Brockenhurst take Rhinefield rd for 2 miles, and site

signed down a lane shared with Camping Club site. A 40-acre site with 200 touring pitches.

FORDINGBRIDGE

New Forest Country Holidays (SU167148)
AWARD Sandy Balls Estate Ltd, Godshill SP6 2JZ ☎ 01425 653042 Signposted
Nearby town: Salisbury
£7-£17 £7-£17 £7-£17
Open all year Booking advisable public hols & Jul-Aug Last arrival 20.00hrs Last departure 11.00hrs
A mostly wooded New Forest site with open fields, river walks and fishing. Facilities and amenities constantly improving. Cross bridge towards Godshill from Fordingbridge, and site on left in 1m. A 30-acre site with 350 touring pitches and 250 statics.
Jacuzzi, steam room, sauna, sunbeds, gym, fitness suite

Credit Cards

FRITHAM
Longbeech Campsite (SU255128)
SO43 7HH ☎ 01703 283771 & 282269 (tourist inf) Signposted
★ £5.60-£8 £5.60-£8 £5.60-£8
Open Etr-Sep Booking advisable Spring bank hol Last arrival 23.30hrs Last departure noon
Large site set attractively amongst trees and close to a disused airfield bordering the New Forest. From Fritham to A35, and site in 1.5m. A 20-acre site with 180 touring pitches.
Lightweight camping area.

Credit Cards

Ocknell Camp Site (SU251119)
SO43 7HH ☎ 01703 283771 & 282269 (tourist inf) Signposted
★ £5.60-£8 £5.60-£8 £5.60-£8
Open Etr-Sep Booking advisable Spring bank hol Last arrival 23.00hrs Last departure noon
An open New Forest site amid trees, shrubs and open heath. From Fritham to A35, and site on right in 1.5m. A 28-acre site with 300 touring pitches.

Credit Cards

HAMBLE

Riverside Park (SU481081)
Satchell Ln SO31 4RH ☎ 01703 453220 Signposted
Nearby town: Southampton
▶▶ 🚐🚗🛆

Open Mar-Oct (rs Nov-Feb open wknds & bank hols for
statics only) Booking advisable bank hols & peak season
Last arrival 21.00hrs Last departure 14.00hrs
*A slightly sloping, pleasant and peaceful site
overlooking the R. Hamble. Located 1m north of Hamble
just off the B3397. A 2-acre site with 60 touring pitches
and 86 statics.*

🔌📶⊙✳🔒🎚📞🛂
➜∪🛆⚡✦🍴

HAYLING ISLAND

Lower Tye Campsite (SZ735020)
Copse Ln PO11 0RQ ☎ 01705 462479
▶▶▶ 🚐🚗🛆

Open Mar-Oct Booking advisable bank hols Last arrival
anytime Last departure noon
*A site that is often very busy at peak holiday periods.
Signed from A3023. A 5-acre site with 150 touring
pitches and 75 statics.*
Rally field.

🔌📶⊙🔆🔍✳🗲🔒🎚🎛✗📞🏪🏛🐕🛂
➜∪🍴🛆⚡✦🍴

🈺

Fleet Farm Caravan & Camping Site (SU724018)
Yew Tree Rd PO11 0QE ☎ 01705 463684 Signposted
Nearby town: Havant
▶▶ 🚐🚗🛆

Open Mar-Oct Booking advisable bank hols & Jul-Aug
*A well-maintained and sheltered site overlooking
Chichester Harbour. Clean basic facilities. A 3-acre site
with 75 touring pitches.*

🔌📶⊙✳🗲🔒🎚🎛🅣✗📞🏪🐕🛂
➜∪🍴⚡✦🍴🈺

LYNDHURST

Denny Wood Campsite (SU334069)
Beaulieu Rd SO43 7FZ ☎ 01703 283771 & 282269
(tourist inf) (2m E off B3056) Signposted
▷ ★ 🚐£5-£6 🚗£5-£6 🛆£5-£6
Open Etr-Sep Booking advisable Spring bank hol Last
departure noon 🚳
*Quiet site in pleasant surroundings of mixed woodland,
grass and gravel surface. A 20-acre site with 170 touring
pitches.*

🔒🎚📞🖃🛂
➜∪

Matley Wood Campsite (SU332075)
Beaulieu Rd SO43 7FZ ☎ 01703 283771 & 282269
(tourist inf) (2m E off B3056) Signposted
▷ ★ 🚐£5-£6 🚗£5-£6 🛆£5-£6
Open Etr-Sep Booking advisable Spring bank hol Last
departure noon

*Clearings in pleasant partially wooded area. An 8-acre
site with 70 touring pitches.*

🖃🛂
➜∪

MILFORD ON SEA

Lytton Lawn (SZ293937)
Lymore Ln, Everton SO41 0TX ☎ 01590 642513 &
643339 Signposted
Nearby town: Lymington
▶▶▶ 🚐£8-£20 🚗£8-£20 🛆£8-£20

Open Mar-5 Jan Booking advisable at all times Last
arrival 22.00hrs Last departure 10.00hrs
*An ideal family site with refurbished facilities and plans
for future improvements. From Lymington take A337
towards Christchurch for 2.5m, turn left on B3058, and
site turning on left .5m along Dowton Lane. A 9.5-acre
site with 126 touring pitches.*
Dishwashing facilities.
See advertisement under Colour Section

🔌📶⊙🍷✳🗲🔒🎚🅣📞🛒🚽🍴🐎🐕🛂♿
➜∪🍴⚡🍴🈺

Credit Cards 🏧💳💳💳💳

OWER

Green Pastures Farm (SU321158)
SO51 6AJ ☎ 01703 814444 Signposted
Nearby town: Romsey
▶▶ 🚐fr £7 🚗fr £7 🛆fr £7
Open 15 Mar-Oct Booking advisable bank hols & peak
periods

Open, level, grassy site in rural surroundings. Situated on edge of New Forest W of Ower and off A31 between Romsey and Cadnam. Take exit 2 off M27. A 5-acre site with 45 touring pitches.

🔌 📶 ☉ ✳ 🛇 ⌀ 🗷 🐾 🛒
→ ▶ 🎣
🔁

RINGWOOD

Copper Kettle (SU152039)
266 Christchurch Rd BH24 3AS ☎ 01425 473904
Signposted
▶ ▶ ▶ ★ 🚐 £8.45-£14 🚐 £7.70-£11.85 ▲ £8.45-£10.85
Open Mar-Oct Booking advisable Whit & Jul-Aug Last arrival 22.00hrs Last departure noon
A small, secluded, level grassy site, with hedges and fields to rear, situated .5m from Ringwood. A 3-acre site with 56 touring pitches.
Dishwashing sink.

🔌 📶 ☉ 🔲 ✳ 🛇 ⌀ 🗷 📞
→ ∪ ▶ △ 🎣 🛒
🔁

SWAY

Setthorns (SU262004)
Wootton BH25 5UA ☎ 01703 283771 & 282269 (tourist inf) Signposted
▷ ★ 🚐 £5.20-£10.60 🚐 £5.20-£10.60 ▲ £5.20-£10.60
Open all year Booking advisable Spring bank hol & peak season Last departure noon
Pleasant level site in woodland. Take Sway rd from Brockenhurst to crossroads, turn left, and site 1.5m on left. A 60-acre site with 320 touring pitches.

🔌 ✳ 🛇 ⌀ 🗂 📞 🛒
→ ∪ ▶
Credit Cards 🃏 🪙 💳

WARSASH

Dibles Park (SU505060)
Dibles Rd SO3 9SA ☎ 01489 575232 Signposted
Nearby town: Fareham
▶ ▶ ★ 🚐 fr £7 🚐 fr £7 ▲ fr £6
Open Etr or Apr-Oct Booking advisable bank hols & Jul-Aug Last arrival 20.30hrs Last departure 13.00hrs
Level, grass site with young trees and bushes, near River Hamble and the Solent. Immaculate toilets. From M27 junc 8 onto A27 signed Bursledon. Cross river bridge and follow signs on right. A 0.75-acre site with 14 touring pitches and 46 statics.

🔌 📶 ☉ ✳ 🛇 🗷 🗂 📞 🚿
→ ∪ 🎣 🔲 🛒
🔁

WINCHESTER

Morn Hill Caravan Club Site (SU522295)
Morn Hill SO21 1HL ☎ 01962 869877
▶ ▶ ★ 🚐 fr £12 🚐 fr £12 ▲ fr £11.50
Open Mar-Nov Booking advisable bank hols & Jul-Aug

Last arrival 20.00hrs Last departure noon
A large site divided into two areas, and well broken up by trees and shrubs. The site lies 2m E of Winchester. A 9-acre site with 150 touring pitches.
Veg prep area.

🔌 📶 ☉ 🏳 ✳ ⛰ 🛇 ⌀ 🗷 🗂 📞
→ ∪ ▶ 🎣
Credit Cards 🃏 💳

HEREFORD & WORCESTER

BROADWAY

Leedon's Park (SP080384)
Childswickham Rd WR12 7HB ☎ 01386 852423
Signposted
▶ ▶ ▶ 🚐 £7-£9 🚐 £7-£9 ▲ £7-£9
Open all year Booking advisable peak periods Last arrival 20.00hrs Last departure 11.00hrs
A large site on the edge of the Vale of Evesham, 1m from the historical village of Broadway; an ideal base ➡

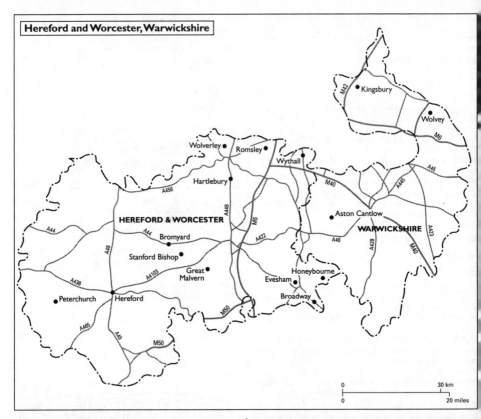

| Hereford and Worcester, Warwickshire |

from which to tour the Cotswolds. A 16-acre site with 450 touring pitches and 86 statics.

See advertisement under GLOUCESTER

🦽 🚐 ⛺ ⊙ 🔲 🥤 ⚡ ✂ 🔌 🗔 ☀ ⚠ ⬛ ⬭ ⬯ ⬆ Ⓣ
✕ ☎ ♿ 🐎 🛒 ⚼ ♿
➡ ∪ ▶
₤

Credit Cards 💳 💳 💳 💳 💳

Bromyard Downs Caravan Club Site (SO679543)
Brockhampton WR6 5TE ☎ 01885 482607 (1.5m E)
▷ ⛺ 🚐
Open 26 Mar-Oct Booking advisable bank hols
A rural woodland site in beautiful countryside between Hereford and Worcester. Site is arranged in two peaceful linked areas. Take care approaching entrance downhill from Brockhampton. A 4-acre site with 44 touring pitches.

🦽 ☀ ⬛ ⬭ ⬆ Ⓣ ☎ ⚼
➡ ∪ ▶ ⚜

Credit Cards 💳 💳 💳

EVESHAM

Weir Meadow Holiday & Touring Park (SP047443)
Lower Leys WR11 5AB ☎ 01386 442417 Signposted
▶ ▶ ▶ ★ ⛺ £6.85-£8.50 🚐 £6.85-£8.50
Open Etr or Apr-Oct Booking advisable bank hols Last arrival dusk Last departure noon
Although in the centre of town the site has a peaceful riverside setting. Turn off Port Street by Workmen's Bridge in Evesham, A44. A 4-acre site with 100 touring pitches and 120 statics.
Slipway, boating, fishing and sailing.

🦽 🦽 ⊙ 🔲 🥤 ☀ ⚠ ⬛ ⬭ Ⓣ ☎ 🏛 🗄 ⚼ ♿
➡ ∪ ▶ ⚓ ⚙ ⚜

HARTLEBURY

Shorthill Caravan & Camping Centre (SO844690)
Crossway Green, Worcester Rd DY13 9SH ☎ 01299 250571 Signposted
Nearby town: Stourport-on-Severn
▶ ⛺ £6-£8 🚐 £6-£8 ⛺ £2-£5
Open all year Booking advisable Etr, bank hols & Jul-Aug Last arrival 21.00hrs Last departure noon
Set behind a roadside restaurant, this small transit site

has a grassed area with a small pool and children's play ground. A 2-acre site with 25 touring pitches and 3 statics.

🎮 🐾 ⊙ 🔋 ✗ 🐕
➜ ∪ ▶ ⅄ 🎵 🏊

HEREFORD

Caravan Club Site (SO501420)
Hereford Racecourse, Roman Rd HR4 9QN ☎ 01432 272364 Signposted
▶ ▶ ▶
Open 28 Apr-24 Sep Booking advisable bank hols Last arrival 20.00hrs Last departure noon
Quiet, well-maintained sloping grass site with pitches on the perimeter of the racecourse. Visitors must move their units on racedays. Adjacent to A49 Leominster road and A4103. A 5-acre site with 60 touring pitches.
Free access to racing on race days.

🎮 🐾 ⊙ 🖵 🔋 🅣 📞
➜ ∪ ▶ 🔲

HONEYBOURNE

Ranch Caravan Park (SP113444)
WR11 5QG ☎ 01386 830744 Signposted
Nearby town: Evesham
▶ ▶ ▶ ★ 🚐 £5-£16 🚍 £5-£16
Open Mar-Nov (rs Mar-May & Sep-Nov swimming pool closed, shorter club hours) Booking advisable school hols Last arrival 20.00hrs Last departure noon
A clean, well-run site with trees and bushes, set in farmland in the Vale of Evesham 2m from B4035. A 12-

acre site with 100 touring pitches and 180 statics.
See advertisement on page 129

🎮 🐾 ⊙ 🔋 🚩 ⥁ 🔌 🖵 ☀ 🍴 🎣 🔋 🅣 ✗ 📞
♿ 🐕 🏊
➜ ∪ 🎵
Credit Cards 💳 💳 💳 🅂

MALVERN

Riverside Caravan Park (SO833463)
Little Clevelode WR13 6PE ☎ 01684 310475 Signposted
▶ ▶ ▶ 🚐 fr £6 🚍 fr £6
Open Mar-Dec Booking advisable bank hols & end Jul-Aug Last arrival 22.00hrs Last departure noon
An open field site with some sloping pitches and a large play area. From A449 signed on to B4424. A 10-acre site with 70 touring pitches and 130 statics.
Slipway for boats, fishing on river.

🎮 🐾 ⊙ 🔋 ⥁ 🔌 🖵 ☀ 🍴 🎣 🔋 🅣 📞 🐕 🏊
➜ ∪ ▶ 🎵

PETERCHURCH

Poston Mill Caravan & Camping Park (SO355373)
HR2 0SF ☎ 01981 550225 & 01584 711280
Nearby town: Hereford
▶ ▶ ▶ ★ 🚐 £6.50-£7.50 🚍 £6.50-£7.50 ⛺ £3.50-£7.50
Open Mar-Nov (rs Dec-Feb) Booking advisable bank & summer hols Last departure noon
A level, grassy site with mature trees in hilly country near River Dore, 11m W of Hereford on B4348. A 5-acre site with 64 touring pitches and 20 statics.

🎮 🐾 ⊙ 🔋 🚩 ⥁ 🔌 ☀ 🍴 🎣 🔋 🅣 ✗ 📞 🛒
♿ 🍽 🏖 🐕 ♿
➜ ∪ ▶ 🎵 🏊
£ᵇ

ROMSLEY

Camping & Caravanning Club Site (SO955795)
Fieldhouse Ln B62 0NH ☎ 01562 710015 (in season) & 01203 694995
Nearby town: Halesowen
▶ ▶ ★ 🚐 £9.30-£10 🚍 £9.30-£10 ⛺ £9.30-£10
Open end Mar-early Nov Booking advisable bank hols & peak periods Last arrival 21.00hrs Last departure noon
A very pretty, well tended park surrounded by wooded hills. Turn off B4551 at Sun Inn, then take 5th turn left, and the park is 300 yds on. Please see the advertisement on page 27 for details of Club Members' benefits. A 6.5-acre site with 130 touring pitches.

🎮 🐾 ⊙ 🔋 🔌 ☀ 🏔 🔋 🎣 📞 🛒 ♿

Credit Cards 💳 💳 💳

STANDFORD BISHOP

Boyce Caravan Park (SO674539)
WR6 5UB ☎ 01885 483439 Signposted
Nearby town: Bromyard
▶ ▶ ★ 🚐 fr £7.50 🚍 fr £7.50 ⛺ £4-£7.50

Open Mar-Oct Booking advisable bank hols Last arrival 18.00hrs Last departure noon
A pleasant site. From B4220 Malvern road take sharp turn opposite Herefordshire House Pub, R in .25m. A 4-acre site with 30 touring pitches and 70 statics.

🏕️ 📶 ☉ 📻 🍳 ⚟ ⚠️ 🚰 🔦 🐕 ♿
➔ ∪ 🎱 ♪

WOLVERLEY

Camping & Caravanning Club Site (SO833792)
Brown Westhead Park DY10 3PX ☎ 01562 850909 & 01203 694995 Signposted
Nearby town: Kidderminster
▶ ▶ ▶ ★ 🚐 £9.30-£10 🚐 £9.30-£10 ▲ £9.30-£10
Open end Mar-early Nov Booking advisable bank hols & Jul-Aug Last arrival 21.00hrs Last departure noon
Very pleasant grassy site on edge of the village, with good access to nearby motorways. At junction of A449 and B4189 take road signed Wolverley, and site .25m on right. Please see the advertisement on page 27 for details of Club Members' benefits. A 12-acre site with 120 touring pitches.

🏕️ 📶 ☉ 🍳 ⚟ ⚠️ 🔦 ♿
Credit Cards 🆑 🔳 🔳

WYTHALL

Chapel Lane Caravan Club Site (SP073750)
B47 6JX ☎ 01564 826483 (1m W) Signposted
Nearby town: Birmingham
▶ ▶ ▶ 👬 🚐 🚐
Open all year Booking advisable bank hols, Feb, Mar & wknds May-Sep Last arrival 20.00hrs
Rural site with a pleasant open aspect, convenient for the M1, M6 and M42 as well as the National Exhibition Centre. From M42, junc 3, take A435 towards Birmingham, and site is on left at first roundabout. A 10-acre site with 90 touring pitches.
Washing up area with hot water.

🏕️ 📶 ☉ 📻 🍳 ❄️ ⚟ 🚰 🌿 🔳 🔲 🔦
➔ ∪ ▶ ♪ 🔳
Credit Cards 🆑 🔳

HERTFORDSHIRE

For the map of this county, see
Essex

HEMEL HEMPSTEAD

Breakspear Way Caravan Club Site (TL085076)
Buncefield Ln, Breakspear Way HP2 4TZ
☎ 01442 68286 (2m E) Signposted
▶ ▶ ▶ ★ 🚐 £10.50-£11.50 🚐 £10.50-£11.50
Open Mar-Dec Booking advisable bank hols & wknds Jun-Sep Last arrival 20.00hrs Last departure noon

A quiet, grassy site with trees screening the surrounding countryside, within 1 mile of junc 8 of M1. Off A414 immed past petrol stn. A 4.5-acre site with 60 touring pitches.

🏕️ 📶 🍳 ❄️ ⚟ 🚰 🌿 🔲 🔦
➔ ∪ ▶ ♪ 🔳
Credit Cards 🆑 🔳

HODDESDON

Lee Valley Caravan Park (TL383082)
Dobbs Weir, Essex Rd EN11 0AS ☎ 01992 462090 Signposted
▶ ▶ 🚐 fr £6.05 🚐 fr £6.05 ▲ fr £4.25
Open Etr-Oct Booking advisable public hols Last arrival 21.30hrs Last departure noon
Neat, well kept site on level ground near river. An 8-acre site with 100 touring pitches and 100 statics.
Fishing.

🏕️ 📶 ☉ 📻 🍳 ⚟ 🚰 🌿 🔲 🔦 🐕 🔳 ♿
➔ 🎣 🎱 ♪
Credit Cards 🆑 🔳

HUMBERSIDE

For the map of this county, see
Lincolnshire

BARTON-UPON-HUMBER

Silver Birches Tourist Park (TA028232)
Waterside Rd DN18 5BA ☎ 01652 632509 Signposted
▶ ▶ 🚐 £4.50-£5 🚐 £4.50-£5 ▲ £3-£3.50
Open Apr-Oct Booking advisable bank hols Last arrival 23.00hrs Last departure 20.00hrs
A very pleasant, well-screened site, convenient for Humber Bridge as well as Humberside and Lincolnshire. Situated S of bridge. Take A15 into Barton and site is clearly signed. A 2-acre site with 24 touring pitches.
Putting green.

🏕️ 📶 ☉ ❄️ ⚟ 🚰 🌿 🔲 🔦 🔳 ♿
➔ ∪ ♪

BRANDESBURTON

Dacre Lakeside Park (TA118468)
YO25 8SA ☎ 01964 543704 Signposted
Nearby town: Hornsea
▶ ▶ ▶ 🚐 🚐 ▲
Open Mar-Oct Booking advisable bank hols Last arrival 21.00hrs Last departure noon
A pleasant, level grassy site beside a lake with good adjacent sports facilities. On the A165 midway between Beverley and Hornsea. A 4-acre site with 90 touring pitches.
Windsurfing, fishing, tennis, squash & bowling green.

🏕️ 📶 ☉ 📻 🍳 ❄️ 🏐 🚰 🌿 🔲 🔦 🐕 🔳 ♿
➔ ∪ ▶ ⛵ ♪

BRIDLINGTON

The Poplars Touring Site & Motel (TA194701)
45 Jewison Ln, Sewerby YO15 1DX ☎ 01262 677251
Signposted
▶ ▶ ★ 🚐 £6-£7 🚐 £6-£7 ▲ £6-£7
Open all year Booking advisable bank hols & school summer hols Last arrival 22.00hrs Last departure noon
A pleasant little site with mature trees, set in an urban area adjacent to a main road. From Bridlington follow the Flamborough road (B1255) then turn left into Jewison Lane, signed Bempton, for the site entrance on left. A 1.25-acre site with 30 touring pitches.

FANGFOSS

Fangfoss Old Station Caravan Park (SE747527)
Old Station House YO4 5QB ☎ 01759 380491
Signposted
Nearby town: York
▶ ▶ ▶ 🚐 £6.50-£7 🚐 £6.50-£7 ▲ £5-£7
Open Mar-Oct Booking advisable bank hols Last arrival 22.30hrs Last departure noon
A well-maintained site in a pleasant rural area. The track and sidings of the old railway station are grassed over and provide excellent hardstanding with a level landscaped field adjacent. Take A166 to Stamford Bridge where site clearly signed. A 4-acre site with 45 touring pitches.

HULL

See **Sproatley**

RUDSTON

Thorpe Hall Caravan & Camping Park (TA108677)
Thorpe Hall YO25 0JE ☎ 01262 420393 & 420394
Signposted
Nearby town: Bridlington
▶ ▶ ▶ 🚐 £5-£8.70 🚐 £5-£8.70 ▲ £5-£7.90
Open Mar-Oct Booking advisable bank hols & peak periods Last arrival 22.00hrs Last departure noon
A very attractive and well-ordered site in rural surroundings on edge of village. 5m from Bridlington on B1253. A 4-acre site with 90 touring pitches.
Covered outside washing up sinks with hot water.

SKIPSEA

Far Grange Park (TA181530)
Windhook, Hornsea Rd YO25 8SY
☎ 01262 468248 & 468293 Signposted
Nearby town: Hornsea
▶ ▶ ▶ ▶ ▶ 🕈 🕯 ⊛ **Holiday Centre** ★ 🚐 £7-£11
🚐 £7-£11 ▲ £7-£11

Far Grange Caravan Park

Far from being expensive
Far from being basic
Far Grange is a holiday by the sea for less than you think

Set in an idyllic location on the East Yorkshire coast, between Bridlington and Hornsea. A quiet place in the country or fun and entertainment for the family. Far Grange Park offers something for everyone. Come and see for yourself that the standards we set are exceptionally high

★ **Full facilities for tourers, tents and motor homes** ★ **Luxury Rose Award Holiday Homes** ★ **Holiday Homes for sale** ★

For further information please telephone or write:

Windhook, Skipsea, Driffield, East Yorkshire YO25 8SY
Tel: 01262 468293/468248

Open Mar-Oct Booking advisable bank & school hols Last arrival 21.00hrs Last departure 11.00hrs
A well-developed holiday site with pleasing public buildings and well-laid out grounds of shrubs, hedges and trees. Adjacent to a private sandy beach on a fairly quiet part of the coast. On B1242, 2m S of village on seaward side next to golf course. A 30-acre site with 365 touring pitches and 334 statics.
Fishing, snooker, gym, sauna, solarium.

Credit Cards 🅺

Low Skirlington Caravan Park (TA188528)
YO25 8SY ☎ 01262 468213 & 468466 Signposted
Nearby town: Bridlington
► ► ► ★ 🚐 £8-£10.50 🚐 £8-£10.50 ▲ £8-£10.50
Open Mar-Oct Booking advisable Jul-Aug
Part-level, part-sloping, grass site with young trees and bushes, set in meadowland adjacent to sea and beach 3m N of Hornsea on B1242. A 24-acre site with 285 touring pitches and 450 statics.
Sauna, sunbed, jacuzzi & bowls.
See advertisement under BRIDLINGTON

SPROATLEY

Burton Constable Caravan Park (TA186357)
Old Lodges HU11 4LN ☎ 01964 562508 Signposted
► ► ► 🚐🚐▲
Open Mar-Oct Booking advisable bank hols Last arrival 23.00hrs Last departure dusk
A beautiful site close to boating and fishing lakes in the grounds of Burton Constable Hall. Off A165 to B1328 to Sproatley, signed. A 20-acre site with 109 touring pitches and 66 statics.

STAMFORD BRIDGE

Weir Caravan Park (SE713557)
YO4 1AN ☎ 01759 371377 Signposted
► ► ► ★ 🚐 £7.75-£8.75 🚐 £7.75-£8.75 ▲ £7.75-£8.75
Open Mar-Oct Booking advisable bank hols & Jul-Aug Last arrival 21.30hrs Last departure noon
Slightly sloping grass site near urban area and River Derwent. 50yds off A166 on entering village from York. An 8-acre site with 50 touring pitches and 125 statics.
Fishing & boating on site. Sauna & Solarium.

KENT

ASHFORD

Broad Hembury Holiday Park (TR009387)
Steeds Ln, Kingsnorth TN26 1NQ
☎ 01233 620859 Signposted
Nearby town: Canterbury
► ► ► ♠ ♦♦ ★ 🚐 £8-£10 🚐 £8-£10 ▲ £6-£10
Open all year Booking advisable Jul-Aug Last departure noon
This is a small farm site surrounded by sheep grazing land and high hedges. It is well-secluded from the B2070 and approx 4m from centre of Ashford. A 3-acre site with 60 touring pitches and 25 statics.
Sports field with football & volley ball.

Credit Cards 🅺 ▭

BIDDENDEN

Woodlands Park (TQ867372)
Tenterden Rd TN27 8BT ☎ 01580 291216 Signposted
Nearby town: Tenterden
► ► ★ 🚐 £6.50-£8 🚐 £6.50-£8 ▲ £6.50-£8
Open Mar-Oct (rs Mar-Apr weather permitting) Booking advisable bank hols Last arrival anytime Last departure anytime

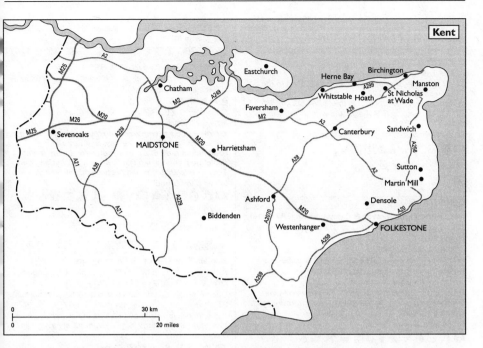

Kent

A site of level grassland bordered by hedges and trees. 1.5m S of Biddenden on northern side of A262. Ideal centre for Kent, Sussex and Channel ports. A 9-acre site with 100 touring pitches and 205 statics.
Camping accessory sales.

🎪 📞 ⊙ 🖥 ❄ 🍴 🏧 🛆 🖊 ➕ 🆃 ✖ 📞 🚿 🍴 🛒
→ ∪ ⌚ ◎ ♪

£

BIRCHINGTON

Quex Caravan Park (TR321685)
Park Rd CT7 0BH ☎ 01843 841273 Signposted
▶ ▶ ▶ ★ 🚐 £10-£15 🚐 £10-£15
Open Mar-Oct (rs Mar water off if weather cold) Booking advisable bank hols Last arrival 20.00hrs Last departure noon
Small parkland site, quiet and secluded, with very good sanitary facilities. From Birchington (A28) turn SE into Park Road, site in 1m. An 11-acre site with 88 touring pitches and 120 statics.
See advertisement under DOVER

🎪 📞 ⊙ 🖥 🍴 ❄ 🛆 🖊 ➕ 📞 🚿 🛒
→ ∪ ⌚ 🔆 ⛺ ♪

Credit Cards 💳 💳 💳 💳

Two Chimneys Caravan Park (TR320684)
Shottendane Rd CT7 0HD ☎ 01843 841068 & 843157 Signposted
▶ ▶ ▶ ★ 🚐 £6.50-£13 🚐 £6.50-£13 ▲ £6.50-£13
Open Mar-Oct (rs Mar-May & Oct)

shop/bar/pool/takeaway restricted) Booking advisable bank & school hols Last arrival 23.00hrs Last departure noon
A good, well-managed site with new toilets and showers, and well-tended grounds. A 4-acre site with 75 touring pitches and 65 statics.
Sauna, spa bath, solarium, amusement arcade.

🎪 📞 ⊙ 🖥 🍴 ⚡ 🔍 ♨ ❄ 🍴 🏧 🛆 🖊 ➕ 🆃 📞 🏛
🛒 ♿
→ ∪ ⌚ ⛵ 🔆 ⛺ ♪

£

Credit Cards 💳 💳

CANTERBURY

Camping & Caravanning Club Site (TR173575)
Bekesbourne Ln CT3 4AB ☎ 01227 463216 (in season) & 01203 694995 Signposted
▶ ▶ ▶ ★ 🚐 £9.30-£10 🚐 £9.30-£10 ▲ £9.30-£10
Open all year Booking advisable bank hols & peak periods Last arrival 21.00hrs Last departure noon
An attractive tree-screened site in pleasant rural surroundings. Off A257 Canterbury-Sandwich road. Please see the advertisement on page 27 for details of Club Members' benefits. A 20-acre site with 210 touring pitches.

🎪 📞 ⊙ 🖥 🍴 ❄ 🛆 🖊 🐕 🛒
→ ∪ ⌚ ⛺

Credit Cards 💳 💳 💳

CHATHAM

Woolmans Wood Caravan Park (TQ746638)
Bridgewood ME5 9SB ☎ 01634 867685 Signposted
▶ ▶ ⌐ ⊞ Å

Open all year Last departure 14.00hrs ⚡
*Small site alongside the city airport and close to the
London-Dover road. 3.25m S of Rochester. From M2
motorway leave at junction 3, then via A229 and B2097,
.75m from junction 3. A 4-acre site with 60 touring
pitches.*
Caravan servicing, washing & valeting.

🔌 📶 ⊙ ⌐ ✳ 🛢 ⊘ ⊟ T ⌇ ⊓
→ ∪ ▶ ⅄ 🍴 🔨 🔟 🎿

⊞

DENSOLE

Black Horse Farm Caravan & Camping Park (TR211418)
385 Canterbury Rd CT18 7BG ☎ 01303 892665
Signposted
Nearby town: Folkestone
▶ ▶ ▶ ★ ⌐ £6.50-£7.50 ⊟ £6.50-£7.50 Å £6.50-£7.50
Open all year Booking advisable peak periods Last
arrival anytime Last departure anytime
*Level, grass site with good facilities and views over
farmland. Adjoining A260 Folkestone-Canterbury road.
A 4-acre site with 45 touring pitches.*
3 acre field for recreation.

🔌 📶 ⊙ 🔟 ⌐ ✳ 🛢 ⊘ ⊟ ➡ 🐴 🎿 ♿
→ ∪ ▶

DOVER

See **Martin Mill**

EASTCHURCH

Warden Springs Caravan Park (TR019722)
Warden Point ME12 4HF ☎ 01795 880216 Signposted
Nearby town: Sheerness
▶ ▶ ▶ ⌐ ⊞ Å

Open Mar-Oct Booking advisable 2 mths prior Last
arrival 22.00hrs
*A large static site with a cliff top touring area overlooking
the sea. Take A249 to Sheerness and turn right at
roundabout onto B2231 Eastchurch road. Turn left at
Eastchurch church and take first right to Warden Point. A
1-acre site with 48 touring pitches and 250 statics.*
9 hole pitch & putt.

🔌 📶 ⊙ 🔟 ⟨ 🔍 ⊡ ⅄ ⌂ 🛢 ⌇ 🔨 🏠 🎿 ♿
→ ∪ 🎿

Credit Cards 🔲 💳

FAVERSHAM

Painters Farm Caravan & Camping Site (TQ990591)
Painters Forstal ME13 0EG ☎ 01795 532995 Signposted
▶ ▶ ⌐ £6-£7.60 ⊟ £6-£7.60 Å £4.80-£5.75
Open Mar-Oct Booking advisable bank hols Last arrival
23.59hrs
*Level, grass, farm site on outskirts of Faversham in very
peaceful surroundings. Signed from A2 at Faversham. A
3-acre site with 50 touring pitches.*

🔌 📶 ⊙ ✳ 🛢 ⊘ ⊟ T 🏠 🐴
→ ∪ ▶ 🍴

FOLKESTONE

Little Satmar Holiday Park (TR260390)
Winehouse Ln, Capel Le Ferne CT18 7JF ☎ 01303 251188 (2m W off A20) Signposted
▶ ▶ ▶ ★ ⚠ £6.75-£8.75 ⚠ £6.75-£8.75 ⚠ £4.50-£8.75
Open Mar-Oct Booking advisable bank hols & Jul-Aug Last arrival 23.00hrs Last departure 14.00hrs
A quiet, well-screened site well away from the road. A useful base for touring Dover/Folkestone area. A 5-acre site with 46 touring pitches and 80 statics.

🎯 🏕 ☉ 🗑 🢁 🔍 ✳ 🅰 🔒 🖉 🛢 🆃 📞 🥾
→ ∪ ▶ 🍴 ✏
💷

Camping & Caravanning Club Site (TR245375)
The Warren CT19 6PT ☎ 01303 255093 (in season) & 01203 694995
▶ ▶ ★ ⚠ £9.30-£10 ⚠ £9.30-£10
Open end Mar-end Sep Booking advisable bank hols & peak periods Last arrival 21.00hrs Last departure noon
This site commands marvellous views across the Strait of Dover and is well located for the channel ports. It nestles on the side of the cliff and is tiered in some areas. Signed from A20 roundabout. Please see the advertisement on page 27 for details of Club Members' benefits. A 4-acre site with 82 touring pitches.

🏕 ☉ 🢁 ✳ 📞 🥾

Credit Cards 💳 💳 💳

Little Switzerland Camping & Caravan Site (TR248380)
Wear Bay Rd CT19 6PS ☎ 01303 252168 Signposted
▶ ▶ ⚠ ⚠ ⚠
Open Mar-Oct Booking advisable from Mar Last arrival mdnt Last departure noon
A small site perched on the cliffs overlooking the Dover Straits. Signed from A2 and A20 E of Folkestone. A 4-acre site with 18 touring pitches and 12 statics.

🎯 🢁 🏕 ☉ 🗑 ✳ 🍴 ✖ 📞 🥾 🛢 🐕 🔲 🥾
→ ∪ ▶ ◎ ⚠ 🍴 ✏

HARRIETSHAM

Hogbarn Caravan Park (TQ885550)
Hogbarn Ln, Stede Hill ME17 1NZ ☎ 01622 859648 Signposted
Nearby town: Maidstone
▶ ▶ ▶ ♦ ⚠ ⚠ ⚠
Open Mar-Oct Booking advisable bank hols & Jul-Aug Last arrival 22.00hrs Last departure noon
A very good country site, with mainly large, fenced in pitches. Situated off A20. A 5-acre site with 60 touring pitches and 70 statics.
Coffee bar & Sauna.
See advertisement on page 39.

🎯 🏕 ☉ 🗑 🢁 🔍 ◻ ✳ 🅰 🔒 🖉 🆃 📞 🐕 🥾
🥾 ♿
→ ∪ ▶ 🍴 ✏
💷

HERNE BAY

Hillborough Park (TR209679)
Reculver Rd CT6 6SR ☎ 01227 374618 Signposted
▶ ▶ ▶ ★ ⚠ fr £9.50 ⚠ fr £9.50
Open Apr-Oct Booking advisable wknds & public hols Last arrival 22.00hrs Last departure 22.00hrs ⚑
Set on high ground a few minutes' from the sea and shopping centre. A large static site with separate area for tourers. Signed from A299 at Reculver. A 1-acre site with 30 touring pitches and 400 statics.
5-a-side soccer pitch.
See advertisement on page 39.

🎯 🏕 ☉ 🗑 🢁 🢂 🔍 🅿 🅰 🔒 🖉 🆃 ✖ 📞 🦽 ♿
→ ∪ ▶ 🏸 🍴 ✏ 🥾
💷

Westbrook Farm Caravan Park (TR158673)
Sea St CT6 8BT ☎ 01227 375586 Signposted
Nearby town: Canterbury
▶ ▶ ▶ ⚠ ⚠ ⚠
Open Mar-Oct (rs Apr-Spring bank hol) Booking advisable bank hols Last arrival 21.00hrs
Small site within easy reach of the Thanet Way (A299) and Herne Bay and close to railway line. The club house is an attractive 16th-Century farmhouse surrounded by trees. A 5-acre site with 100 touring pitches and 79 statics.
See advertisement on page 39.

🎯 🏕 ☉ 🗑 🢁 🔍 🔲 ✳ 🅿 🅰 🔒 🖉 🛢 🆃 📞 🦽 🔲
🐕 🥾
→ ∪ ▶ ◎ ⚠ 🍴 ✏

HOATH

South View (TR205648)
Maypole Ln CT3 4LL ☎ 01227 860280 Signposted
Nearby town: Canterbury
▶ ▶ ▶ ♦ ★ ⚠ £8 ⚠ £8 ⚠ £8
Open all year Booking advisable bank hols Last arrival 23.00hrs Last departure 22.00hrs
A small rural site, level and well secluded. Off A299 or A28. A 3-acre site with 45 touring pitches.

🎯 🏕 ☉ 🗑 🢁 ✳ 🅰 🔒 🖉 🛢 🥾 ♿
→ ∪ ▶ ◎ ⚠ 🍴 ✏
💷

MAIDSTONE

Pine Lodge Touring Park (TQ815549)
Ashford Rd, Nr Bearsted, Hollingbourne ME17 1XH
☎ 01622 730018 (2m NW on A20, from junc 8 M20) Signposted
▶ ▶ ⚠ ⚠ ⚠
Open all year Booking advisable bank hols Last arrival 22.00hrs Last departure 14.00hrs ⚑
A very well laid out new site close to Leeds Castle and the A20. Much planting of trees will result in good screening. A 7-acre site with 100 touring pitches.
Waste disposal points.

🎯 🏕 ☉ ✳ 🅰 🔒 🖉 🆃 📞 🥾
→ ∪ ▶ 🍴 ✏ 🗑

MANSTON

Manston Caravan & Camping Park (TR348662)
Manston Court Rd CT12 5AU ☎ 01843 823442
Signposted
Nearby town: Margate
► ► ► ★ ⊕ £6.50-£9 ⊕ £6.50-£8.50 ▲ £4-£10
Open Etr-Oct (rs Apr shop open weekends only) Booking
advisable bank hols & Jul-Aug Last arrival 23.55hrs Last
departure 11.00hrs
*A level grassy site with mature trees situated near
Manston Airport and convenient for the seaside resorts
on the Isle of Thanet. A 5-acre site with 100 touring
pitches and 46 statics.*

🔊 🇷 ⊙ 🖲 ॿ ☀ ⚠ 🛉 ⌀ Ⓣ ❤ 🐕 🌄
→ ∪ ▶ ᡃ 👪 ♫ 🗓
⊞

MARTIN MILL

**Hawthorn Farm Caravan Park
(TR342464)**
CT15 5JU
☎ 01304 852658 & 852914 Signposted
Nearby town: Dover
► ► ► ♦ 🛉🛉 ★ ⊕ £2.75-£3.50 ⊕ £2.75-£3.50 ▲ £2-£2.50
Open Mar-Oct water off if weather cold Booking
advisable bank hols & Jul-Aug Last arrival 22.00hrs Last
departure noon
*This pleasant rural site is screened by young trees and
hedgerows. Its grounds include a rose garden and
woods. Signed from A258. A 15-acre site with 160
touring pitches and 176 statics.*
See advertisement under DOVER

🔊 🇷 ⊙ 🖲 ☀ 🛉 ⌀ ❤ 🌄
→ ∪ ▶ 🛆 ᡃ 👪 ♫

Credit Cards 🔲 🔤 🔤

〇〇〇〇〇〇〇〇〇〇

ST NICHOLAS AT WADE

St Nicholas at Wade Camping Site (TR254672)
Court Rd CT7 0NH ☎ 01843 847245 Signposted
Nearby town: Margate
► ⊕ £6-£9 ⊕ £6.50-£7.50 ▲ £6.50-£8
Open Etr-Oct Booking advisable Jul-Aug Last arrival
22.00hrs Last departure 16.00hrs
*A small field with a toilet block, close to village and
shop, off A299 and A28. A 3-acre site with 75 touring
pitches.*

🔊 🇷 ⊙ ☀ ⚠ 🛉 ⌀ Ⓣ 🌄
→ ∪ ♫ 🗓

SANDWICH

Sandwich Leisure Park (TR326581)
Woodnesborough Rd CT13 0AA ☎ 01304 612681
Signposted
► ► ► ★ ⊕ £6.50-£9 ⊕ £6.50-£9 ▲ £4-£9
Open Mar-Oct Booking advisable Etr, Spring bank hol &
Jul-Aug Last arrival 20.00hrs Last departure 11.00hrs
*A useful touring site on the edge of Sandwich, with well
laid out pitches and very clean toilets. Signed from A256*

*at Sandwich. A 5.5-acre site with 100 touring pitches
and 103 statics.*
Washing-up area.

🔊 🇷 ⊙ 🖲 ॿ ☀ ⚠ 🛉 ⌀ ❤ 🐕 🌄
→ ∪ ▶ ᡃ 👪 ♫
⊞

SEVENOAKS

Camping & Caravanning Club Site (TQ577564)
Styants Bottom Rd, Styants Bottom, Nr Seal TN15 0ET
☎ 01732 762728 (in season) & 01203 694995
► ► ► ♦ ★ ⊕ £9.30-£10 ⊕ £9.30-£10 ▲ £9.30-£10
Open end Mar-early Nov Booking advisable bank hols &
peak periods Last arrival 21.00hrs Last departure noon
*A quiet park in the centre of NT woodlands, with
buildings blending well into the surroundings. Please
see the advertisement on page 27 for details of Club
Members' benefits. A 4-acre site with 60 touring pitches.*

🔊 🇷 ⊙ 🖲 ॿ ☀ ⚠ 🛉 ❤ 🌄 ♿

Credit Cards 🔲 🔤 🔤

SUTTON

Sutton Vale Caravan Park (TR339498)
CT15 5DH ☎ 01304 374155
Nearby town: Dover
► ► ► ★ ⊕ £8.50-£10.50 ⊕ £8.50-£10.50
Open Mar-Jan Booking advisable bank hols & Jul-Aug
Last arrival 19.00hrs Last departure noon
*Small and well-sited park with limited space for tourers.
Mainly static with little privacy. From A258 in Ringwould
take unclass rd to site in 1.5m. A 6-acre site with 20
touring pitches and 114 statics.*
Sports field, croquet.

🔊 🇷 ⊙ 🖲 ॿ ᡃ ◀ ☐ ☀ ♀ ⚠ 🛉 ⊡ Ⓣ ✕ ❤ ♨
🏕 ☂ 🐕 ⊟ 🌄
→ ∪ ▶ 🛆 ᡃ 👪 ♫
⊞

Credit Cards 🔲 🔤

WESTENHANGER

Caravan Club Site (TR128371)
Folkestone Racecourse ☎ 01303 261761 Signposted
Nearby town: Folkestone
► ► ⊕ ⊕ ▲
Open Apr-Sep Booking advisable Jul-Aug Last arrival
20.00hrs Last departure noon
*Situated in rural surroundings 7m W of Folkestone and
3m from nearest beach. Conveniently positioned for
Channel ports. From junc 11 of M20 onto A261 at
roundabout with A20, signed Sellinge. A 4-acre site with
60 touring pitches.*

🔊 🇷 ⊙ ☀ 🛉 ⌀ Ⓣ ❤ 🐕
→ ∪ ▶ ᡃ 👪 ♫ 🌄

Credit Cards 🔲 🔤

WHITSTABLE

Blue Waters Touring Harbour (TR145675)
St John's Rd CT5 2RY ☎ 01227 792246 Signposted
Nearby town: Herne Bay
▶ ▶ ▶ 🚐 🚙

Open Etr-Oct Booking advisable public hols Last arrival
21.30hrs ♨

*A large static site with an equally large touring field. A
12-acre site with 20 touring pitches and 452 statics.*
Amusement arcade & adventure trail.
See advertisement on page 39.

LANCASHIRE

BLACKPOOL

Mariclough Hampsfield Camping Site (SD366326)
Preston New Rd, Peel Corner FY4 5JR ☎ 01253 761034
(on A583 0.5m S of M55 Jct 4)
▶ ★ 🚐 £6-£8.50 🚙 £4-£7.50 ▲ £4-£7.50
Open Etr-Nov Booking advisable high season bank hols
(for caravans) Last arrival 22.30hrs Last departure noon
*A small, tidy, family camping site located on A583 and
on the outskirts of Blackpool, set in open countryside. A
2-acre site with 50 touring pitches and 2 statics.* ➡

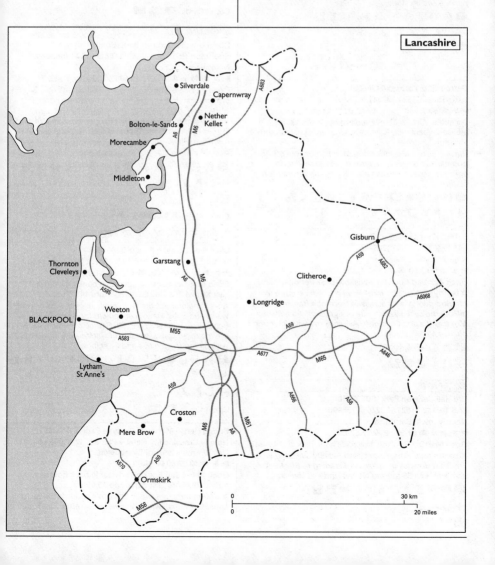

Lancashire

Coffee shop, TV & games room in high season.

🎮 🛞 ☉ 🦯 ❄ 🏔 🔒 🖉 🗓 🕆 ✗ ☎ 🧴
➜ ∪ ▶ ⅄ 🍽 ✈

Sandside Caravan & Camping Park (SD472681)
The Shore LA5 8JS ☎ 01524 822311 Signposted
▶ ▶ ▶ 🚐 🚐 🅰
Open Mar-Oct Booking advisable bank hols & Jul-Aug
A well-maintained site on pleasant sloping ground overlooking Morecambe Bay, with distant views of the Lake District. Leave junction 35 of M6; A6 through Carnforth, turn right at Little Chef in Bolton-le-Sands, over level-crossing to site. A 6-acre site with 130 touring pitches and 35 statics.

🎮 🛞 ☉ 🦯 🦯 ❄ 🏔 🔒 🖉 🗓 ☎ 🧴
➜ ∪ ▶ ⬙ ⅄ 🍽 ✈
£

Credit Cards 💳 💳 💳 💳 💳 💳 💳

Detron Gate Farm (SD478683)
LA5 9TN ☎ 01524 732842 & 733617 (night) Signposted
▶ ▶ 🚐 🚐 🅰
Open Mar-Oct (rs Mar-May shop hours) Booking advisable bank hols Last arrival 22.00hrs Last departure 18.00hrs
Rural grassy site overlooking Morecambe Bay off A6. A popular site on sloping ground with a small farm adjacent. An 8-acre site with 100 touring pitches and 42 statics.

🎮 🛞 ☉ 🦯 🍴 🖵 ❄ 🏔 🔒 🖉 🗓 🕆 ☎ 🧴
➜ ∪ ▶ ⅄ ✈

Bolton Holmes Farm (SD481693)
LA5 8ES ☎ 01524 732854
Nearby town: Lancaster
▶ ★ 🚐 fr £3.50 🚐 fr £3.50 🅰 fr £3.50
Open Apr-Sep Booking advisable peak periods
A gently sloping site forming part of a farm complex, offering good views across Morecambe Bay and to the hills of the Lake District. Site is signed off A6 between Morecambe and Carnforth. A 5-acre site with 30 touring pitches and 45 statics.

🎮 🛞 ☉ ❄ 🔒 🗓 🧴
➜ ∪ ⅄ ✈ 🔟 🧴

Old Hall Caravan Park (SD533716)
LA6 1AD ☎ 01524 733276 & 735996
Nearby town: Carnforth
▶ ▶ ▶ ★ 🚐 £7.50-£9 🚐 £7.50-£9
Open Mar-Oct Booking advisable bank hols & Jul-Aug
A continuously improving site in lovely secluded woods. 1m from Borwick on unclass rd leading to B6243. A 3-acre site with 38 touring pitches and 128 statics.

🎮 🛞 ☉ 🦯 🦯 🏔 🔒 🗓 🧴 🐕 🔟 🧴 ♿
➜ ∪ ⅄ ✈
£

Camping & Caravanning Club Site (SD727416)
Edisford Bridge, Edisford Rd BB7 3LA ☎ 01200 25294 (in season) & 01203 694995 (1m W off B6243) Signposted
▶ ▶ ★ 🚐 £9.30-£10 🚐 £9.30-£10 🅰 £9.30-£10
Open end Mar-early Nov Booking advisable bank hols & peak periods Last arrival 21.00hrs Last departure noon
Set on the banks of the River Ribble, this site is ideal for fishing and walking as well as enjoying the adjacent park. Situated 1m out of town on the B6243. Please see the advertisement on page 27 for details of Club Members' benefits. A 5-acre site with 80 touring pitches.

🎮 🛞 ☉ 🦯 ❄ 🔒 🖉 🗓 ☎ 🧴
➜ ▶ 🍽 ✈

Credit Cards 💳 💳 💳

Royal Umpire Caravan Park (SD504190)
Southport Rd PR5 7HP ☎ 01772 600257 Signposted
Nearby town: Chorley
▶ ▶ ▶ 👫 ★ 🚐 £5-£12.20 🚐 £5-£12.20 🅰 £5-£9.71
Open 22 Dec-6 Nov Booking advisable bank hols & peak season Last arrival 22.30hrs Last departure noon
A pleasant, level site with good facilities and high standard of maintenance, set in open countryside, and signed off A581 from Chorley.. A 10-acre site with 200 touring pitches.
Assault course, five a side football pitch.

🎮 🛞 ☉ 🦯 🦯 🍴 ❄ 🏔 🔒 🖉 🗓 🕆 🧴 🏍 🐕 🧴 ♿
➜ ∪ ▶ ✈
£

Credit Cards 💳 💳 💳 💳 💳

Claylands Caravan Park (SD496485)
Cabus PR3 1AJ ☎ 01524 791242 (2m N) Signposted
▶ ▶ ▶ ▶ ★ 🚐 £8.25 🚐 £8.25 🅰 £8.25
Open Mar-Oct Booking advisable bank hols & Jul-Aug
Last arrival 23.00hrs Last departure 14.00hrs
A well-maintained site with lovely river and woodland walks and good views, convenient for A6 and M6 between junctions 32 and 33. Signed off A6 down private rd on Lancaster side of Garstang. A 14-acre site with 64 touring pitches and 22 statics.

🎮 🛞 ☉ 🦯 🦯 ❄ 🍴 🏔 🔒 🖉 🗓 🕆 ✗ 🧴 🎏 🐕 🧴
♿
➜ ∪ ▶ ✈

Credit Cards 💳 💳

Bridge House Marina & Caravan Park (SD483457)
Nateby Crossing Ln, Nateby PR3 0JJ ☎ 01995 603207 (1m W on unclass rd) Signposted
▶ ▶ ▶ 🚐 £7.80 🚐 £7.80
Open Mar-4 Jan Booking advisable bank hols Last arrival 22.00hrs Last departure 13.00hrs
A well-maintained site in attractive countryside by the Lancaster Canal, with good views towards the Trough of

Bowland. Just off A6, on unclass rd signed Knott End. A 4-acre site with 50 touring pitches and 20 statics.

🎦 🏪 ☉ 🗊 🥛 ※ 🛝 🛢 🖉 ⊞ T 📞 🏋

→ 🎵

GISBURN

Rimington Caravan Park (SD825469)
Hardacre Lane, Rimington BB7 4DS ☎ 01200 445355 (off A682 1m S of Gisburn) Signposted
Nearby town: Clitheroe
► ► ► 🚐 £6.50-£7.50 🚐 £6.50-£7.50 ▲ £6.50-£7.50
Open Apr-Oct (rs Mar hardstanding available only)
Booking advisable bank hols & Jul-3 Sep Last arrival 21.00hrs Last departure 20.00hrs
A well-cared for site set in an attractive rural valley close to the Pendle Hills and situated just off A682 Gisburn-Nelson road 1m from town centre. A 4-acre site with 30 touring pitches and 150 statics.

🎦 🛒 🏪 ☉ 🗊 🥛 🔦 ※ ♀ 🛢 🖉 ⊞ T 📞 🏋

→ ∪ 🎵

💷

Todber Caravan Park (SD835469)
BB7 4JJ ☎ 01200 445322 Signposted
Nearby town: Nelson
► ► ► 🚐 £7 🚐 £7 ▲ £7
Open Mar-Oct (rs Mar-Etr clubhouse open wknds only)
Booking advisable public hols & for electric hook-up Last arrival 20.00hrs Last departure 18.00hrs
A popular rural site on sloping ground with good views all round, off A682. A 5-acre site with 100 touring pitches and 257 statics.
Indoor playroom & games field.

🎦 🏪 ☉ 🗊 🥛 🔦 ※ ♀ 🛝 🛢 ⊞ T 📞 🐕 🏋

💷

LONGRIDGE

Beacon Fell View Caravan Park (SD618382)
110 Higher Rd PR3 2TY ☎ 01772 785434
► ► ► ★ 🚐 £7-£12 🚐 £7-£12 ▲
Open 8 Apr-28 Oct Booking advisable bank & school hols Last arrival 21.00hrs Last departure 18.00hrs
An elevated site with views over Beacon Fell. Leave A6 at Broughton on B5269 into Longridge and follow B6243 out of town centre, then take L fork signed Jeffrey Hill; site is .75m on R. A 7-acre site with 97 touring pitches and 397 statics.
Free evening entertainment, pool tables, darts.

🎦 🏪 ☉ 🗊 🥛 🔦 ♀ 🛝 🛢 🖉 📞 🛖 🐕 🏋

→ ∪ 🚽 🎵

Credit Cards 📇

LYTHAM ST ANNES

Eastham Hall Caravan Site (SD379291)
Saltcotes Rd FY8 4LS ☎ 01253 737907 Signposted
► ► ► ★ 🚐 £7-£8.50 🚐 £7-£8.50
Open Mar-Oct Booking advisable bank hols & Jul Last arrival 22.00hrs Last departure 14.00hrs
A level, secluded site with trees and hedgerows, in rural

surroundings. From Preston on A584, turn right onto B5259 to site in .75m. A 15-acre site with 200 touring pitches and 200 statics.

🎦 🏪 ☉ 🗊 🥛 🔦 ※ 🛝 🛢 🖉 ⊞ T 📞 🐕 🏋

→ ∪ 🚽 🛶 ⛵

MERE BROW

Leisure Lakes (SO408176)
PR4 6JX ☎ 01772 813446 & 814502
Nearby town: Southport
► ► ► 🚐 fr £8.50 🚐 fr £8.50 ▲ fr £8.50
Open all year Booking advisable bank hols, Jun-Aug & wknds Last arrival 21.00hrs Last departure 16.30hrs
A level grassy site in spacious parkland with ample amenities including watersports, fishing and walking. Site is just off A565 Preston-Southport road approx 5 miles from Southport. A 9-acre site with 86 touring pitches.
Windsurfing, canoe hire, golf range, cycle hire.

🎦 🏪 ☉ 🗊 ※ ♀ 🛝 🛢 🖉 ✕ 📞 🛖 🎏 🏋 ♿

→ 🚽 🛶 ⛵ 🎣 🎵

MIDDLETON (NEAR MORECAMBE)

Hawthorne Camping Site (SD415575)
Carr Ln LA3 3LL ☎ 01524 52074
► ► ► 🚐 🚐 ▲
Open Etr-Oct Booking advisable public hols Last arrival 21.00hrs Last departure 11.00hrs
Level grass site with trees and bushes set in woodland, with access to sea and beach at Middleton Sands. On unclass rd from Heysham past Pontins Middleton Towers to beach. A 6-acre site with 70 touring pitches and 50 statics.
Beer gardens.

🎦 🏪 ☉ 🗊 🔦 🗔 ※ ♀ 🛝 🛢 🖉 ⊞ T ✕ 📞 🎏 🏋

→ ∪ 🚽 🛶 🎵

Melbreak Caravan Park (SD415584)
Carr Ln LA3 3LH ☎ 01524 852430 Signposted
Nearby town: Morecambe
► ► ► 🚐 fr £6 🚐 fr £6 ▲ fr £6
Open Mar-Oct Booking advisable Jul-Aug Last arrival 22.00hrs Last departure noon
Small, well run, tidy site in open countryside S of Morecambe. Site on unclass rd from Heysham towards Middleton Sands. A 2-acre site with 22 touring pitches and 10 statics.

🎦 🏪 ☉ 🗊 🥛 ※ 🛢 🖉 ⊞ T 🛖 🏋

→ ∪ 🚽 🎵

💷

MORECAMBE

Riverside Caravan Park (SD448615)
Snatchems LA3 3ER ☎ 01524 844193 (take unclass road S off B5273) Signposted
Nearby town: Lancaster
► ► ► 🚐 £5.50 🚐 £5.50 ▲ £5-£5.50
Open Mar-Oct Booking advisable public hols & high season Last arrival 22.00hrs Last departure noon
A nice level grassy site with views over River Lune and ➥

Morecambe Bay. On unclass road off B5273 near Heaton. A 2-acre site with 50 touring pitches.

🎮 🐾 ☉ ⚑ ✳ ⚠ 🔒 ⊞ T 📞 🐕 🔄 🐾 ♿
→ ∪ ▶ 📹 ⚓ 🗑

💷

Credit Cards

Venture Caravan Park (SD436633)

Langridge Way, Westgate LA4 4TQ
☎ 01524 412986 & 412585 Signposted
▶ ▶ ▶ ★ 🚐 fr £8 🚐 fr £8 ▲ fr £8

Open Mar-Oct (rs Nov-Feb touring vans only, one toilet block open) Booking advisable bank hols & peak periods Last arrival 22.00hrs Last departure noon

Large, mainly static site off the A589, close to the centre of town. A 5-acre site with 56 touring pitches and 304 statics.

Amusement arcade & off licence.

🎮 🐾 ☉ 🗄 ⚑ 🍴 ☐ ✳ ⚠ 🔒 🌿 ⊞ T 📞 ♿
→ ∪ ▶ ⚓ ⚓

💷

Hawthorns Caravan & Camping Park (SD514686)
LA6 1EA ☎ 01524 732079 Signposted
Nearby town: Carnforth
▶ ▶ ▶ 🚐 🚐 ▲

Open Mar-Oct Booking advisable bank hols Last arrival 22.00hrs Last departure noon

A very well-kept and planned site in a rural setting on the edge of the village. Some good recreational facilities. From junc 35 of M6 take B6254 towards Kirkby Lonsdale through village. A 3-acre site with 25 touring pitches and 43 statics.

Putting green, library & table tennis.

🎮 🐾 ☉ 🗄 ⚑ ♠ ✳ ⚠ 🔒 ⊞ 📞 ♨ ☂ 🐕
→ ∪ ▶ ⚓ ⚓ 📹 ⚓ ⚓

Abbey Farm Caravan Park (SD434098)

Dark Ln L40 5TX ☎ 01695 572686 Signposted
▶ ▶ ▶ ★ 🚐 £6-£7 🚐 £6-£7 ▲ £4.25-£7

Open all year Booking advisable public hols & Jul-Aug Last arrival 22.00hrs Last departure 13.00hrs

A well-maintained rural site with level, grassy pitches close to town. In the grounds of Burscough Abbey, signed from the town centre on unclass rd to A5209 to Burscough.. A 5-acre site with 56 touring pitches and 44 statics.

Undercover washing up area.

🎮 🛒 🐾 ☉ 🗄 ⚑ ✳ ⚠ 🔒 🌿 ⊞ T 📞 ♨ 🐕 🐾
♿
→ ▶ 📹 ⚓

Holgate's Caravan Park (SD455762)
Cove Rd LA5 0SH ☎ 01524 701508
Signposted
▶ ▶ ▶ ▶ 🐾 👫 ⊕ ★ 🚐 £12.85-£14.40 🚐 £12.85-£14.40
▲ £12.85-£14.40

Open mid Feb-7 Nov (rs 21 Dec-mid Feb) Booking advisable school & public hols & wknds Last arrival 22.00hrs Last departure 14.00hrs

A superb family holiday centre set in wooded countryside adjacent to the sea, this is the Regional Winner for Northern England of the AA's 1996 Campsite of the Year Award. For full details of award winners, refer to the colour section at the front of the book. From Carnforth centre take unclass Silverdale rd & follow tourist signs after Warton. A 10-acre site with 70 touring pitches and 350 statics.

Sauna, spa bath, steam room & mini-golf.

See advertisement under Colour Section

🎮 🐾 ☉ 🗄 ⚑ ♠ ✳ 🍷 ⚠ 🔒 🌿 ⊞ T ✗ 📞 ⛲
🐕 🐾 ♿
→ ∪ ▶ ⚓

💷

Credit Cards

Kneps Farm Holiday Park (SD353429)

River Rd FY5 5LR ☎ 01253 823632 Signposted
Nearby town: Blackpool
▶ ▶ ▶ ▶ 👫 ★ 🚐 £7-£9.50 🚐 £7-£9.50 ▲ £7-£9.50

Open Mar-Oct Booking advisable at all times Last arrival 20.00hrs Last departure noon

A level stony and grassy site with mature trees near a river and with good facilities. 5m N of Blackpool. Leave A585 at roundabout onto B5412 to Little Thornton. Turn right at St Johns Church into Stanah Road, leading to River Road. A 4-acre site with 72 touring pitches and 88 statics.

Bird watching hide.

🎮 🛒 🐾 ☉ 🗄 ⚑ ✳ ⚠ 🔒 🌿 ⊞ T ✗ 📞 🛒 ⛲
☂ 🐾 ♿
→ ∪ ▶ ⚓

💷

Credit Cards

High Moor Farm Caravan Park (SD388365)

PR4 3JJ ☎ 01253 836273 Signposted
Nearby town: Blackpool
▶ 🚐 fr £6 ▲ fr £5

Open Mar-Oct Booking advisable bank hols & Jul-Aug Last arrival 21.00hrs Last departure 14.00hrs

A small site in open farmland about 6m from Blackpool. Situated N of M55 (exit 3) off A585 Fleetwood road on B5260. A 4-acre site with 60 touring pitches.

🎮 🐾 ☉ 🗄 ✳ ⚠ 🔒 ⊞ 📞 ⛲ 🐕 🐾
→ ∪ ▶ 📹 ⚓

LEICESTERSHIRE

For the map of this county, see Nottinghamshire

CASTLE DONINGTON

Park Farmhouse Hotel (SK414254)
Melbourne Rd, Isley Walton DE74 2RN ☎ 01332 862409
Signposted
► ► 🚐 £6-£9 🚐 £6-£9
Open Mar-Nov Booking advisable summer season Last
arrival 20.00hrs Last departure noon
*A brand new site at rear of hotel beside Donington Park
racecourse, .5m off A453 towards Melbourne. Booking
essential on race days, but a quiet rural site at other
times. A 5-acre site with 34 touring pitches.*

🖾🅡⊙🌂🗶🕻 ㊑
→ ∪🏳 ⓞ 🎪 🕽 🏊
㊐

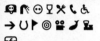

Credit Cards 🅂 ▆ ▆ 🅾 ▤ 🅂

NORTH KILWORTH

Kilworth Caravan Park (SP605838)
LE17 6JE ☎ 01858 880597 & 880385
► ★ 🚐 fr £4.50 🚐 fr £4.50
Open all year Last arrival 22.00hrs Last departure noon
*Gently sloping grass and gravel site with mixed
vegetation, and basic but clean and well maintained
facilities. Set in hilly wood and meadowland near canal,
with access to A427 Market Harborough road. On A427,
.75m W of North Kilworth on L. Busy road and extreme
care needed. A 10-acre site with 50 touring pitches.*

🖾🅡⊙🝙
→ ∪🏳 🍴 🕽 🏊

LINCOLNSHIRE

FLEET HARGATE

Matopos Caravan & Campsite (TF388248)
Main St PE12 8LL ☎ 01406 422910 Signposted
Nearby town: Holbeach
► ► ► ♠ ★ 🚐 fr £6 🚐 fr £6 🅰 fr £6
Open Mar-Oct Booking advisable 1-10 May Last arrival
22.30hrs Last departure noon
*A well-kept and pretty site with some mature and many
newly-planted trees. Off A17 midway between Long
Sutton and Holbeach, signed. A 3-acre site with 45
touring pitches.*

🖾🅡⊙🗟🌂 ✳🝙🖉📥🐕🏊

MABLETHORPE

Golden Sands Holiday Park (TF501861)
Quebec Rd LN12 1QJ ☎ 01507 477871 & 472671
► ► ► ★ 🚐 £5-£12.50 🚐 £5-£12.50 🅰 £5-£12.50
Open 8 Apr-28 Oct Booking advisable Jul-Sep Last
departure 10.00hrs
*A clean and well-kept seaside holiday site. 1m W of
town off A1031 Cleethorpes road. A 23-acre site with
400 touring pitches.*
Mini bowling alley, snooker/pool, indoor fun palace.

🖾🅡ⓞ🎾🍽 🦐♣🍷🎢🗶🕻🍴🛏🏊㊑

Camping & Caravanning Club Site (TF500839)
Highfield, Church Ln LN12 2NU
☎ 01507 472374 (in season) & 01203 694995 Signposted
► ► ★ 🚐 £8.40-£9 🚐 £8.40-£9 🅰 £8.40-£9
Open end Mar-end Oct Booking advisable bank hol &
peak periods Last arrival 21.00hrs Last departure noon
*Level, mainly grassy site off main road about 1m from
sea. Take A1104 from Alford to Mablethorpe, turn R into
Church Lane. Please see the advertisement on page 27
for details of Club Members' benefits. A 6-acre site with
105 touring pitches.*

🖾🅡⊙🎾✳🎢🝙🖉🕻🏊
→ ∪🏳 🎪 🕽

Credit Cards 🅂 ▆ ▤

Kirkstead Holiday Park (TF509835)
North Rd, Trusthorpe LN12 2QD ☎ 01507 441483
Signposted
► ★ 🚐 £6-£9 🚐 £6-£9 🅰 £4.50-£6
Open Mar-Nov Booking advisable bank hols & Jul-Aug
Last arrival mdnt Last departure 15.00hrs
*A pleasant family-run site with great potential. Situated
1m out of Mablethorpe towards Sutton-on-Sea, signed
Kirkstead off Alford Rd. A 6-acre site with 30 touring
pitches and 45 statics.*
Snooker room, childrens room, evening bar meals.

🖾🅡⊙🗟🎾🦐🗖✳🍷🎢🝙🖉🖾🕻🛏🏤🍴
🐕🏊
→ ∪🏳 🎪 🕽
㊐

MARKET RASEN

Walesby Woodlands Caravan Park (TF117906)
Walesby Rd LN8 3UN ☎ 01673 843285 Signposted
► ► ► 🚐 £6.50-£8 🚐 £6.50-£8 🅰 £6.50-£8
Open Mar-Oct Booking advisable public hols Last arrival
22.00hrs Last departure 17.00hrs
*A thoroughly well-planned, immaculate site. Out of
Market Rasen on B1203 and turn L for .75m. A 3-acre
site with 60 touring pitches.*
Solarium.

🖾🅡⊙🗟✳🎢🝙🖉🖾🆃🕻㊑
→ ∪🏳 🕽 🏊
㊐

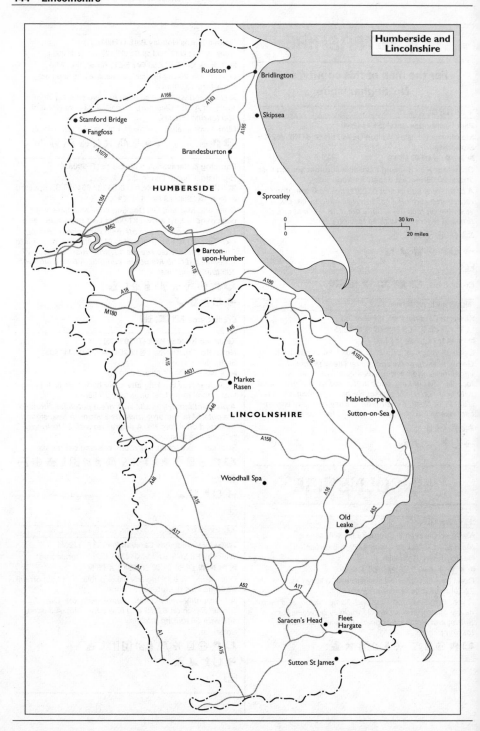

Humberside and Lincolnshire

Rudston

Bridlington

Skipsea

Stamford Bridge

Fangfoss

Brandesburton

A166

A163

A165

A1079

A1084

HUMBERSIDE

Sproatley

M62

A63

0   30 km

0   20 miles

Barton-upon-Humber

A15

A180

A18

M180

A46

A15

A631

A16

A1031

Market Rasen

A46

Mablethorpe

Sutton-on-Sea

LINCOLNSHIRE

A158

Woodhall Spa

A46

A15

A16

A52

Old Leake

A17

A1

A52

A17

Saracen's Head

Fleet Hargate

A1

A15

Sutton St James

Caravan Club Site (TF123883)
Legsby Rd ☎ 01673 842307 Signposted
▶▶ ⊞⊟Å
Open 28 Mar-23 Sep Booking advisable Last arrival 22.00hrs Last departure 15.00hrs
Well-run, mainly level, grass site on racecourse 1m SE of town centre off A63 Louth road. A 3-acre site with 60 touring pitches.
Reduced rate for racing.
🔌📶☉🖵⚠🛈🕐📞🦯
➔∪▶▣

OLD LEAKE

White Cat Park (TF415498)
Shaw Ln PE22 9LQ ☎ 01205 870121 Signposted
Nearby town: Boston
▶▶▶ ★ ⊞£4.25-£5.25 ⊟£4.25-£5.25 Å £4.25-£5.25
Open mid Mar-mid Nov Booking advisable bank hols Last arrival 22.00hrs Last departure 14.00hrs
An efficient and pleasant site in quiet rural surroundings just off A52, 7m NE of Boston.. A 2.5-acre site with 40 touring pitches and 4 statics.
🔌📶☉✳⚠🛈🗑🕐📞🦯
➔ 🎵

SARACEN'S HEAD (NEAR HOLBEACH)

Whaplode Manor Caravan Park (TF341278)
Whaplode Manor PE12 8AZ ☎ 01406 422837 Signposted
Nearby town: Holbeach
▶▶ ⊞£6 ⊟£6 Å £6
Open Etr-Nov Booking advisable 1st wk in May & Jul-Aug
This pleasant, level, grassy site adjoins open farmland and is well screened by mature trees situated off A17 at rear of a large 18th century manor house. A 1-acre site with 20 touring pitches.
🔌📶☉🔦✳⚠🛈🗑🖸
➔🦯

Credit Cards 🆑 💳

SUTTON-ON-SEA

Hawthorn Farm Caravan Club Site (TF519801)
Crabtree Ln LN12 2RS ☎ 01507 441503 (1.25m S) Signposted
▶▶ ⊞⊟
Open Apr-Oct Booking advisable bank hols & Jul-Aug Last arrival 20.00hrs no cars by tents
An open, level site with good facilities and play equipment, .75m from a safe bathing beach. An 8.5-acre site with 120 touring pitches.
🔌📶☉🗑⚠🛈🗑🕐📞🦮🦯♿
➔▶⛵🛟

Credit Cards 🆑 💳 🔷

SUTTON ST JAMES

Foremans Bridge Caravan Park (TF409197)
PE12 0HU ☎ 01945 440346
Nearby town: Long Sutton
▶▶ ★ ⊞£5.50 ⊟£5.50 Å £4.50-£5.50
Open Mar-Dec Booking advisable Last arrival 23.00hrs
A nicely-kept, trim site with good sanitary facilities. Take B1390 Long Sutton to Sutton St James rd, and site in 2m on L immediately after bridge. A 2.5-acre site with 40 touring pitches and 5 statics.
🔌📶☉🖵🔧✳🛈🗑🕐📞🦮🦯
➔▶🎵
💷

WOODHALL SPA

Bainland Country Park (TF215640)
Horncastle Rd LN10 6UX
☎ 01526 352903 Signposted
Nearby town: Horncastle
▶▶▶▶▶ 🏕🏃 ♻ Holiday Centre ⊟£7.50-£23 ⊟£7.50-£23 Å £7.50-£18
Open all year Booking advisable all year Last arrival 20.00hrs Last departure 11.30hrs
More a country club than a purely touring park, this is one of the best equipped parks in the country and its impressive array of leisure facilities, combined with its high standards of maintenance, have earned it the regional award for Central England in the 1996 AA Campsite of the Year competition. For full details of all the awards, see the colour section at the front of the ➡

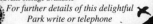

book. On B1191 about 2m E of town. A 12-acre site with
100 touring pitches and 10 statics.
Jacuzzi, solarium, sauna, par 3 golf, putting, boule.

🗙🔌🚐🏧🎣🏇🐕🐴🐂♿
➜∪🏳⊚🎦🎵

🔳

Credit Cards 🔳 🔳 🔳 🔳

Camping & Caravanning Club Site (TF225634)
Wellsyke Ln, Kirkby-on-Bain LN10 6YU
☎ 01526 352911 (in season) & 01203 694995
▷ ★ 🚐 £6.60-£7 🚐 £6.60-£7 ▲ £6.60-£7
Open end Mar-end Oct Booking advisable bank hols &
Jul-Aug Last arrival 21.00hrs Last departure noon
*A pleasant site in silver birch wood and moorland. Take
B1191 towards Horncastle. After 5m turn right towards
Kirby-on-Bain. Signed. Please see the advertisement on
page 27 for details of Club Members' benefits. A 6-acre
site with 90 touring pitches.*

🔋🎣☉🔲🍴❄🎵♿
➜∪🏳🎦🎵🚂

Credit Cards 🔳 🔳 🔳

LONDON

For the map, see
Essex

For the map, see Essex

E4 CHINGFORD

Lee Valley Campsite (TQ381970)
Sewardstone Rd E4 7RA ☎ 0181 529 5689 Signposted
▶ ▶ ▶ ▶ ♦ ★ 🚐 £9.50 🚐 £9.50 ▲ £9.50
Open Apr-Oct Booking advisable bank hols & Jul-Aug
Last arrival 22.00hrs Last departure noon
*Well-run useful North London site with easy access to
town. Overlooking King George's reservoir and close to
Epping Forest. From M25 junct 26 to A112 and signed. A
12-acre site with 200 touring pitches.*

🔋🎣☉🔲🍴❄🎵♿🐕♿
➜∪🏳🎦🎵🚂

Credit Cards 🔳 🔳 🔳 🔳 🔳

N9 EDMONTON

Lee Valley Leisure Centre Camping & Caravan (TQ360945)
Meridian Way N9 0AS
☎ 0181 345 6666 ext 380 & 0181 803 6900 Signposted
▶ ▶ ★ ➡ fr £9 ➡ fr £9 ⛺ fr £9
Open all year Booking advisable Jul-Aug Last departure noon
Close to London, part of a large sporting complex with use of swimming pool, roller skating and golf driving range. Signed from A10. A 4.5-acre site with 200 touring pitches.
Membership of adjacent sports complex.

🎡🐾⊙🍴🔌 🍴🔍❋🛟🚿🏧 🚽🅣🍴🛎🚃🛒
🍴👥
➜➤⛺⛳🏊🎱🎵
💷

Credit Cards 💳 💳 💳 💳

SE19 CRYSTAL PALACE

Crystal Palace Caravan Club Site (TQ341714)
Crystal Palace Pde SE19 1UF ☎ 0181 778 7155
▶ ▶ ▶ ➡ ➡ ⛺
Open all year Booking advisable all times
A newly redeveloped site nearly at the foot of the Crystal Palace TV mast, arranged in a series of terraces on the edge of a pleasant park. Many attractions for children. A 6-acre site with 150 touring pitches.
Veg prep area.

🎡🐾⊙🍴❋🛟🚿🏧 🚽🅣🛎🚃🛒👥
➜➤🎱🎵

Credit Cards 💳 💳

MERSEYSIDE

For the map of this county, see Shropshire

WEST KIRBY

Wirral Country Park Caravan Club Site (SJ234838)
Station Rd L61 0HN ☎ 0151 648 5228 (2.5m SE)
▶ ▶ ➡ ➡
Open 26 Mar-8 Nov Booking advisable bank hols & wknds Last arrival 20.00hrs Last departure noon
Several flat, grassy pitching areas separated by young planting and overlooking the Dee estuary. Located in a 2,000-acre country park, and signed off A540. An 8-acre site with 106 touring pitches.
Veg prep area.

🎡🐾⊙🍴🔌🏔🛟🚿🏧 🚽🅣🛎👥🛒
➜∪➤⊙⛳🏊🎱🎵

Credit Cards 💳 💳

NORFOLK

BARNEY

The Old Brick Kilns (TG007328)
Little Barney Ln, Barney NR21 0NL
☎ 01328 878305 Signposted
Nearby town: Fakenham
▶ ▶ ▶ ▶ 🏕👫 ➡ £8.25-£10.25 ➡ £8.25-£10.25
⛺ £8.25-£10.25
Open Mar-Oct (rs low season bar food/takeaway selected nights only) Booking advisable bank hols & Jul-Aug Last arrival 22.00hrs Last departure noon
A secluded and peaceful site with a small boating pool and mature trees. Excellent, well-planned toilet facilities. Approach from the A148 near Thursford towards Barney village and in .25m turn into no-through road. Site in .5m. A 6.5-acre site with 60 touring pitches.
Boules, outdoor draughts/chess, family games area.
See advertisement under FAKENHAM

🎡🐾⊙🍴🔌🔍🛒❋🛟🏔🛎🚿🏧 🚽🅣🍴🛎👥
🍴🏠🏕🐕🛒👥
➜🎱

Credit Cards 💳 💳 💳

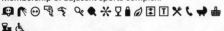

BAWBURGH

Caravan Club Site (TG150102)
Royal Norfolk Agrricultural, Association Showground, Long Ln NR9 3LX ☎ 01603 742708
▶ ▶ ▶ ➡ ➡
Open 26 Mar-11 Oct Booking advisable bank hols & mid Jul
A tree-bordered site in the corner of the showground, at the end of a country lane. A 5-acre site with 60 touring pitches.
Veg prep area.

🛟
➜➤🛒

BELTON

Rose Farm Touring & Camping Park (TG488033)
Stepshort NR31 9JS ☎ 01493 780896 Signposted
Nearby town: Great Yarmouth
▶ ▶ ▶ ★ ➡ £4-£6 ➡ £4-£6 ⛺ £4-£6
Open all year Booking advisable
A very neat site with a good toilet block and tidy facilities. Follow signs to Belton off A143, turn right at Stepshort, and the site is first on right. A 6-acre site with 80 touring pitches.

🎡🐾⊙🍴🔌🔍🛒❋🏔🛟🚿🏧 🚽🅣🛎🐕🛒👥
➜∪➤🎱🎵

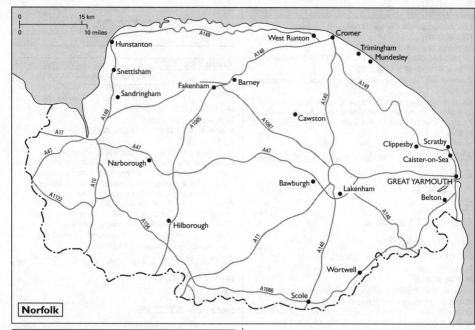

Norfolk

Wild Duck Caravan & Chalet Park (TG475028)
NR31 9NE ☎ 01493 780268
► ► ► 🚐 🚐 Å
Open Whit-Oct (rs Etr-Whit partly open limited
entertainment) Booking advisable Jul-Aug Last arrival
23.00hrs Last departure 10.00hrs
Level grassy site in forest with small cleared areas for
tourers and well laid out facilities. Signed from A143. A
20-acre site with 150 touring pitches and 230 statics.
See advertisement under GREAT YARMOUTH

🏠 📻 ⊙ 🖥 🏳 📶 🔍 🍴 ❋ 🍺 🎡 🛁 🛒 ⊞ Ⓣ ✕ 📞
🛗
→ ∪ ▶ ⊁ 🎪 🎣
Credit Cards 🏧 💳

CAISTER-ON-SEA

Grasmere Caravan Park (TG521115)
9 Bultitude's Loke, Yarmouth Rd NR30 5DH
☎ 01493 720382 Signposted
Nearby town: Great Yarmouth
► ► ► 🚐 £5-£6.95 🚐 £5-£6.95
Open Apr-Oct Booking advisable school & bank hols
Last arrival 22.00hrs Last departure 11.00hrs 🚫
Mainly level grass and gravel site with mature trees. Set
in meadowland in an urban area with access to A149. A
2-acre site with 46 touring pitches and 62 statics.

🏠 📻 ⊙ 🖥 ❋ 🏳 🛁 🛒 ⊞ 📞 🦽 ♿ ⅙
→ ∪ ▶ ⊁ 🎪 🎣

Old Hall Leisure Park (TG521122)
High St NR30 5JL ☎ 01493 720400 Signposted
Nearby town: Great Yarmouth
▶ ▶ ▶ ★ ⊞ £6-£9 ⊞ £6-£9
Open Spring bank hol wk & 22 Jun-1 Sep (rs Apr-21 Jun
pool closed, bar/rest limited opening) Booking advisable
Spring bank hol & Jul-Aug Last arrival mdnt Last
departure 10.00hrs ⊘
*An urban site close to a busy main road. Very neat and
precise layout. Some tourers overlooked by statics. A 2-
acre site with 35 touring pitches and 38 statics.*
See advertisement under GREAT YARMOUTH

🐶 📶 ⊙ 🗄 🗏 ⇗ ☀ ♀ ⚠ ⓘ ⊞ ✕ 📞
→ ∪ ⌐ ⅄ 📹 🎣 🔌

£

Credit Cards ⬛ ⬛ ⬛ ⬛ ⬛

CAWSTON

Haveringland Hall Caravan Park (TG153213)
NR10 4PN ☎ 01603 871302 Signposted
Nearby town: Alysham
▶ ▶ ★ ⊞ £6-£7.50 ⊞ £6-£7.50 ▲ £6-£7.50
Open Mar-30 Oct Booking advisable public hol wks &
Jul-Aug Last arrival 22.00hrs Last departure noon
*A very pleasant site set in woodland and meadowland
with direct access to lake. Level pitches in different area
with interesting mature trees. 10m N of Norwich on
Cawston road. A 25-acre site with 65 touring pitches and
80 statics.*

14 acre fishing lake.

🐶 📶 ⊙ ☀ ⚠ ⓘ ⊞ T 📞 🏠 🏕 🐕 🐾 🔌
→ ∪ ⌐ 🎣

£

CLIPPESBY

Clippesby Holidays (TG423147)
NR29 3BJ ☎ 01493 369367 Signposted
Nearby town: Great Yarmouth
▶ ▶ ▶ ★ ⊞ £8-£15 ⊞ £8-£15 ▲ £8-£15
Open late Spring bank hol-last wk Sep (rs Etr, Mayday
wknd & Oct half term some facilities may close) Booking
advisable school hols Last arrival 17.30hrs Last
departure 11.00hrs
*A lovely country house estate with vans hidden among
trees and a friendly welcome. From A1064 at Acle to
B1152 and signed. A 30-acre site with 90 touring pitches.
Putting, bowls, bicycle hire & tea room.*

🐶 📶 ⊙ 🗄 🗏 ⇗ ♀ ⚡ ☀ ♀ ⚠ ⓘ ⊘ ⊞ T ✕ 📞
🏕 🐕 🐾 ♿
→ ∪ ◎ ⚠ ⅄ 🎣

£

Credit Cards ⬛ ⬛ ⬛ ⬛ ⬛

CROMER

Seacroft Camping Park (TG206424)
Runton Rd NR27 9NJ ☎ 01263 511722 Signposted
▶ ▶ ▶ ▶ ⊞ £9.25-£13.50 ⊞ £9.25-£13.50
▲ £9.25-£13.50
Open Mar-Oct Booking advisable school hols, 22-31 May
& 4 Sep Last arrival 23.00hrs Last departure noon
*A very good touring site, well laid out and landscaped.
Toilets and showers tiled and spotless. 1m W of Cromer
on A149 coast road. A 5-acre site with 120 touring
pitches.*
Baby change.

🐶 📶 ⊙ 🗄 🗏 ⇗ ♀ ⚡ 🗄 ☀ ♀ ⚠ ⓘ ⊘ ⊞ T ✕ 📞
🔌 🍺 🏠 🏕 🐕 🐾 ♿
→ ∪ ⌐ ◎ ⚠ 📹 🎣

£

Credit Cards ⬛ ⬛ ⬛ ⬛ ⬛

Forest Park Caravan Site (TG233405)
Northrepps Rd NR27 0JR ☎ 01263 513290 Signposted
▶ ▶ ▶ ⊞ £6.50-£9.50 ⊞ £6.50-£9.50
Open Apr-Oct Booking advisable Etr, Spring bank hol &
Jul-Aug Last arrival 22.00hrs Last departure 14.00hrs
*Surrounded by forest, this gently sloping parkland
offers quiet and sheltered pitches. Signed from A149
and B1159. A 30-acre site with 429 touring pitches and
372 statics.*
BMX track.

🐶 📶 ⊙ 🗄 🗏 ⇗ ♀ ☀ ♀ ⚠ ⓘ ⊘ ⊞ T ✕ 📞 🔌 🐾
→ ∪ ⌐ ⅄ 📹 🎣

Credit Cards ⬛ ⬛

Caravan Club Site (TF926288)
Fakenham Racecourse NR21 7NY ☎ 01328 862388
Signposted
▶▶▶ ⊞ ⊞ ▲
Open 26 Mar-10 Oct Booking advisable Etr & May-Aug
Last departure noon
A level grassy site with mature trees, three-quarters of a mile SW of town off A1065 Swaffham road. An 11.5-acre site with 150 touring pitches.
TV aerial hook-ups & satellite channels.

⬚ ⬚ ⬚ ⬚ ⬚ ⬚ ⬚ ⬚ ⬚ ⬚ ⬚ ⬚ ⬚ ⬚ ⬚ ⬚ ⬚
&

→ ∪ ▶ ♪

See **Caister-on-Sea**

Vauxhall Holiday Park (TG520083)
4 Acle New Rd NR30 1TB ☎ 01493 857231
Signposted
▶▶▶▶ ★ ⊞ £10-£17 ⊞ £10-£17 ▲ £10-£17
Open Etr then mid May-Sep Booking advisable mid Jul-Aug Last arrival 21.00hrs Last departure 10.00hrs ⚲
A very large holiday complex with plenty of entertainment and access to beach, river, estuary, lake and main A47. A 16-acre site with 256 touring pitches and 446 statics.
Hairdressing & entertainment.

⬚ ⬚ ⬚ ⬚ ⬚ ⬚ ⬚ ⬚ ⬚ ⬚ ⬚ ⬚ ⬚ ⬚ ⬚ ⬚
⬚ ⬚ &

→ ∪ ▶ ◎ ⬚ ⬚ ⬚ ♪

Credit Cards ⬚

Caravan Club Site (TG526103)
Great Yarmouth Racecourse, Jellicoe Rd NR30 4AU
☎ 01493 855223 (1.5m N)
▶▶▶ ⊞ ⊞
Open 26 Mar-11 Oct Booking advisable bank hols, Jun-Aug & Sep race wk
An open site in a good position next to the racecourse and golf course, just 300 yards from the quieter end of the sea front. A 5.25-acre site with 122 touring pitches.
Veg prep area.

⬚

→ ∪ ▶ ⬚ ♪ ⬚

The Covert Caravan Club Site (TL810967)
High Ash IP26 5BZ ☎ 01842 878356 (1m S)
Nearby town: Swaffham
▷ ⊞ ⊞
Open Mar-Nov Booking advisable bank hols & wknds
May-Sep Last arrival 20.00hrs Last departure noon
A quiet, secluded site in Forestry Commission woodland, with pitching areas in little open glades. From Swaffham on A1065 turn R about 2.25m past Hilborough. From Thetford on A134 turn R at rndbt in
➟

151

UNHITCH, PITCH AND RELAX AT

GREAT YARMOUTH
Vauxhall
HOLIDAY PARK

NEW LUXURY INDOOR POOL

FREE ENTERTAINMENT

Top quality facilities with superb new indoor luxury pool!

- ◆ OVER 250 SITES FOR TOURING CARAVANS
- ◆ ALL-ELECTRIC SITES
- ◆ GRASS AND HARD STANDINGS
- ◆ AWNINGS FREE
- ◆ NEW LUXURY INDOOR POOL
- ◆ SUNBATHING TERRACES
- ◆ ALL WEATHER FUN

5 star entertainment absolutely free

PHONE 01493 857231 NOW FOR YOUR FREE BROCHURE
QUOTE REF: 4   4 ACLE NEW ROAD   GREAT YARMOUTH NR30 ITB

Mundford onto A1065 and site on L in 2m. A 9.5-acre site with 130 touring pitches.

🅰 ✳ 🛈 ⊘ 🚼 T ↳ 🐕
→ ∪ ▶ 🞷 🛒
Credit Cards 🂠 ▭ ▭

HUNSTANTON

Searles of Hunstanton (TF671400)
South Beach PE36 5BB ☎ 01485 534211 & 532342
Signposted
▶ ▶ ▶ ▶ ▶ ✪ Holiday Centre 🚐 £9-£14.50 🚐 £9-£14.50 ▲ £8-£13.50
Open Etr-Oct (rs Mar-May & Oct certain facilities not open) Booking advisable bank hols & Jul-Aug Last arrival 21.00hrs Last departure 11.00hrs
A large seaside holiday complex with well-managed facilities, adjacent to sea and beach. On B1161, in South Hunstanton, off A149 King's Lynn road. An 18-acre site with 350 touring pitches and 450 statics.
Stables, entertainment programme & hire shop.
🅰 🚐 🕅 ⊙ 🗗 🖁 ⚡ ⚔ ⚫ ✳ 🍴 🏛 🛈 ⊘ 🚼
T ✗ ↳ 🧺 🍴 🍴 🐕 🛒 ♿
→ ∪ ▶ ⊙ 🛆 ⚓ 📺 🞷
£
Credit Cards 🂠 ▭ ▭ 🄂

KING'S LYNN
See **Narborough**

LAKENHAM

Camping & Caravanning Club Site (TG237063)
Martineau Ln NR1 2HX ☎ 01603 620060 (in season) & 01203 694995
Nearby town: Norwich
▶ ▶ 🚐 £8.40-£9 🚐 £8.40-£9 ▲ £8.40-£9
Open end Mar-end Sep Booking advisable bank hols & Jul-Aug Last arrival 21.00hrs Last departure noon
A small site on the outskirts of Norwich close to a river and screened by trees from the city. From A47 take A146 left to traffic lights, then left and left again. Please see the advertisement on page 27 for details of Club Members' benefits. A 2.5-acre site with 50 touring pitches.
🕅 ⊙ 🖁 ✳ ↳ 🐕 🛒
→ ∪ ▶ ⚓ 📺 🞷
Credit Cards 🂠 ▭ ▭

MUNDESLEY

Links Caravan Site (TG305365)
Links Rd NR11 8AE ☎ 01263 720665 Signposted
Nearby town: North Walsham
▶ ▶ ★ 🚐 £5-£6 🚐 £5-£6 ▲ £5-£6
Open Etr-1st wk Oct Booking advisable bank hols & peak season Last arrival 22.00hrs Last departure noon
A pleasant site on a south-facing slope with level pitches, offering distant rural views. From B1159 at Mundesley turn into Church Road. A 2-acre site with 32 touring pitches.
🅰 🕅 ⊙ ✳ 🏛
→ ∪ ▶ ⊙ 🞷 🗗 🛒

NARBOROUGH

Pentney Park (TF742141)
Gayton Rd, Pentney PE32 1HU ☎ 01760 337479
Signposted
Nearby town: Swaffham
▶▶▶▶ ★ ⊞ £8-£10 ⊞ £8-£10 ▲ £8-£10
Open all year (rs Nov-Feb outdoor swimming pool
closed) Booking advisable bank hols Last arrival
22.30hrs Last departure 11.00hrs
*A well-run touring site set in woods and meadowland
adjacent to A47 Swaffham-King's Lynn Road. A 16-acre
site with 200 touring pitches.*

🐕 �🅿 &
→ 🥄
£

Credit Cards 💳 💳

SANDRINGHAM

**Camping & Caravanning Club Site
(TF692271)**
The Sandringham Estate, Double
Lodges PE36 6EA ☎ 01485 542555 (in season) &
01203 694995 Signposted
Nearby town: King's Lynn
▶▶ ♠ ⚄ ★ ⊞ £9.40-£10.20 ⊞ £9.40-£10.20
▲ £9.40-£10.20
Open end Feb-end Nov Booking advisable bank hols &
high season Last arrival 21.00hrs Last departure noon
A prestige site, very well landscaped with toilets and other

*buildings blending in with the scenery. Please see the
advertisement on page 27 for details of Club Members'
benefits. A 12.5-acre site with 250 touring pitches.*

Credit Cards 💳 💳 💳

Caravan Club Site (TF682268)
The Sandringham Estate, Glucksburg Woods PE35 6EZ
☎ 01553 631614 (1.5m SW) Signposted
Nearby town: King's Lynn
▶▶ ★ ⊞ £12-£13.50 ⊞ £12-£13.50
Open late May-mid Oct Booking advisable bank hols &
Jul-Aug Last arrival 20.00hrs Last departure noon
*A site set on gently rising ground in woodland on the
royal estate, and surrounded by the 600-acre country
park. A 9-acre site with 120 touring pitches.*

→

Credit Cards 💳 💳

SCOLE

Willows Camping & Caravan Park (TM139790)
Diss Rd IP21 4DH ☎ 01379 740271 Signposted
Nearby town: Diss
▶▶▶ ⊞ £6.50-£7 ⊞ £6.50-£7 ▲ £6.50-£7
Open May-Sep Booking advisable Spring bank hol &
school hols Last arrival 23.00hrs Last departure noon
*Level, peaceful site on the banks of the River Waveney,
bordered by willow trees. Take A143 from Scole to Diss,*
➡

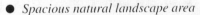

site 400yds on left after Scole crossroads. A 4-acre site with 32 touring pitches.
Washing-up sinks.

🎭 📻 ⊙ ✳ 🅰 🔋 🛆 🚻 ⬆ T
➜ ▶ 🖊 🗑 🐾

Scratby Hall Caravan Park (TG501155)
NR29 3PH ☎ 01493 730283 Signposted
Nearby town: Great Yarmouth
▶ ▶ ▶ ♠ ★ 🚐 £4-£8.50 🚐 £4-£8.50 ⅄ £4-£8.50
Open Spring bank hol-mid Sep (rs Etr-Spring bank hol & mid Sep-Oct reduced hours & shop closed) Booking advisable Spring bank hol wk & Jul-Aug Last arrival anytime Last departure noon
A quiet, level grass site surrounded by trees, close to beach and the Norfolk Broads. Signed off B1159. A 5-acre site with 108 touring pitches.
Washing-up & food preparation room.

🎭 📻 ⊙ 🗑 🎏 🔍 ✳ 🔋 🛆 ⬆ T 📞 🐾 ♿
➜ ∪ ▶ ✚ 🖊

Diglea Caravan & Camping Park (TF656336)
Beach Rd PE31 7RB ☎ 01485 541367 Signposted
Nearby town: Hunstanton
▶ ▶ ▶ ★ 🚐 £5-£7.50 🚐 £5-£7.50 ⅄ £5-£7.50
Open Apr-Oct Booking advisable bank hols & mid Jul-Aug Last departure noon
Undulating pasture land, close to the sea and in rural surroundings. Signed from A149. A 9-acre site with 200 touring pitches and 150 statics.

🎭 📻 ⊙ 🗑 ✳ 🎏 🅰 🔋 🛆 ⬆ T 📞 🐕
➜ ∪ 🖊 🐾

Woodlands Caravan Park (TG274388)
NR11 8AL ☎ 01263 833144 Signposted
Nearby town: Cromer
▶ ▶ ▶ ♠ ★ 🚐 £6-£8.75
Open Apr-Oct Booking advisable public hols & Jul-Aug Last arrival 23.00hrs Last departure 11.00hrs
A pleasant woodland site close to the sea but well sheltered from winds. Pitches in open areas among the trees. 4m SE on coast road, B1159. A 10-acre site with 110 touring pitches and 154 statics.
See advertisement on page 150.

🎭 📻 ⊙ 🎏 🔍 🅰 🔋 ⬆ 📞 🚐 🚃 🐾 ♿
➜ ∪ ▶ 🍽 🖊

Camping & Caravanning Club Site (TG189419)
Holgate Ln NR27 9NW ☎ 01263 837544 (in season) & 01203 694995
Nearby town: Cromer
▶ ▶ ▶ ♠ ★ 🚐 £9.40-£10.20 🚐 £9.40-£10.20
⅄ £9.40-£10.20

Open end Mar-end Oct Booking advisable bank hols & peak periods Last arrival 21.00hrs Last departure noon
A lovely, well-kept site with mainly level pitches on pleasantly undulating ground. Surrounded by woodland. Approach from A148 about 2m SW of Cromer, signposted into unclass road and reached only by a narrow and rough hill access road. Please see the advertisement on page 27 for details of Club Members' benefits. A 12-acre site with 250 touring pitches.

🎭 📻 ⊙ 🗑 🎏 🖵 ✳ 🅰 🔋 🛆 ⬆ T 📞 🚐 ♿
➜ ∪ ▶ 🍽 🖊 🐾

Credit Cards 🔳 💳 💳

Little Lakeland Caravan Park (TM279849)
IP20 0HG ☎ 01986 788646 Signposted
Nearby town: Harleston
▶ ▶ ▶ ♠ ★ 🚐 £6.20-£7.80 🚐 £6.20-£7.80
(rs Mar-Etr restricted laundry facilities) Booking advisable bank hols & peak periods Last arrival 22.00hrs Last departure noon
A well-kept and pretty site built round a lake and with individual pitches in hedged enclosures. 2m NE of Harleston. A 4.5-acre site with 40 touring pitches and 16 statics.
Library & fishing on site.

🎭 📻 ⊙ 🎏 ✳ 🅰 🛆 ⬆ 🖵
➜ ∪ ▶ ✚ 🍽 🖊 🐾

Lone Pine Camping Site (TM274843)
Low Rd IP20 0HJ ☎ 01986 788596 & 01379 852423 Signposted
Nearby town: Harleston
▶ ★ 🚐 £4-£4.50 ⅄ £4-£4.50
Open May-Sep Booking advisable bank hols
A sheltered grassy site with saplings and bushes set in downs and meadowland. Signed from village by post office. A 2-acre site with 27 touring pitches.

📻 ⊙ ✳ 🔋 🛆 🐾
➜ ∪ 🖊

NORTHAMPTONSHIRE

For the map of this county, see Berkshire

Top Lodge Caravan Club Site (SK979984)
Fineshade NN17 3BB ☎ 01780 444617
Nearby town: Corby
▷ 🚐 🚐
Open Apr-Sep Booking advisable bank hols & wknds Last arrival 20.00hrs Last departure noon
A tranquil, open meadowland site surrounded by woodland. Site off A43 on left approx 2.25m from A47 junc at Duddington. Signed off A43 'Fineshade - Top

Lodge' along single track for .5m. A 5.5-acre site with 80 touring pitches.

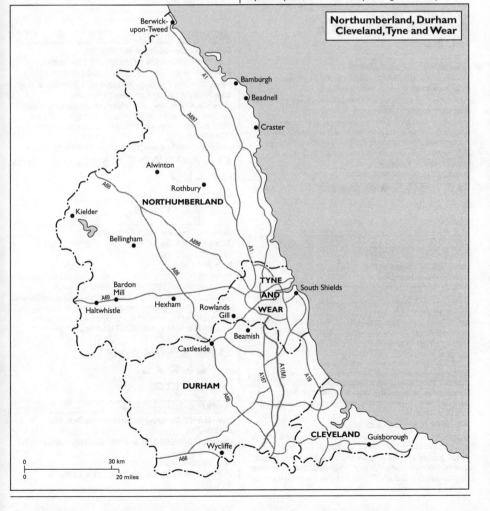

Credit Cards

Mill Marina (SP994781)
Midland Rd NN14 4JR ☎ 01832 732850 Signposted
Nearby town: Kettering
▶ 🚐 £8.60-£10.10 🚐 £7.60-£9.10 ▲ £6.60-£8.10
Open Apr-Dec (rs Jan-Mar static pitches only) Booking advisable public hols & summer wknds Last arrival 21.00hrs Last departure 18.00hrs
Level riverside site with mature trees and bushes, with pleasure trips by boat from site. Take Thrapston exit from A14 or A605, signed. A 3-acre site with 42 touring

pitches and 5 statics.
Slipway for boats & canoes, coarse fishing on site.

NORTHUMBERLAND

Clennell Hall (NT928072)
Clennell NE65 7BG ☎ 01669 50341 Signposted
Nearby town: Rothbury
▶ ▶ ▶ 🚐🚐▲
Open all year (rs Jan & Feb by arrangement only)

**Northumberland, Durham
Cleveland, Tyne and Wear**

Open all year (rs Jan & Feb by arrangement only)
Booking advisable summer & bank hols Last arrival
22.00hrs Last departure 16.00hrs
*A tranquil rural site on the fringe of the National Park
NW of Rothbury. A 13-acre site with 50 touring pitches
and 18 statics.*

❄️ 🏕️ ☉ 📻 🔧 🔌 ⌷ ☼ ⟁ 🏔️ 🔦 ∅ ✕ ☎ ☎ ♿
➔ 🥄

BAMBURGH

Glororum Caravan Park (NU166334)
Glororum Farm NE69 7AW ☎ 01668 214457 Signposted
▶ ▶ ▶ ★ 🚐 £6-£8 🚐 £6-£8 ▲
Open Apr-Oct Booking advisable school hols Last arrival
22.00hrs Last departure 10.00hrs
*A well-run site with good facilities, pleasantly situated
off B1341, 1m W of Bamburgh. The open countryside
setting gives views of Bamburgh Castle and
surrounding farmland. A 6-acre site with 100 touring
pitches and 150 statics.*

🔧 🏕️ ☉ 📻 🔧 ☼ 🏔️ 🔦 ∅ ⊞ ☎ ☎
➔ ∪ ▶ 🥄

Waren Caravan Park (NU155343)
Waren Mill NE70 7EE ☎ 01668 214366 Signposted
▶ ▶ ▶ ☀ 🚐 🚐 ▲
Open Apr-Oct Booking advisable Spring bank hol & Jul-
Aug Last arrival 22.00hrs Last departure noon
*Attractive seaside site close to beach, surrounded by a
slightly sloping grassy embankment affording shelter
for caravans. Immaculate sanitary facilities. Situated 2m
E of town on B1342. A 4-acre site with 105 touring
pitches and 325 statics.*
100 acres of private heathland.

🔧 🏕️ ☉ 📻 🔧 ⟍ ● ☼ 🏔️ 🔦 ∅ ⊞ T ✕ ☎ 🛒 🏛️
🏯 ☂ 🐕 ☎
➔ ▶ 🥄

BARDON MILL

Ashcroft Farm (NY782645)
NE47 7JA ☎ 01434 344409
Nearby town: Hexham
▷ ★ 🚐 £3-£3.50 🚐 £3-£3.50 ▲ £2-£2.50
Open Apr-Oct Booking advisable Last arrival 21.00hrs
Last departure 13.00hrs
*Level farm site adjacent to A69, between Haltwhistle
and Hexham. A 2-acre site with 20 touring pitches.*
Fishing by arrangement.

➔ ☎

BEADNELL

Camping & Caravanning Club Site (NU233284)
Anstead NE67 5BX ☎ 01665 720586 (in season) &
01203 694995
▶ ▶ ★ 🚐 £8.80-£9.60 ▲ £8.80-£9.60
Open end Mar-early Oct Booking advisable bank hols &
Jul-Aug Last arrival 21.00hrs Last departure noon
*Level, grassy site set in coastal area with access to sea,
beach and main road. From A1 follow B1340 signposted
Seahouses-Bamburgh. Please see the advertisement on*

*page 27 for details of Club Members' benefits. A 6-acre
site with 150 touring pitches.*

🏕️ ☉ 📻 🔧 ☼ 🔦 ∅ ☎ 🛒
➔ ∪ ▶ ⤓ 🥄

Credit Cards 🔳 🔳 🔳

BELLINGHAM

Brown Rigg Caravan & Camping Park (NY835826)
NE48 2JY ☎ 01434 220175
▶ ▶ ▶ 🚐 £6.50 🚐 £6.50 ▲ £4
Open wk before Etr-Oct Booking advisable bank &
school hols Last arrival 20.30hrs Last departure 13.30hrs
*This well laid out site is in a pleasant rural setting, run
by enthusiastic resident owners. On B6320 .5miles S of
Bellingham. A 5.5-acre site with 60 touring pitches.*

🔧 🏕️ ☉ 📻 🔧 ⟍ ☼ 🏔️ 🔦 ∅ ⊞ T ☎ 🐕 🛒
➔ ∪ ▶ 🔺 🥄
🎫

BERWICK-UPON-TWEED

Ord House Caravan Park (NT982515)
East Ord TD15 2NS ☎ 01289 305288 Signposted
▶ ▶ ▶ ★ 🚐 £7.50-£11.50 🚐 £7.50-£11.50
Open Mar-Jan Booking advisable bank hols & Jul-Aug
Last arrival 23.00hrs Last departure noon
*A very well-run site set in pleasant surroundings with
mature trees and bushes. Situated on the A698, 1m
from Berwick. A 6-acre site with 70 touring pitches and
200 statics.*
Crazy golf, tabletennis, badminton,9 hole pitch/putt

❄️ 🛒 🏕️ ☉ 📻 🔧 ☼ ⟁ 🏔️ 🔦 ∅ ⊞ T ✕ ☎ 🐕 🛒
➔ ▶ ⤓ ☕ 🥄
🎫

Credit Cards 🔳 🔳 🔳

Seaview Caravan Club Site (NU003517)
Billendean Rd, Spittal TD15 1QU ☎ 01289 305198
(0.5m S) Signposted
▶ ▶ ▶ ☀☀ 🚐 🚐
Open 26 Mar-1 Nov Booking advisable bank hols & Jul-
Aug Last arrival 20.00hrs Last departure noon
*Mainly level site with terraced pitches, and great views
of the Tweed, the three bridges crossing it, and the old
town. Off A1167 at Spittal, .5m from Berwick-upon-
Tweed. A 6-acre site with 120 touring pitches.*
Veg prep area.

🔧 🏕️ ☉ 📻 🔧 ☼ 🔦 ∅ ⊞ T ☎ ♿
➔ ▶ 🔺 ⤓ ☕ 🥄 🛒

Credit Cards 🔳 🔳

CRASTER

**Dunstan Hill Camping & Caravanning Club Site
(NU234206)**
Dunstan Hill NE66 3TQ ☎ 01665 576310 (in season) &
01203 694995
Nearby town: Alnwick
▶ ▶ ▶ ★ 🚐 £9.30-£10 🚐 £9.30-£10 ▲ £9.30-£10

Open end Mar-early Nov Booking advisable Spring bank hol & Jul-Aug Last arrival 21.00hrs Last departure noon
An immaculately maintained site with pleasant landscaping close to the beach and historic town of Alnwick, but in a countryside setting. 1m from Embleton. Please see the advertisement on page 27 for details of Club Members' benefits. An 8-acre site with 150 touring pitches.

Credit Cards

HALTWHISTLE

Camping & Caravanning Club Site (NY685622)
Burnfoot, Park Village NE49 0HZ ☎ 01434 320106 (in season) & 01203 694995 Signposted
▶▶▶✦ ♨ £9.30-£10 ♨ £9.30-£10 ▲ £9.30-£10
Open end Mar-early Nov Booking advisable bank hols & high season Last arrival 21.00hrs Last departure noon
An attractive site on the banks of the River South Tyne, amid mature trees, on the Bellister Castle Estate. Please see the advertisement on page 27 for details of Club Members' benefits. A 3-acre site with 60 touring pitches.

Credit Cards

HEXHAM

Caravan Club Site (NY919623)
Hexham Racecourse NE46 3NN ☎ 01434 606847 Signposted
▶▶▶ ♨♨▲
Open Etr-1 Oct Booking advisable wknds & bank hols for electric hook-up Last arrival 20.00hrs Last departure noon
A part-level and part-sloping grassy site on racecourse overlooking Hexhamshire Moors. A 4-acre site with 60 touring pitches.

Credit Cards

Causey Hill Caravan Park (NY925625)
Benson's Fell Farm NE46 2JN ☎ 01434 602834 & 604647
▶▶▶★ ♨ £7.50-£8.50 ♨ £7.50-£8
Open Apr-Oct Booking advisable public hols & Jul-Sep Last arrival 19.00hrs Last departure noon no cars by tents
A well-maintained site on very sloping ground with some level pitches. Attractively screened by trees. To avoid steep hill out of Hexham, follow B6305, signed Allendale, Alston, turn left in 3m onto unclass rd, and left again 300yds past race course. Site in 100yds. A 2-acre site with 30 touring pitches and 105 statics.
Off Licence.

KIELDER

Kielder Campsite (NY626938)
NE48 1EJ ☎ 01434 220242 & 250291 for Warden Signposted
▶▶▶★ ♨ £7.50-£9 ♨ £7.50-£9 ▲ £3.50-£5.50
Open Etr-Sep Booking advisable Whitsun & Jun-Aug Last arrival 23.00hrs Last departure 10.00hrs
Set in riverside fields with Kielder Water a few minutes' drive away. Proceed N from Kielder village towards the Scottish Border for approx 500yds, the site is on the right-hand side (E) of the road. A 10-acre site with 70 touring pitches.

Credit Cards

Kielder Water Caravan Club Site (NY660877)
Leaplish Waterside Park NE48 1AX
☎ 01434 250278
(4m SE) Signposted
▶▶▶✦♨♨▲
Open all year Booking advisable bank hols Last arrival 20.00hrs Last departure 18.00hrs
Gently sloping site reaching down to Kielder Water and backed by trees. Ideal for an active holiday. An 8-acre site with 118 touring pitches.

Credit Cards

ROTHBURY

Coquetdale Caravan Park (NU055007)
Whitton NE65 7RU ☎ 01669 620549 Signposted
▶▶★ ♨ £8-£10 ♨ £8-£10 ▲ £7-£10
Open mid Mar/Etr-Oct Booking advisable school hols Last arrival anytime Last departure anytime
Partly level and sloping grass site in hilly country adjacent to River Coquet, and overlooked by Simonside Hills and moorland; .5m SW of Rothbury on Newton road. A 2-acre site with 50 touring pitches and 180 statics.
Adventure playground, 5-a-side football posts.

NOTTINGHAMSHIRE

CLUMBER PARK

Camping & Caravanning Club Site (SK626748)
The Walled Garden S80 3BA ☎ 01909 482303 (in season) & 01203 694995 Signposted
Nearby town: Worksop
▶▶★ ♨ £8.20-£8.80 ▲ £8.20-£8.80
Open end Mar-end Oct Booking advisable bank hols & Jul-Aug Last arrival 21.00hrs Last departure noon

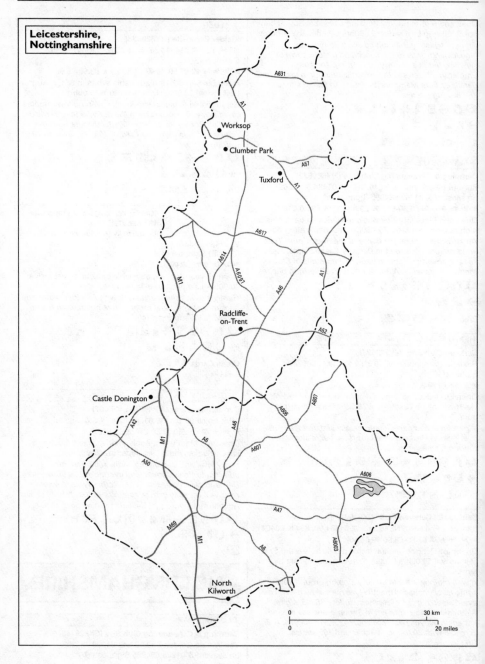

Leicestershire,
Nottinghamshire

Worksop

Clumber Park

Tuxford

Radcliffe-
on-Trent

Castle Donington

North
Kilworth

0   30 km
0   20 miles

Pleasant and peaceful site, well-maintained and situated in the splendid wooded surroundings of Clumber Park. Members only caravans. Follow signs for chapel and site signed beside cricket field. Please see the advertisement on page 27 for details of Club Members' benefits. A 4.5-acre site with 55 touring pitches.

🏕⊙✳🅿∅🖫🖭📞🐾🛇

→∪🚐♪

Credit Cards 🆑 💳 💳

NOTTINGHAM

See **Radcliffe on Trent**

RADCLIFFE ON TRENT

Thornton's Holt Camping Park (SK638377)
Stragglethorpe NG12 2JZ ☎ 0115 9332125 & 9334204 Signposted
Nearby town: Nottingham
▶▶▶ ★ 🚐 £6.50-£7.50 🚐 £6.50-£7.50 ⛺ £6.50-£7.50
Open Apr-1 Nov (rs 2 Nov-Mar limited facilities) Booking advisable bank hols & wknds mid May-Oct Last arrival 23.00hrs Last departure 13.00hrs
A level grass site with young trees and bushes, set in meadowland .5m S of A52 and 2m N of A46. Nearby (2m) is the National Water Sports Centre. A 6-acre site with 84 touring pitches.
Washing-up facilities.

🔥🏕⊙🖥🎱🎣 ✦✳🗻🅿∅🖫🖭📞🐎♞🛇👤

→∪🚩⛰🎣🎮♪

£

TUXFORD

Greenacres Touring Park (SK751719)
Lincoln Rd NG22 0JN ☎ 01777 870264 Signposted
Nearby town: Retford
▶▶▶ 🚐 £6 🚐 £6 ⛺ £6
Open Apr-Oct Booking advisable public hols Last arrival 23.00hrs Last departure 18.00hrs
Level and slightly sloping grass site with trees, set in rural area outside Tuxford, .75m E of A1 on A6075 over railway bridge. A 4-acre site with 40 touring pitches and 14 statics.

🔥🏕⊙🖥✳🗻🅿∅🖫🖭📞🐾🛇

→∪♪

£

Orchard Park Touring Caravan & Camping Park (SK754708)
Marnham Rd NG22 0PY ☎ 01777 870228
▶▶▶ ★ 🚐 £6.25-£6.50 🚐 £6.25-£6.50 ⛺ £6.25-£6.50
Open Mar-Oct Booking advisable bank hols Last arrival mdnt
A very pleasant developing site with newly-built toilet block. From Tuxford on A6075 .25m NE turn left to Marnham. Site signed on right in 800yards. A 3.5-acre site with 60 touring pitches.
Family shower room.

🔥🏕⊙✳🗻🅿∅🖫🖭📞🐎🐾🛇

→∪♪

£

WORKSOP

Clumber Park Caravan Club Site (SK628768)
Lime Tree Av, Clumber Park S80 3AE ☎ 01909 484758 (4.5m SE) Signposted
▶▶▶♿🚐🚐
Open Apr-Oct Booking advisable bank hols & wknds Last arrival 20.00hrs Last departure noon no cars by tents
Spacious site set within 4,000 acres of parkland of what was once Sherwood Forest. Entry by Aplethead Lodge Gate from A614 to avoid park charges. A 20-acre site with 150 touring pitches.

🔥🏕⊙🖥🎱🗻🅿🖫🖭📞🐎🛇

→∪🚩♪

Credit Cards 🆑 💳

OXFORDSHIRE

For the map of this county, see
Berkshire

BANBURY

Barnstones Caravan & Camping Site (SP455454)
Great Bourton OX17 1QU ☎ 01295 750289 Signposted
▶▶♿★🚐£4.50 🚐£4.50 ⛺£3-£4.50
Open all year Booking advisable public hols

➤

An excellent, well-run and beautifully laid-out site. Signposted from A423 (Coventry) Gt Bourton/Cropredy. A 3-acre site with 49 touring pitches.

🏕️🐾⊙📷🔥🎿🅼🚿🛁🚿🍴🔌📶♨️🚩🐴🛖♿
➡️🔄💰◎➕🚽💺🎣🍽️

🅿️

Mollington Touring Caravan Park (SP443477)
The Yews, Mollington OX17 1AZ ☎ 01295 750731
▶️ ▶️ ⭐ 🏕️ £5-£6 🚐 £5-£6 🏕️ £4
Open all year
A new site on farm land at edge of the village, neat and well run. Leave M40 at junc 11 onto A422 signed Banbury, take A423 signed Southam, and site on left in 3.5m. A 2-acre site with 24 touring pitches.

🏕️🐾⊙🐴🛖
➡️🔄◎🎣🍽️

BENSON

Benson Camping & Caravanning Park (SP613917)
OX10 6SJ ☎ 01491 838304 Signposted
Nearby town: Wallingford
▶️ ▶️ ▶️ 🚐🚐🏕️
Open Apr-Oct Booking advisable bank hols & Jul-Aug
Last arrival 19.00hrs Last departure noon
An attractive riverside site close to a busy road. Signed from A4074 in Benson. A 1-acre site with 26 touring pitches and 25 statics.

🏕️🐾⊙📷🔥🚽💺🆃✖️🔌🍽️♿
➡️🔄💰🔺🎣🍽️🎣

Credit Cards 🔲 🔲

BLETCHINGDON

Diamond Farm Caravan & Camping Park (SP513170)
OX5 3DR ☎ 01869 350909 Signposted
Nearby town: Oxford
▶️ ▶️ ▶️ ▶️ ♨️ ⭐ 🏕️ £5-£9 🚐 £5-£9 🏕️ £5-£9
Open all year (rs Nov-Mar shop & bar closed) Booking advisable bank hols & Jul-Sep Last arrival 22.00hrs Last departure noon
A well-run, quiet rural site in good level surroundings, and ideal for touring the Cotswolds. Situated alongside the B4027, 1m from the A43 and 7m N of Oxford in the heart of the Thames Valley. A 3-acre site with 37 touring pitches.
Cycle/jogging track, snooker table.

🏕️🚐🐾⊙📷🔥🔀♨️✖️🅼🚿🛁🚿🚽✖️🔌🍽️
➡️🔄💰🎣🍽️

🅿️

CASSINGTON

Cassington Mill Caravan Park (SP451099)
Eynsham Rd OX8 1DB ☎ 01865 881081 Signposted
Nearby town: Oxford
▶️ ▶️ ⭐ 🚐 fr £7 🚐 🏕️
Open Apr-Oct Booking advisable bank hols & Jun-Aug
Last arrival 21.00hrs Last departure noon

Secluded pretty site on the banks of the River Evenlode. First turn left 2.5m W of Oxford on A40 to Witney. A 4-acre site with 83 touring pitches and 50 statics.

🏕️🐾⊙✖️🅼🚿🛁🚿🚽🆃🔌🐴🐾♿
➡️🎣🍽️📷

🅿️

Credit Cards 🔲 🔲 🔲 🔲 🔲

CHARLBURY

Cotswold View Caravan & Camping Site (SP365210)
Enstone Rd OX7 3JH ☎ 01608 810314 Signposted
Nearby town: Witney
▶️ ▶️ ▶️ ♨️ 👫 ⭐ 🚐 £7.50-£9 🚐 £7.50-£9 🏕️ £7.50-£9
Open Etr or Apr-Oct Booking advisable bank hols Last arrival 20.00hrs Last departure noon
A really first class Cotswold site, well-screened with attractive views. Signed from A44 on to B4022. A 7-acre site with 90 touring pitches.
Off-licence & cycle hire.

🏕️🚐🐾⊙📷🔥🔀♨️✖️🅼🚿🛁🚿🚽🆃🔌🚩🐴
🍽️♿
➡️🎣🍽️

🅿️

📷📷📷📷📷📷📷📷📷📷

CHIPPING NORTON

Camping & Caravanning Club Site (SP315244)
Chipping Norton Rd OX7 3PN ☎ 01608 641993 & 01203 694995 (1.5m S A361) Signposted
▶️ ▶️ ⭐ 🚐 £9.80-£10.50 🚐 £9.80-£10.50 🏕️ £9.80-£10.50
Open Mar-Nov Booking advisable bank hols & Jul-Aug
Last arrival 21.00hrs Last departure noon
A hilltop site surrounded by trees but close to a busy main road. Toilets very clean. Direct access off A361, but only from the road signed to Chadlington. Please see the advertisement on page 27 for details of Club Members' benefits. A 4-acre site with 75 touring pitches.

🏕️🐾⊙♨️🔌🚽💺🆃🔌🍽️
➡️🔄💰🍽️🎣

Credit Cards 🔲 🔲 🔲

CUMNOR

Spring Farm (SP462032)
Faringdon Rd (A420) OX2 9QY ☎ 01865 863028
Signposted
Nearby town: Oxford
▷ ⭐ 🚐 £3-£4 🚐 £3-£4 🏕️ £2.50-£3
Open Apr-Oct Booking advisable anytime Last arrival 21.00hrs Last departure noon
A pretty, large garden site with clean facilities. A 1.5-acre site with 25 touring pitches.

🐾✖️🆃
➡️🎣🍽️📷🍽️

HENLEY-ON-THAMES

Swiss Farm International Camping (SU759837)
Marlow Rd RG9 2HY ☎ 01491 573419 Signposted
▶ ▶ ▶ ★ 🚐 fr £9.25 🚐 fr £9.25 ⚠ fr £9.25
Open Mar-Oct Booking advisable bank hols
*Pleasantly screened rural site just outside Henley on
A4155. A 6-acre site with 120 touring pitches and 6
statics.*
Football pitch & fishing lake.

🔌🚰📶☉🅿☼⚡🍴🚿✖❓♨🎣🐕🎪♿
➜ ♻✈🔪💽

💷

OXFORD

Oxford Camping International (SP518041)
426 Abingdon Rd OX1 4XN ☎ 01865 246551 Signposted
▶ ▶ ▶ ♦♦ ★ 🚐 £9.95 🚐 £9.95 ⚠ £9.95
Open all year Booking advisable bank hols & Jul-Aug
Last arrival 22.00hrs Last departure noon
*A very busy town site with handy park-and-ride into
Oxford. Situated on the south side of Oxford. Take
A4144 to city centre from the ring road, site is .25m on
left at rear of Texaco filling station. A 5-acre site with
129 touring pitches.*

🔌🚰📶☉🅿☼⚡🍴🔟🎣🐕🎪♿
➜ ♻✈📺💽

💷

Credit Cards

STANDLAKE

Hardwick Parks (SP388047)
Downs Rd OX8 7PZ ☎ 01865 300501 Signposted
Nearby town: Witney
▶ ▶ ▶ ★ 🚐 £6.75-£8.75 🚐 £6.75-£8.75 ⚠ £6.75-£8.75
Open Apr-Oct Booking advisable bank hols Last arrival
21.00hrs Last departure 17.00hrs
*A pleasant riverside site with views across the lake and
its own water activities. Signed from A415 at Standlake.
A 20-acre site with 250 touring pitches and 116 statics.*
Fishing, windsurfing, boating & swimming in lake.

🔌🚰📶☉🅿☼⚡🍴🍴🎣🐕🎪
➜ ♻💽

💷

Credit Cards

AWARD

Lincoln Farm Park
(SP395028)
High St OX8 7RH
☎ 01865 300239 Signposted
Nearby town: Witney
▶ ▶ ▶ ♦ ♦♦ ★ 🚐 £9.50-£11.50 🚐 £9.50-£11.50
⚠ £9.50-£11.50
Open Apr-Oct Booking advisable bank hols, Jul-Aug &
most wknds Last arrival 21.00hrs Last departure noon
*An attractively landscaped park, in a quiet village setting
on A415, with superb facilities and excellent
maintenance. A 7-acre site with 70 touring pitches and
19 statics.*
Indoor leisure centre, putting green.

🔌🚰📶☉🅿☼⚡ ☼🍴🍴📶🔟🎣🐕🎪
➜ ♻✈♨💽

💷

Credit Cards

UPPER HEYFORD

Heyford Leys Mobile Home Park (SP518255)
Camp Rd OX6 3LX ☎ 01869 232048
▶ ▶ ▶ 🚐🚐⚠
Open all year
*A touring field separated from the mobile home park by
a stream and bridge, in a quiet country area. Signed
from B430. A 3-acre site with 21 touring pitches and 47
statics.*

🔌📶☉🅿🍴🎣

WALLINGFORD

Riverside Caravan & Camping Site (SU612892)
OX10 8HN ☎ 01491 823717 out of season 01235 819888
Signposted
▶ ▶ ★ 🚐 £6.20-£8.25 🚐 £6.20-£8.25 ⚠ £6.20-£8.25
Open mid May-mid Sep Booking advisable Last arrival
21.30hrs Last departure 21.30hrs ⊘ no cars by caravans
no cars by tents
*Level grassy meadow site surrounded by trees and next
to the River Thames. For caravans approach from the E*

➡

via Henley and A423. A 2-acre site with 25 touring pitches.

🔥 ⊙ ⟨ ⟨ 🦽
→ ∪ ▶ ⤴ ♨ ♪ 🔲

SHROPSHIRE

BRIDGNORTH

Stanmore Hall Touring Park (SO742923)
Stourbridge Rd WV15 6DT
☎ 01746 761761 (E on A458) Signposted
▶ ▶ ▶ ▶ ♠ ♠♠ ➼ £9.89-£11.55 ➼ £9.89-£11.55 ▲ fr £5.25
Open all year Booking advisable bank hols & Jul-Aug
Last arrival 20.00hrs Last departure noon
A newly refurbished site in peaceful surroundings offering outstanding facilities. Situated on the A458 2m E of Bridgnorth in the grounds of Stanmore Hall and adj to the Midland Motor Museum. National winner of the AA's 1995 Campsite of the Year Award. A 12.5-acre site with 131 touring pitches.

🎮 🔥 ⊙ 🔲 🐟 ✳ ⚠ 🔒 ⟋ 🖲 🕐 ✗ ⟨ ➼ 🏮 ⟆
🐴 🦽 ♿
→ ▶ ♨ ♪

Credit Cards 🔲 🔲 🔲

BROOME

Engine & Tender Inn (SO399812)
SY7 ONT ☎ 01588 660275
▶ ➼ ➼ ▲
Open all year Booking advisable bank hols Last arrival 11.00hrs Last departure 14.00hrs no cars by caravans no cars by tents
A pleasant country pub site with gently sloping ground. In well-drained rural setting with a good set of facilities. W from Craven Arms on B4368, fork left to B4367, and site in village on right in 2m. A 2-acre site with 30 touring pitches and 2 statics.

→ ∪ ▶ ♪ 🔲 🦽

DIDDLEBURY

Glebe Farm (SO508855)
SY7 9DH ☎ 01584 841221 Signposted
Nearby town: Ludlow
▷ ➼ ➼ ▲
Open all year Booking advisable bank hols Last arrival 22.00hrs
Secluded wooded paddock adjacent to small stream in farm grounds. 5m NE of Craven Arms on B4368 to Much Wenlock, situated in village. A 4-acre site with 5 touring pitches.
River & lake fishing available.

🎮 🔥
→ ♪ 🦽

ELLESMERE

See **Lyneal**

HAUGHTON

Camping & Caravanning Club Site (SJ546165)
Ring Bank, Ebury Hill TF6 6BU ☎ 01743 709334 (in season) & 01203 694995
Nearby town: Shrewsbury
▷ ♠ ★ ➼ £6.60-£7 ➼ £6.60-£7 ▲ £6.60-£7
Open end Mar-early Nov Booking advisable bank hols & high season Last arrival 21.00hrs Last departure noon
A wooded hill fort with a central lake overlooking the Shropshire countryside. Well-screened by very mature trees. 4m NE of Shrewsbury on B5062 Newport rd. Please see the advertisement on page 27 for details of Club Members' benefits. An 18-acre site with 160 touring pitches.
Fishing.

🎮 ⚠ 🐕
Credit Cards 🔲 🔲 🔲

HUGHLEY

Mill Farm Holiday Park (SO564979)
SY5 6NT ☎ 01746 785208 Signposted
Nearby town: Much Wenlock
▶ ▶ ▶ ➼ ➼ ▲
Open Mar-Oct Booking advisable peak periods Last arrival 22.00hrs Last departure noon
A well-established farm site set in meadowland adjacent to river, with mature trees and bushes providing screening, situated below Wenlock Edge.. A 7-acre site with 55 touring pitches and 75 statics.
Fishing & horse riding.

🎮 🔥 ⊙ 🐟 ✳ 🔒 ⟋ 🖲 ⟨ 🐕 🐴
→ ∪ ♪

KINNERLEY

Cranberry Moss Camping & Caravan Park (SJ366211)
SY10 8DY ☎ 01743 741444 Signposted
Nearby town: Oswestry
▶ ▶ ★ ➼ £5-£6.20 ➼ £5-£6.20 ▲ £5-£6.20
Open Apr-Oct Booking advisable bank hols & Aug Last departure noon
A very pleasant, quiet site with a variety of trees. NW of Shrewsbury off A5, take B4396 and site is 400yds on left. A 4-acre site with 60 touring pitches.

🎮 🔥 ⊙ ✳ ⚠ 🔒 ⟋ 🖲 🕐 ⟨ 🦽

LYNEAL (NEAR ELLESMERE)

Fernwood Caravan Park (SJ445346)
SY12 0QF ☎ 01948 710221 Signposted
Nearby town: Ellesmere
▶ ▶ ▶ ➼ ➼
Open Mar-Nov Booking advisable bank hols Last arrival 21.00hrs Last departure 17.00hrs
A peaceful site set in wooded countryside, with screened, tree-lined touring area and fishing lake. 2m E of Ellesmere off A528, signed on right. A 5-acre site with 60 touring pitches and 165 statics.
Lake for coarse fishing on site.

🎮 🔥 ⊙ 🔲 🐟 ✳ ⚠ 🔒 🖲 🕐 ⟨ 🦽 ♿
→ ⤴ ♪

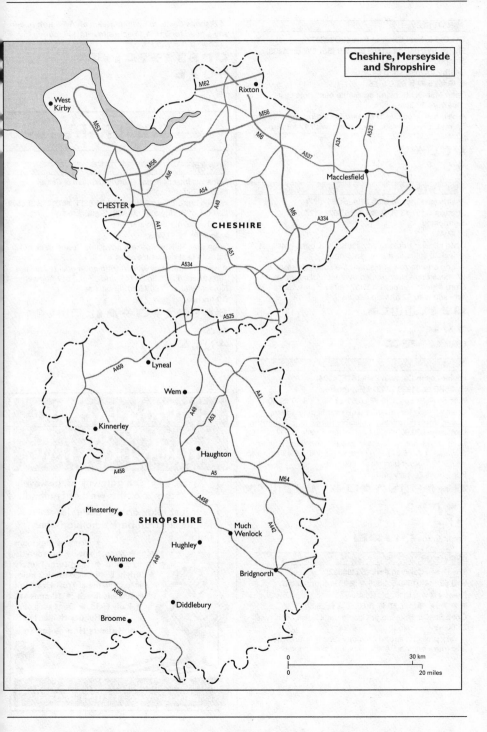

Cheshire, Merseyside
and Shropshire

MINSTERLEY

The Old School Caravan Park (SO322977)
Shelve SY5 0JQ ☎ 01588 650410 (5m SW on A488)
Signposted
Nearby town: Bishop's Castle
▶ 🚐 fr £5 🚐 fr £5 ▲ fr £5
Open Mar-Oct Booking advisable bank hols Last
departure 10.30hrs
*A well-designed site in a beautiful setting, 16miles S of
Shrewsbury on A488. A 1-acre site with 12 touring
pitches.*

🏴 🅿 ☉ ☀ 📞
➔ ∪ 🧦 🏊

MUCH WENLOCK

Presthope Caravan Club Site (SO587977)
Stretton Rd TF13 6DQ ☎ 01746 36234 (2.5m SW)
Signposted
▷ 🚐 🚐
Open all year Booking advisable Etr & bank hols Last
arrival 20.00hrs Last departure noon
*A long and narrow site set on the southern slope of
Wenlock Edge, surrounded by beautiful countryside.
From Much Wenlock on B4371 site on L in 2.5m. A 10-
acre site with 82 touring pitches.*

🏴 ☀ 🎱 🖉 ⊞ Ⓣ 📞 🐕
➔ ∪ 🏊

Credit Cards 🔳 🔳

WEM

Lower Lacon Caravan Park (ST534304)
SY4 5RP ☎ 01939 232376 Signposted
▶ ▶ ▶ 🚐 £6.50-£9.50 🚐 £6.50-£9.50 ▲ £6.50-£9.50
Open all year (rs Nov-Mar club wknds only, toilets
closed if frost) Booking advisable public hols & Jul-Aug
Last arrival 20.00hrs Last departure 19.00hrs
*Level grass site set in meadowland with good sanitary
facilities. 1.5m E of town centre on B5065. A 48-acre site
with 270 touring pitches and 50 statics.*
Pony rides & crazy golf.

🏴 🛒 🅿 ☉ 🖥 🗜 ⟨ ⊛ 🛒 ☀ 🍽 ⚠ 🎱 🖉 ⊞ Ⓣ ✗
📞 🕎 🐕 🏊 ♿
➔ ▶ 🧦

Credit Cards 🔳 🔳 🔳 🔳

WENTNOR

The Green Caravan Park (S0380932)
SY9 5EF ☎ 01588 650605 & 650231 Signposted
Nearby town: Bishop's Castle
▶ ▶ ▶ ★ 🚐 fr £5.50 🚐 fr £5.50 ▲ fr £5.50
Open Etr-Oct Booking advisable bank hols Last arrival
21.00hrs Last departure 13.00hrs
*A very pleasant spot with many recent improvments
and more planned. Mostly level, grassy pitches. 1m NE*

*of Bishops Castle to Lydham Heath on A489 turn rt, and
site signed for 3m. A 15-acre site with 140 touring
pitches and 20 statics.*

🏴 🅿 ☉ 🖥 🗜 ☀ 🍽 🏔 🎱 🖉 ⊞ ✗
➔ ∪ 🧦 🏊
💷

SOMERSET

BAWDRIP

*Fairways International Touring Caravan & Camp
(ST349402)*
Woolavington Corner, Bath Rd TA7 8PP ☎ 01278 685569
(3m NE of Bridgwater off A39) Signposted
Nearby town: Bridgwater
▶ ▶ ▶ ▶ 🚶 🚐 🚐 ▲
Open Mar-15 Nov Booking advisable Spring bank hol &
Jul-Aug Last departure noon
*A well-planned new site offering good quality facilities.
100 yards off A39 on B3141, and 3.5m E of Bridgwater. A
5.5-acre site with 200 touring pitches.*
Off-licence.

🏴 🅿 ☉ 🖥 🗜 ⟨ 🛒 ☀ 🏔 ⚠ 🎱 🖉 ⊞ Ⓣ 📞 🕎 🐕
🏊 ♿
➔ ∪ 💧 ⚓ 🧦

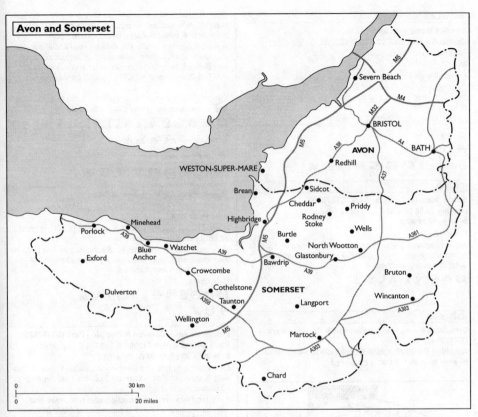

Avon and Somerset

BLUE ANCHOR

Blue Anchor Park (ST025434)
TA24 6JT ☎ 01643 821360 Signposted
Nearby town: Minehead
►►► ★ 🚐 £6-£12 🚐 £6-£12
Open Mar-Oct (rs Mar & Oct shop & swimming pool limited) Booking advisable bank hols & Jul-Aug Last arrival 22.00hrs Last departure 10.00hrs ⊗
Large coastal site, partly wooded on level ground overlooking bay with individual areas screened. .25m E of West Somerset Railway Station on B3191. A 3-acre site with 103 touring pitches and 300 statics.
Crazy golf.

🎮 🏪 ⊙ 🗓 🖥 ❄ ✳ 🏛 🔒 🥄 🔋 🔔 🕻 🛒 � ✴ &

→ ∪ ▶ ◎ ♪

Credit Cards 🔷 💳 🔷 🔷 🔷

BREAN

Northam Farm Camping & Caravan Park (SS299556)
TA8 2SE ☎ 01278 751244 & 751222
►►► 🚐 🚐 ▲
Open Etr-Sep (rs Oct shop & takeaway closed) Booking advisable bank & school hols Last arrival 22.00hrs Last departure noon

An attractive site a short walk from the sea with game, coarse and sea fishing close by. Take road to Burnham, and site on left in 500yds. A 30-acre site with 299 touring pitches and 90 statics.
Pond fishing.

🎮 🛒 🏪 ⊙ 🗓 🖥 ✳ 🏛 🔒 🥄 🔋 🔔 Ｔ 🕻 🛒 🚲 ⍟
🔋 &
→ ∪ ▶ 📹 ♪

BRUTON

Batcombe Vale Caravan Park (ST681379)
Batcombe BA4 6BW ☎ 01749 830246 Signposted
►►► 🚐 £7-£8 🚐 £7-£8 ▲ £7-£8
Open Etr-Sep Booking advisable bank hols & Jul-Aug Last departure noon
A small, attractive and very quiet site in a secluded valley close to three lakes. Standards of maintenance remain high. Take Evercreech road from Bruton, signed. A 4-acre site with 30 touring pitches.
Wild landscaped garden in secluded valley of lakes

🎮 🏪 ⊙ ✳ 🏛 🔒 🔋 🕻 🎏 ✝
→ ∪ ⍟ ⍟ ♪ 🔋

BURTLE

Ye Olde Burtle Inn (ST397434)
Catcott Rd TA7 8NG ☎ 01278 722269
Nearby town: Glastonbury
► Å

Open all year Booking advisable Jul-Aug
Tenting only site in a cider apple orchard. Situated beside pub in centre of village. A 0.75-acre site with 30 touring pitches.
Skittke alley, pool, darts & cycle hire.

☺ ⚠ ✕ ✆
→ ∪ ⏚ ⚑

Credit Cards 🂠 ▬ ▭ ⏺ ▦ ▨ 🅖

CHARD

South Somerset Holiday Park (ST279098)
Howley TA20 3EA ☎ 01460 62221 & 66036
► ► ► ► ⊞ ⊞ Å
Open all year
An immaculate site with impressive facilities and levels of maintenance. 3m W of Chard on A30. A 7-acre site with 75 touring pitches.

🖾 ⍨ ☺ ⚑ ⚟ ⚠ ✆ ⚑ &

CHEDDAR

Broadway House Holiday Caravan & Camping Park (ST448547)
Axbridge Rd BS27 3DB ☎ 01934 742610 Signposted
► ► ► ► ★ ⊞ fr £4 ⊞ fr £2 Å fr £4

Bucklegrove

CARAVAN PARK
AND CAMPING SITE

RODNEY STOKE,
Nr. CHEDDAR
SOMERSET BS27 3UZ
Telephone (01749) 870261

Indoor Heated Pool
Enjoy the peace and beauty of the Somerset countryside at this family run Holiday Park situated at the foot of the Mendip Hills midway between the Cathedral City of Wells and the famous Cheddar Gorge.
★ Modern toilet facilities with bathroom, dishwashing and free showers ★ Disabled toilet and shower ★ Childrens play area ★ Licensed Bar & Conservatory ★ Well stocked shop ★ Launderette ★ Electric Hook Up ★ Gas sales ★ Holiday homes for sale or hire ★ Summer and Winter storage ★ Bus stop at entrance ★ Dogs accepted ★
Rodney Stoke, Cheddar, Somerset, BS27 3UZ. Tel: 01749 870261

Open end May-Sep (rs Mar-end May & Oct-Nov no bar & pool open, limited shop hours) Booking advisable bank hols & end Jul-Aug Last departure noon
A well-equipped family site on slopes of Mendips with exceptional adventure areas for children, jacuzzi and sun bed. Midway between Cheddar and Axbridge on A371. A 30-acre site with 200 touring pitches and 35 statics.
Sunbed, table tennis, crazy golf, full activity prog.
See advertisement under Colour Section

🖾 ⍨ ⍨ ☺ ⚑ ⚟ ⚞ ⚟ ▭ ☀ ⚟ ⚠ ⬛ ⬚ ⊞ ⏹ ✕
✆ ⍨ ⚟ ⊞ ✝ ⚑ ⚑ &
→ ∪ ▶ ☺ ⚑

Credit Cards 🂠 ▬ ▭ ⏺ ▦ ▨ 🅖

Church Farm Camping Site (ST460529)
Church St BS27 3RF ☎ 01934 743048 Signposted
► ► ► ⊞ ⊞ Å
Open Etr-Oct Booking advisable public hols Last arrival 22.00hrs Last departure noon
Spacious, flat, grassy site, well-screened at rear of farm and short walk from Cheddar. A 5-acre site with 44 touring pitches and 3 statics.
Hairdryers.

🖾 ⍨ ☺ ⚟ ⚑ ☀ ⬛ ⬚ ⊞ ⏹ ✆ ⚑
→ ∪ ⏚

Froglands Farm Caravan & Camping Park (ST462529)
BS27 3RH ☎ 01934 742058 & 743304 Signposted
► ► ► ★ ⊞ £6-£8 ⊞ £4-£6 Å £3-£7
Open Etr or Apr-30 Oct Booking advisable Whitsun, Jul-Aug & school hols Last arrival 23.00hrs Last departure 13.00hrs
Farmland site on undulating ground with trees and shrubs, located on A371 Weston-Super-Mare to Wells road on SE outskirts of Cheddar. A 3-acre site with 68 touring pitches.

🖾 ⍨ ☺ ☀ ⬛ ⬚ ⊞ ⚑
→ ∪ ⏚

COTHELSTONE

Toulton Farm (ST191312)
TA4 3DR ☎ 01823 433458 Signposted
▷ ⊞ ⊞ Å
Open all year Booking advisable Last arrival 16.00hrs Last departure 10.00hrs ✗
A quietish farm site on a hillside with views over Vale of Taunton. Care needed at entrance if pulling trailers. From Cothelstone take road opp abbey, and site 1m on left. A 1-acre site with 10 touring pitches.
Horseriding on site.

🖾 ☀ ⚞
→ ∪ ▶ ⚟ ☺ ⚑

CROWCOMBE

Quantock Orchard Caravan Park (ST138357)
TA4 4AW ☎ 01984 618618 Signposted
Nearby town: Taunton
► ► ► ⚟ ★ ⊞ £6.90-£9.25 ⊞ £6.90-£9.25 Å £3-£9.25

QUANTOCK ORCHARD CARAVAN PARK

in the beautiful Quantock hills.
The small, clean and friendly Park for
Touring Caravans & Camping
Situated at the foot of the glorious Quantock hills, this
small, quiet, family-run Park is close to Exmoor and the
coast in the perfect location for touring Somerset and
North Devon.
Our full range of facilities include:
Immaculate timber and tiled washing facilities with free
showers (AA award for excellence winners 93/94 94/95) –
Large en-suite bathroom – Full laundry facilities –
Dishwashing room with microwave (free use) – Beautiful
heated swimming pool – Good children's play area –
Games room/TV room with Sky TV. Level individual
pitches, most with hook-ups, some on hardstanding –
tastefully landscaped – plenty of flowers – level tent
paddock. Mountain Bike hire.
Quality without quantity in a designed area of outstanding
natural beauty.
Dogs welcome on leads. Riding. Fishing. Steam Railway.
Good pub Food – all nearby.
Send s.a.e. for colour brochure and price guide to:
Mr & Mrs E C Biggs
QUANTOCK ORCHARD CARAVAN PARK,
 Crowcombe, Taunton,
Somerset TA4 4AW **AA E**
Tel: (01984) 618618
Excellent Graded **OPEN ALL YEAR** BHHPA Members

Open all year Booking advisable bank hols & Jul-Aug
Last arrival 10.00hrs Last departure noon
An attractive, quiet site at the foot of the Quantocks with
good views, and set back from the A358. A 3.5-acre site
with 65 touring pitches.
Barbecues provided, off-licence on site.

🗗 🚐 🞉 ⊙ 🖻 🦪 🗘 ⚓ ⌑ ✳ ⛰ 🛢 ⌀ ⊞ Ⓣ 📞
🚐 🏤 🏋 &
➔ ∪ 🅿 ⅃

DULVERTON

Exmoor House Caravan Club Site (SS912281)
TA22 9HL ☎ 01398 323268
▶ ▶ ▶ ★ 🚐 fr £8.50 🚐 fr £8.50
Open 26 Mar-3 Jan Booking advisable at all times Last
arrival 20.00hrs Last departure noon
A pretty valley-bottom site, overlooked by wooded
hillsides and within a few hundred yards of the old
village of Dulverton. A 4-acre site with 66 touring
pitches.

🗗 🞉 ⊙ 🖻 🦪 ✳ 🛢 ⌀ Ⓣ 📞 🏋
➔ ∪ 🅿 ⅃

Credit Cards ▦ ▦ ▦

EXFORD

Westermill Farm (SS824398)
TA24 7NJ ☎ 01643 831238 Signposted
Nearby town: Dulverton
▶ ▶ ♠ ★ 🚐 fr £7 🛆 fr £7

Open Apr-Oct (rs Apr-23 May shop closed) Booking
advisable Spring bank hol & Jul-Aug
An idyllic site for peace and quiet, in sheltered valley in
the heart of Exmoor. Four waymarked walks over 500
acre working farm. Leave Exford on the Porlock road,
after .25m fork left. Continue for 2.25m along valley past
another campsite until 'Westermill' sign seen on tree,
then fork left. Not suitable for caravans. A 6-acre site
with 60 touring pitches.
Trout fishing on site. Information centre.

🞉 ⊙ 🖻 🦪 ✳ 🛢 ⌀ 📞 🏋
➔ ∪ ⅃

GLASTONBURY

Old Oaks Touring Park
(ST521394)
Wick Farm, Wick BA6 8JS
☎ 01458 831437 Signposted
▶ ▶ ▶ ♣ ♠ ♦♦ 🚐 £6-£7.50 🚐 £6-£7.50 🛆 £6-£7.50
Open Mar-Oct (rs Oct shop & reception open limited
hours) Booking advisable bank hols & main season Last
arrival 21.00hrs Last departure noon
An ideal family park on a working farm on the east side
of Glastonbury Tor with panoramic views towards the
Mendip Hills. Glastonbury's two famous 1,000 year old
oaks - Gog and Magog - are on site, hence the name.
This is undoubtedly one of the best small parks in the
country and we are delighted to announce that it has
won the 1996 Regional Award of AA Campsite of the
Year for Southern England. For details of the awards,
see the colour section at the front of the book. From
Glastonbury take the Shepton Mallet road. A 2.5-acre
site with 40 touring pitches.
Fishing & off-licence on site.

🗗 🚐 🞉 ⊙ 🖻 🦪 ⅃ ⚓ ✳ ⛰ 🛢 ⌀ ⊞ Ⓣ 📞 🚐
🏋 🏋 &
➔ ⅃

Ashwell Farm House (ST517383)
Ashwell Ln BA6 8LB ☎ 01458 832313 (1m E, off A361)
Signposted
▶ ▶ 🚐 🚐 🛆
Open all year Booking advisable peak periods Last
arrival 22.00hrs Last departure noon
A basic but clean site with good views of the
surrounding countryside. 1m E of Glastonbury off A361.
A 4-acre site with 60 touring pitches.

🗗 🞉 ⊙ ✳ 🛢 ⌀ ⊞ 📞 🏋
➔ ⅃ 🖻 🏋

HIGHBRIDGE

Edithmead Leisure & Park Homes (ST337459)
TA9 4HE ☎ 01278 783475 Signposted
Nearby town: Burnham-on-Sea
▶ ▶ ▶ ★ 🚐 £6-£8 🚐 £6-£8 🛆 £4-£6
Open 9 Feb-11 Jan Booking advisable bank hols & Jul-
Sep Last arrival mdnt Last departure noon
Level, compact site adjacent to M5. From Highcliffe
follow signs to M5 rndbt, and site on right. A 15-acre
site with 250 touring pitches and 65 statics. ➡

Amusement arcade.

🔌 📷 ☉ 🗊 🎣 ☀ ⚲ 🏔 🛏 🖉 Ⓣ ⚂ ♨ 🐕 🐾
→ ∪ ◎ ⚠ ♟ 🎣

New House Farm Caravan & Camping Park (ST338469)
Walrow TA9 4RA ☎ 01278 782218 & 788729 Signposted

▶▶▶ ★ 🚍 £5-£6 🚐 £5-£6 Å £3-£6

Open Mar-Oct Booking advisable Jul & Aug Last arrival
23.30hrs Last departure 18.30hrs

*A flat and very well-maintained site, well-sheltered by
boundary hedging and trees. 3m from beaches. A 4-acre
site with 30 touring pitches.*

🔌 📷 ☉ 🗊 ☀ 🏔 🛏 🐾
→ ∪ 🅿 ⚠ ♟ 🎣 🐾

LANGPORT

Thorney Lakes Caravan Park (ST430237)
Thorney West Farm, Muchelney TA10 0DW
☎ 01458 250811

▶▶ ★ 🚍 fr £6 🚐 fr £6 Å fr £6

Open Mar-Jan Booking advisable

A 6-acre site with 16 touring pitches.
Trout & Coarse fishing on site.

🔌 📷 ☉ 🗊 ♿
→ 🐾

MARTOCK

Southfork Caravan Park (ST448188)
Parrett Works TA12 6AE ☎ 01935 825661 Signposted
Nearby town: Yeovil

▶▶▶ 🚶 🚍 fr £7 🚐 fr £7 Å fr £7

Open all year Booking advisable bank hols & Jul-Aug
Last arrival 23.00hrs Last departure noon

*Well-kept and equipped level site, 1.5m from centre of
Martock with good country views. An ideal touring
centre. A 2-acre site with 30 touring pitches and 2
statics.*

Caravan service/repair centre & accessories shop.

🔌 📷 ☉ 🗊 🎣 ☀ 🏔 🛏 🖉 🗊 Ⓣ ⚂ 🐕 🐾 🐾
→ ∪ 🅿 🎣

💷

MINEHEAD

Camping & Caravanning Club Site (SS958471)
Hill Rd, North Hill TA24 5SF ☎ 01643 704138 (in season)
& 01203 694995 Signposted

▶▶▶ ♣ ★ 🚍 £8.40-£9 Å £8.40-£9

Open end Mar-end Sep Booking advisable bank hols &
Jul-Aug Last arrival 21.00hrs Last departure noon no
cars by caravans

*A secluded site offering glorious views of the Bristol
Channel and Quantocks. The approach road is narrow
with sharp bends. Please see the advertisement on page
27 for details of Club Members' benefits. A 4-acre site
with 60 touring pitches.*

📷 ☉ 🎣 ☀ 🛏 🖉 🗊 ⚂
→ ∪ 🅿 ⚲ ♟ 🎣 🗊 🐾

Credit Cards 🔳 🔳 🔳

Minehead & Exmoor Caravan Site (SS950457)
Minehead & Exmoor Caravan Park, Porlock Rd TA24
8SN ☎ 01643 703074 (1m W adj to A39) Signposted

▶▶▶ ★ 🚍 £6 🚐 £6 Å £6

Open Mar-Oct Booking advisable bank hols & Jul-Aug
Last arrival 23.00hrs Last departure noon

*Small, terraced, grassy site near the town with many
young trees and plants. Bordered by a stream on the
edge of Exmoor. Adjacent to the A39. A 2.5-acre site
with 50 touring pitches.*

🔌 📷 ☉ 🗊 🎣 ☀ 🏔 🛏 🖉 🗊 Ⓣ ⚂ 🐾 ♿
→ ∪ 🅿 ⚲ ♟ 🎣

Credit Cards 🔳

NORTH WOOTTON

Greenacres Camping (ST553416)
Barrow Ln BA4 4HL ☎ 01749 890497 Signposted

▶▶ ♣ Å

Open Apr-Oct Booking advisable school hols Last arrival
21.00hrs Last departure noon 🚫

*An immaculately maintained site peacefully set within
sight of Glastonbury Tor. Mainly family orientated with
many thoughtful extra facilities provided. A 4.5-acre site
with 30 touring pitches.*

📷 ☉ 🎣 ☀ 🏔 🛏 🖉 🗊
→ ∪ 🅿 ♟ 🎣 🗊 🐾

PORLOCK

Burrowhayes Farm Caravan & Camping Site (SS897460)
West Luccombe TA24 8HU ☎ 01643 862463
(SE of Porlock .25m off A39)
Nearby town: Minehead
▶ ▶ ▶ ★ 🚐 £5-£6.50 🚐 £5-£6.50 ▲ £5-£6.50

Open 15 Mar-Oct Booking advisable Etr, Spring bank hol & Jun-Sep Last departure noon
A delightful site on the edge of Exmoor, on slope to the river, and ideal for exploring surrounding area. An 8-acre site with 140 touring pitches and 20 statics.
Pony-treking available.

🖼 🐾 ⊙ 🗑 ☀ 🔌 🗑 ⊺ 🔔 🐴 🐛
➔ ▶ ◎ △ ⅄ 🎪 🎵

Porlock Caravan Park (SS882469)
TA24 8NS ☎ 01643 862269 Signposted
▶ ▶ ▶ 🚐 🚐 ▲

Open 15 Mar-Oct Booking advisable Etr, Whitsun & Jul-Aug Last arrival 23.00hrs Last departure noon
A well-planned site, in valley with shrubs and trees, and an ideal touring centre for Exmoor. A 3-acre site with 40 touring pitches and 56 statics.

🖼 🐾 ⊙ 🗑 🍴 ☀ 🏔 🔌 🗑 ⊺ 🔔 🐴 🐛
➔ ∪ ▶ ⅄ 🎵

PRIDDY

Mendip Heights Caravan & Camping Park (ST522519)
Townsend BA5 3BP ☎ 01749 870241 Signposted
Nearby town: Wells
▶ ▶ ▶ 🚐 £8.50 🚐 £8.50 ▲ £8.50

Open Etr or Apr-Oct Booking advisable bank & school hols
Quiet family site in high open-countryside overlooking the Mendip Hills and valleys, signposted from A39 at Green Ore. A 4.5-acre site with 90 touring pitches and 1 static.
Archery, canoeing, absailing, caving, table tennis.

🖼 🐾 ⊙ 🗑 🍴 ☀ 🏔 🔌 🗑 ⊺ 🔔 🐛
➔ ∪

RODNEY STOKE

Bucklegrove Caravan & Camping Park (ST487502)
BS27 3UZ ☎ 01749 870261 Signposted
Nearby town: Wells
▶ ▶ ▶ ▶ ★ 🚐 £5-£9.50 🚐 £5-£9.50 ▲ £5-£9.50

Open Mar-Oct Booking advisable bank hols & peak periods Last arrival 22.30hrs Last departure noon
A well-sheltered site on the southern slopes of the Mendip Hills providing superb views of Somerset. An ideal touring base off A371. A 5-acre site with 125 touring pitches and 35 statics.
See advertisement under CHEDDAR

💀 🛒 🐾 ⊙ 🗑 🍴 🔔 🗑 ☀ 🍷 🏔 🔌 🗑 ⊺ 🔔
🔲 🐛 ♿
➔ ∪ 🎪 🎵
💷

Credit Cards 🟦 🟦 🟦 🟦 🟦

TAUNTON

Ashe Farm Camping & Caravan Site (ST279229)
Thornfalcon TA3 5NW ☎ 01823 442567 Signposted
▶ ▶ ▶ ★ 🚐 £5.50-£10 🚐 £5.50-£10 ▲ £5.50-£10

Open Apr-Oct Booking advisable Jul-Aug
Attractive site with clean facilities. Situated off A358, 4m SE of Taunton, 3.5m from junc 25 of M5. A 3-acre site with 30 touring pitches and 2 statics.

🖼 🐾 ⊙ 🍴 🍷 🔍 🔍 ☀ 🏔 🔌 🗑 ⊺ 🔔 🐴 🐛
➔ ∪ ▶ 🎪 🎵 📼

Holly Bush Park (ST220162)
Culmhead TA3 7EA ☎ 01823 421515 (5m S on B3170, turn right heading for village of Culmhead) Signposted
▶ ▶ ▶ ★ 🚐 £4.50-£6 🚐 £4.50-£6 ▲ £4.50-£6

Open mid Feb-mid Jan Booking advisable bank hols & high season Last arrival 22.00hrs Last departure noon
A good basic site, ideal as overnight stop yet well positioned around attractive countryside with easy access to Wellington and Taunton. A 2-acre site with 40 touring pitches.

🖼 🐾 ⊙ 🗑 ☀ 🔌 🗑 ⊺ 🔔 🐴 🐛
➔ ∪ ▶ 🎵
💷

WATCHET

Doniford Bay Holiday Park (ST095433)
TA23 0TJ ☎ 01984 632423
▶ ▶ ▶ ★ 🚐 £7.50-£14.50 🚐 £7.50-£14.50 ▲ £7.50-£14.50

Open Apr-mid Oct Booking advisable Jul-Aug Last departure 10.00hrs
A level site with some hardstanding pitches for caravans and surfaced internal roadways. E of Watchet off A39 and overlooking the sea (Minehead Bay). A 5-acre site with 120 touring pitches.
Free evening entertainment, amusements, Go-Karts.

🖼 🐾 ⊙ 🗑 🍷 🔍 🍷 🏔 ✂ 🔔 🍺 🐛 ♿
➔ ∪

WELLINGTON

Gamlins Farm Caravan Park (ST083195)
Gamlins Farm, Greenham TA21 0LZ ☎ 01823 672596 (4m W) Signposted
▶ ▶ ▶ 🚐 £6-£7 🚐 £6-£7 ▲ £4-£7

Open Apr-Sep Booking advisable bank hols Last departure noon
A well-planned site in a secluded position with panoramic views. Situated off the A38 on the Greenham road. A 3-acre site with 25 touring pitches.

🖼 🐾 ⊙ 🍷 ☀ 🔔 🐴
➔ ∪ 🎪 🗑 🐛

Cadeside Caravan Club Site (ST147214)
Nynehead Rd TA21 9HN ☎ 01823 663103 (1m E)
▷ 🚐 🚐

Open 26 Mar-4 Oct Booking advisable bank hols
A simple rural site, well-screened with hedges and trees at the edge, and distant views to the surrounding hills.

➡

Within ten minutes' walk of Wellington. A 4.75-acre site with 60 touring pitches.

🔒 🐕
→ ∪

WELLS

Homestead Caravan & Camping Park (ST532474)
Wookey Hole BA5 1BW ☎ 01749 673022 Signposted
▶ ▶ ▶ ★ ⊞ £8.10 ⊞ £7.60 ▲ £8.30
Open Etr-Oct Booking advisable Last arrival 22.00hrs
Last departure noon
Attractive small site by stream with mature trees. Set in hilly woods and meadowland with access to river and Wookey Hole. .5m NW off A371 Wells-Cheddar road. A 2-acre site with 60 touring pitches and 28 statics.
Childrens fishing.

🎮 🚜 🌮 ⊙ ⓞ ☌ ✳ 🔋 🖋 ⊞ ☎ 🔋
→ ∪ ▶ 📺 🎵
⊞

WINCANTON

Wincanton Racecourse Caravan Club Site (ST708295)
BA9 8BJ ☎ 01963 34276 Signposted
▶ ▶ ★ ⊞ £5-£6 ⊞ £5-£6 ▲ £5-£7.50
Open Apr-Sep (rs Apr-5 May limited space/electric point on race day) Booking advisable bank hols Last arrival 20.00hrs Last departure noon
A well-kept level grassy site on Racecourse Downs one mile from the town centre on A303. Turn off main road at Hunters Lodge to A3081 from either direction. A 2-acre site with 50 touring pitches.
9 hole golf course.

🎮 🌮 ⊙ 🖥 🖋 ⊘ ⊞ ☎ 🐴 🐕 ♿
→ ∪ ▶ 📺 🎵 🖥
Credit Cards 💳 💳 💳

STAFFORDSHIRE

CANNOCK CHASE

Camping & Caravanning Club Site (SK039145)
Old Youth Hostel, Wandon
WS15 1QW ☎ 01889 582166 & 01203 694995 Signposted
▶ ▶ ♣ 🚶 ★ ⊞ £9.80-£10.50 ⊞ £9.80-£10.50
▲ £9.80-£10.50
Open Mar-Nov Booking advisable bank hols & Jul-Aug
Last arrival 21.00hrs Last departure noon
Very popular site in an excellent location in the heart of the Chase. A gently sloping site with timber-built facility blocks. Please see the advertisement on page 27 for details of Club Members' benefits. A 5-acre site with 60 touring pitches.

🌮 ⊙ 🔳 ☎ ♿
Credit Cards 💳 💳 💳

CHEADLE

Quarry Walk Park (SK045405)
Coppice Ln, Croxden Common, Freehay ST10 1RQ
☎ 01538 723495
▶ ▶ ★ ⊞ fr £6.50 ⊞ fr £6.50 ▲ fr £6.50
Open all year Booking advisable bank hols Last arrival 23.00hrs Last departure noon
A brand new park in an old quarry, well-screened with mature trees and shrubs. Situated 1m from A522 Cheadle-Uttoxeter Rd at Freehay, A 14-acre site with 40 touring pitches.

🎮 🌮 ⊙ 🏔 🔋 ⊞ ☎
→ ∪ 🎵 🔋

LEEK

Blackshaw Moor Caravan Club Site (SK012603)
ST13 8TW ☎ 01538 300203 (2.75m NE)
▶ ▶ ♣ 🚶 ⊞ ⊞ ▲
Open 26 Mar-Oct Booking advisable bank hols & wknds
Attractive terraced site with striking views of the Peaks. An 8.5-acre site with 87 touring pitches and 20 statics.

🎮 🌮 ⊙ 🖥 🔳 🔋 ⊞ ☎ 🐕 🔋 ♿
→ ∪ ▶ 🎵 🎵
Credit Cards 💳 💳

Q Q Q Q Q Q Q Q Q Q

OAKAMOOR

Star Caravan & Camping Park (SK066456)
Cotton ST10 3BN ☎ 01538 702256 & 702219
(1.25m NE off B5417) Signposted
Nearby town: Leek
▶ ▶ ⊞ ⊞ ▲
Open Feb-Dec Booking advisable anytime Last arrival anytime Last departure 19.00hrs
A pleasant, well screened site situated within one mile of Alton Towers. !.25m N of Oakamoor off B5417, 1.5m S of A52. A 20-acre site with 90 touring pitches and 58 statics.

🎮 🌮 ⊙ 🔳 🏔 🔋 ⊘ ⊞ Ⓣ ☎ 🐕 🔋
→ ∪ ▶ 🎵 🖥

RUGELEY

Silver Trees Caravan Park (SK014173)
Stafford Brook Rd, Penkridge Bank WS15 2TX
☎ 01889 582185 Signposted
▶ ▶ ★ ⊞ £6-£8 ⊞ £6-£8
Open May-Sep (rs Apr & Oct shop & pool closed)
Booking advisable public hols Last arrival 23.00hrs Last departure noon
Situated on rising ground on Cannock Chase amidst attractive woodland. Off Penkridge-Rugeley road, 2m from Rugeley. A 10-acre site with 50 touring pitches and 50 statics.

🎮 🌮 ⊙ 🖥 🔳 ☌ ♦ 🔳 ✳ 🏔 🔋 ☎ 🐕 🔋
→ 📺
See advertisement on page 172.

STOKE ON TRENT

See **Trentham**

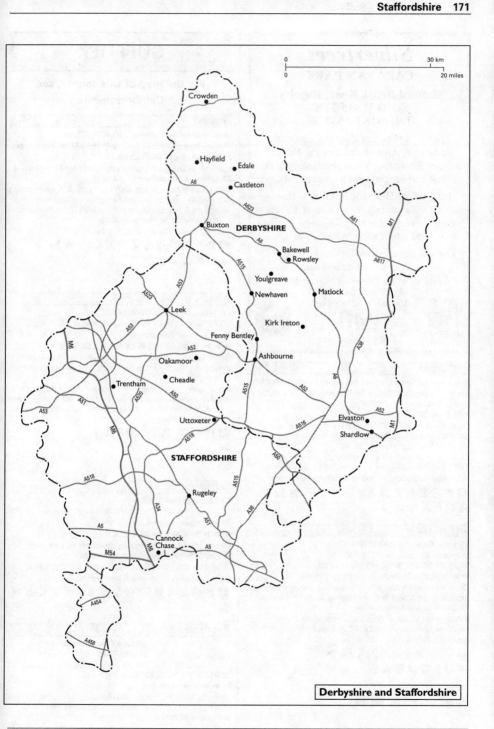

Derbyshire and Staffordshire

Silvertrees
CARAVAN PARK

**Stafford Brook Road, Rugeley,
Staffs WS15 2TX.
Tel: (01889) 582185**

Set in the heart of Cannock Chase, a
designated Area of Outstanding Natural
Beauty, Silvertrees offers peaceful, relaxing,
scenic surroundings for a country holiday.

LUXURY SHOWER BLOCK – Tennis
court – Swimming pool – colour TV and
games room – electric hook-ups – touring
and motor caravans welcome.

Luxury "Rose Award" holiday homes, all
services, for hire and sale.

*Close to Alton Towers, Drayton Manor
Park and Zoo, West
Midlands Safari Park.*

AA **E**

Colour Brochure

TRENTHAM

Trentham Gardens Caravan & Leisure Park (SJ864409)
Trentham Gardens, Stone Rd ST4 8AX ☎ 01782 657341
Signposted
▶▶▶ 🚐🚐▲

Open all year (rs Oct-Etr shop bar cafe closed) Booking
advisable bank hols & during major events Last arrival
23.00hrs Last departure 18.00hrs
*Wooded meadowland site by lakes. Access to A34 and
exit 15 of M6. A 30-acre site with 250 touring pitches.*
Watersports on lake, shooting & fishing, kart centre

🔧🐾☉🖼️☀️♀️🏍️🛡️🛢️🛅Ⓣ✗🔌🎋🐴🐕♿
➜∪🏳️⛄🍗🎣

UTTOXETER

Caravan Club Site (SK099334)
Uttoxeter Racecourse ST14 8BD
☎ 01889 564172 & 562561 Signposted
▶▶ ★ 🚐 £5-£10 🚐 £5-£10 ▲ £3.50-£13.50

Open Apr-Oct (rs Mar & Nov limited opening) Booking
advisable bank hols & race meeting dates Last arrival
20.00hrs Last departure noon
*Situated on SE edge of small market town, mainly level
site in hilly country. Off B5017. A 3-acre site with 83
touring pitches.*

🔧🐾☉☀️♀️🛡️🛢️🛅Ⓣ🔌🎋🐴
➜∪🏳️⛄🍗🎣🖼️🔌

💷

Credit Cards 🟦 🟥 🟫

SUFFOLK

For the map of this county, see
Cambridgeshire

BUNGAY

Outney Meadow Caravan Park (TM333905)
Outney Meadow NR35 1HG ☎ 01986 892338 Signposted
▶▶▶ 🚐 £6-£11 🚐 £6-£11 ▲ £6-£11

Open all year Booking advisable public hols Last arrival
22.00hrs Last departure 21.00hrs
*An excellent holiday site with river sports. A well-spaced
out area for tourers adjacent to common and river. W of
village on A143, adjoining the roundabout. A 6-acre site
with 60 touring pitches and 30 statics.*
Fishing, rowing boat and canoe hire.

🔧🐾☉🖼️🍳☀️♀️🛡️🛢️🛅Ⓣ🔌🎋🐴🐕♿
➜∪🏳️⛄🍗🎣
💷

BUTLEY

Tangham Campsite (TM355485)
IP12 3NP ☎ 01394 450707 Signposted
Nearby town: Woodbridge
▶▶▶ ★ 🚐 £6.50-£8 🚐 £6.50-£8 ▲ £6.50-£8

Open Apr-Oct (rs Nov-11 Jan no toilets or showers cdp
only) Booking advisable bank hols Last arrival 22.00hrs
Last departure noon
*Good, quiet, level grass site, situated on the edge of a
deep forest with attractive walks. From Woodbridge take
B1084, after 5m turn right into forest. A 7-acre site with
90 touring pitches.*

🔧🐾☉☀️🏍️♀️🛡️🛢️🛅Ⓣ🔌♿
➜∪🏳️
💷

DUNWICH

Cliff House (TM475692)
Minsmere Rd IP17 3DQ ☎ 01728 648282 Signposted
Nearby town: Southwold
▶▶▶▶ ★ 🚐 fr £8 🚐 fr £8 ▲ fr £5

Open Etr or Apr-Oct Booking advisable all year Last
arrival 23.00hrs Last departure 11.00hrs
A 10-acre site with 95 touring pitches and 78 statics.
Campers wash room, pool, table tennis & darts.

🔧🐾☉🖼️🍳🔌🏠☀️♀️🏍️🛡️🛢️✗🔌🏪🐴
♿

EAST BERGHOLT

**Grange Country Park
(TM098353)**
The Grange CO7 6UX
☎ 01206 298567 & 298912 Signposted
▶▶▶▶🚿👪🚐🚐▲

Open 31 Mar-Oct (rs Oct-Mar) Booking advisable for
stays of 1 wk or more Last arrival 22.00hrs Last
departure 18.00hrs

This level, grassy site is situated in hilly woodland with some moorland nearby. The park is sheltered by mature trees and bushes and provides first class sanitary facilities. 3m off A12 between Colchester and Ipswich. Winner of the 1994 Best Campsite of the Year Award for the Central England. An 8-acre site with 120 touring pitches and 55 statics.

🔌📶🕽☉🗄🏧⚡🖧☀️🍴🎢🅿️🚿✕☎🛏
🏕🐕🐾
➜ ♨ 🏊 ⛱ ✴ 🚤 🏄

♈♈♈♈♈♈♈♈

FELIXSTOWE

Peewit Caravan Park (TM290338)

Walton Av IP11 8HB ☎ 01394 284511 Signposted

▶▶▶▶ 🚐🚐▲

Open Apr or Etr-Oct (rs early & late season shop closed) Booking advisable school & bank hols Last arrival 21.00hrs Last departure 11.00hrs

A useful town site, not overlooked by houses. The site is neat and tidy with spotless toilets, and the beach a few minutes away by car. Signed from A45 in Felixstowe. A 3-acre site with 65 touring pitches and 220 statics.

Bowling green, washing up sink.

🔌📶🕽☉🗄🅿️☀️🍴⚡🖧🎢☎🐕🐾♟🗑
➜ ✴ 🏊 🚤

GISLEHAM

Chestnut Farm Touring Park (TM510876)

NR33 8EE ☎ 01502 740227 Signposted

Nearby town: Lowestoft

▶▶ ★ 🚐 £5-£6 🚐 £5-£6 ▲ £5-£6

Open Apr-Oct Booking advisable bank hols Last arrival mdnt

A nice little farm site with well-maintained toilets in a peaceful setting. At southern roundabout of Kessingland bypass go west signposted Rushmere, Mutford and Gisleham. Take second turning on left. A 3-acre site with 20 touring pitches.

Fishing on site.

🔌📶🕽☉✴🗑🐕🐾♟
➜ ♨ 🏊 ☉ ⛱ ✴ 🏊 🚤

💷

IPSWICH

Priory Park (TM198409)

IP10 0JT ☎ 01473 727393 Signposted

▶▶▶ 🚐 £8.25-£26 🚐 £8.25-£26 ▲ £8.25-£26

Open all year (rs Oct-Apr limited number of sites, shop/club closed) Booking advisable bank & school hols Last arrival 21.00hrs Last departure noon

Well-screened south-facing site with panoramic views overlooking Orwell. Convenient for Ipswich southern bypass and Felixstowe car ferry. From bypass take Nacton exit then follow signs Ipswich/Airport for 300yds to site entrance. A 10-acre site with 110 touring pitches and 260 statics.

9 hole golf, small boat launching, table tennis.

See advertisement on page 174

🔌🛥🕽☉🗄⚡♟🔍✴🍴🏧⚡🖧🎢✕☎🚿
🐕
➜ ♨ 🅿️ ⛱ 🏊 🚤 🎢

Low House Touring Caravan Centre (TM227425)

Bucklesham Rd, Foxhall IP10 0AU ☎ 01473 659437 (eves) (4m E)

▶▶ 🚐 £6.50-£8 🚐 £6.50-£8 ▲ £6.50-£8

Open all year Booking advisable anytime Last departure anytime

A very neat and tidy site with good toilet facilities. From A45 south ring road take slip road to A1156 signed East Ipswich. Turn right in 1m and right again in .5m. Site on left. A 3.5-acre site with 30 touring pitches.

Temporary membership of sports centre opposite.

🔌📶🕽☉✴🍴🏧🎢☎🚿
➜ ♨ 🅿️ 🏊 🚤 🗑

💷

KESSINGLAND

Kessingland Beach Holiday Village (TM535852)

Beach Rd NR33 7RN ☎ 01502 740636 & 740879 Signposted

Nearby town: Lowestoft

▶▶▶▶ ★ 🚐 £6-£11 🚐 £6-£11 ▲ £5-£9

Open Etr-Oct Booking advisable Jul-Aug Last arrival 21.00hrs Last departure 14.00hrs

An excellent seaside holiday park with plenty of entertainment for all ages. A 5-acre site with 90 touring

➡

pitches and 330 statics.
Bowling green, sauna, amusements, tennis courts.

🔌📞🎣☉🗑️🎾 🏹🔍🔍☀️🚻🏛️🗜️🖊️✂️📞🛒
🚒🎣♿

➔⛵☔📽️🎣🎵

Credit Cards 🔳 💳

Camping & Caravanning Club Site (TM521862)
Suffolk Wildlife Park, Whites Ln NR33 7SL
☎ 01502 742040 (in season) & 01203 694995 (.5m S, off
A12)
Nearby town: Lowestoft
▶▶▶ ★ 🚐 £9.30-£10 🚍 £9.30-£10 ▲ £9.30-£10
Open end Mar-end Oct Booking advisable bank hols &
Jul-Aug Last arrival 21.00hrs Last departure noon
*An open site next to a wildlife park, with beaches close
by. Very tidy and well maintained. Concessions to
wildlife park. Please see the advertisement on page 27
for details of Club Members' benefits. A 4.5-acre site
with 90 touring pitches.*

🔌📞🎣☉🗑️🎣☀️📞🐕🚒♿
➔⛵☔📽️🎣🎵

Credit Cards 🔳 💳

LEISTON

Cakes & Ale (TM432637)
Abbey Ln, Theberton IP16 4TE ☎ 01728 831655 & 01473
736650 Signposted
Nearby town: Aldeburgh
▶▶▶ 🚐 fr £8 🚍 fr £8 ▲ fr £4
Open Apr-Oct (rs low season club, shop/reception open
limited hours) Booking advisable public & school hols
Last arrival 21.00hrs Last departure 16.00hrs
*A large, well spread out site with many trees and bushes.
Ideal centre for touring. From A12 at Saxmundham turn
E onto B1119 for 3 miles. Then follow by-road over level
crossing and signs to caravan park. A 5-acre site with 50
touring pitches and 200 statics.*
See advertisement under IPSWICH

🔌🛒📞☉🗑️🎣🔍☀️🚻🏛️🗜️🖊️📞🐕🚒
➔⛵📽️🎵

LOWESTOFT
See **Kessingland**

MILDENHALL

Round Plantation Caravan Club Site (TL726754)
Brandon Rd IP28 7JE ☎ 01638 713089 (1m NE)
▷ ★ 🚐 £7.75 🚍 £7.75
Open Mar-Oct Booking advisable bank hols Last arrival
20.00hrs Last departure noon
*A pleasant, carefully landscaped forest site, with open
pitching areas within the woodland, and quiet walks
from the site. From A11 at Barton Mills rndbt take
A1101, turn R in .75m at Half Moon PH into Brandon Rd
signed Brandon & Lakenheath. Site in .75m on R. A 15-
acre site with 100 touring pitches.*

🔌☀️🖊️🗜️🎣🚰📺📞🐕
➔⛵📽️🎵🚒

Credit Cards 🔳

NEWMARKET

Camping & Caravanning Club Site (TL621626)
Rowley Mile Racecourse CB8 8JL ☎ 01638 663235
Signposted
▶▶ 🚐🚍▲
Open May-Sep Booking advisable
*A level grassy site on Newmarket Heath with panoramic
country views, 1m W of town centre, off A1304. Please
see the advertisement on page 27 for details of Club
Members' benefits. A 10-acre site with 90 touring
pitches.*

🔌📞☉🎣🏛️📞🚒
➔▶

Credit Cards 🔳 💳 💳

SAXMUNDHAM

Whitearch Touring Caravan Park (TM379610)
Main Rd, Benhall IP17 1NA ☎ 01728 604646
▶▶ ★ 🚐 fr £8.50 🚍 fr £8.50 ▲ fr £8.50
Open Apr-Oct Booking advisable bank hols
*Attractive valley site with lake for coarse fishing and
new, very clean toilet block. On the junction of A12 and
B1121. A 5-acre site with 30 touring pitches.*
Fishing lake

🔌📞☉☀️🏛️🗜️🖊️📞🚒🏹🐕🚒♿
💷

Marsh Farm Caravan Site (TM385608)
Sternfield IP171HW ☎ 01728 602168 (1.5m S)
Signposted
▷ 🚐 £5-£7 🚍 £5-£7
Open all year Booking advisable Jun-Aug Last arrival
22.30hrs Last departure 22.30hrs
*Very attractive venture site with adjoining lakes offering
coarse fishing. A 6-acre site with 30 touring pitches.*

☠️🏛️🗃️🚒🏹🐕🚒
➔⛵▶📽️🎵🗑️

SHOTTISHAM

St Margaret's House (TM323447)
IP12 3HD ☎ 01394 411247 Signposted
Nearby town: Woodbridge
▶▶ ★ 🚐 £4-£4.50 🚍 £4-£4.50 ▲ £4-£4.50
Open Apr or Etr-Oct Booking advisable bank hols & Jul-
Aug Last arrival 22.00hrs Last departure noon
*A pleasant little family run site in attractive village
setting. Turn off B1083 at village and in .25m find site to
SE of church. A 3-acre site with 30 touring pitches.*

🔌📞☉☀️🗜️🖊️📺🔲
➔⛵▶🎵🚒

WALDRINGFIELD

Moon & Sixpence (TM263454)
Newbourn Rd IP12 4PP ☎ 01473 736650 Signposted
Nearby town: Woodbridge
▶▶▶ ♣ 🚐 £4-£16 🚍 £4-£16 ▲ £4-£16
Open Apr-Oct (rs low season club/shop/reception open
limited hours) Booking advisable school & bank hols
Last arrival 21.00hrs Last departure noon ➥

A splendid, well-planned site, with a lakeside sandy beach. Tourers are in a valley around the lake. Signed from A12 at Martlesham. A 5-acre site with 90 touring pitches and 150 statics.
2 acre lake with sandy beach.
See advertisement under IPSWICH

🔌 🚽 📻 ☉ 🗑 🍳 ✳ ♿ 🏧 🅿 🛒 ✕ 🍴 🛒 🏠 🐴 🍹

→ ∪ ▶ ⛽ 🎪 ♩

Credit Cards 🏧 💳

SURREY

For the map of this county, see Sussex, East

For the map of this county, see Sussex, East

CHERTSEY

Camping & Caravanning Club Site (TQ051667)
Bridge Rd KT16 8JX ☎ 01932 562405 & 01203 694995
▶ ▶ ▶ 🚐 � Å
Open all year
A pretty riverside site with many trees and shrubs, and well-looked after grounds. Fishing and boating allowed on the River Thames. Please see the advertisement on page 27 for details of Club Members' benefits. A 12-acre site with 200 touring pitches.
Table tennis, pool, fishing.

🔌 📻 ☉ 🍳 🗖 🏧 🦮 🅿 🛒 ♿

→ ♩

Credit Cards 🏧 💳 🏦

EAST HORSLEY

Camping & Caravanning Club Site (TQ077558)
Ockham Rd North KT24 6PE
☎ 01483 283273 & 01203 694995
▶ ▶ ▶ 🚿 🚐 🚐 Å
Open end Mar-early Nov
Beautiful lakeside site with plenty of trees and shrubs, and separate camping fields. Well-organised, friendly owners. Situated between A3 and A246, on the B2039. Please see the advertisement on page 27 for details of Club Members' benefits. A 12-acre site with 135 touring pitches.
Table tennis & fishing.

🔌 📻 ☉ 🍳 🗳 🏧 🅿 🛒

LALEHAM

Laleham Park Camping Site (TQ052684)
Thameside TW18 1SH ☎ 01932 564149 Signposted
▶ ▶ 🚐 🚐 Å
Open Apr-Sep Booking advisable Jul-Aug Last arrival 21.00hrs Last departure noon no cars by caravans no cars by tents
Site set in a field among trees beside a peaceful stretch of the River Thames. From M3 onto A308 into village and Ferry Rd. A 7-acre site with 100 touring pitches and 65 statics.

2 grass volleyball courts.

🔌 📻 ☉ 🗑 🏧 ♿ 🦮

→ ▶ 🍴 🎪 ♩ 🛒

LINGFIELD

Long Acres Caravan & Camping Park (TQ368425)
Newchapel Rd RH7 6LE ☎ 01342 833205 Signposted
Nearby town: East Grinstead
▶ ▶ ▶ ★ 🚐 fr £7.50 🚐 fr £7.50 Å fr £3
Open all year Booking advisable bank hols & for electric hook ups Last arrival 22.30hrs Last departure 13.00hrs
A pleasant ex-farm site, well-screened and well-maintained, with modern heated toilet facilities. Under Gatwick flight path. From A22 turn E into Newchapel Rd, signed. A 7-acre site with 60 touring pitches.
Quad bikes, free fishing, pony rides & Go-Karts.

🔌 📻 ☉ 🗑 ✳ 🏧 🅿 🦮 🗖 🎯 🛒 🏠 🐴 🐴 🛒

→ ∪ ▶ 🎪 ♩

💷

SUSSEX, EAST

BATTLE

Normanhurst Court Caravan Club Site (TQ711148)
Stevens Crouch TN33 9LR ☎ 01424 773808 (3m W) Signposted
▶ ▶ ▶ 🚿 🏃 ★ 🚐 £3.50-£7.50 🚐 £3.50-£7.50
Open 26 Mar-1 Nov Booking advisable bank hols & Jul-Aug Last arrival 20.00hrs Last departure noon
A garden site with splendid specimen trees and shrubs. Some open areas for pitching with views to the distant Downs. Sharp turn off B2204 into site. An 18-acre site with 180 touring pitches.
Veg prep area.

🔌 📻 ☉ 🗑 🍳 ✳ 🏧 🅿 🎯 🗖 🦮 🐴 🛒 ♿

→ ∪ ▶ ♩

Credit Cards 🏧 💳 🏦 🏧 📋

Senlac Park Caravan & Camping Site (TQ722153)
Main Rd, Catsfield TN33 9DU ☎ 01424 773969 & 752590 Signposted
▶ ▶ ★ 🚐 £6.50-£9 🚐 £6.50-£9 Å £6.50-£9
Open Mar-Oct Booking advisable bank hols Last arrival 21.00hrs Last departure noon
A pretty woodland site with many secluded bays, well landscaped and attractively laid out. From Battle take A271, then turn left on to B2204 signed Bexhill. A 5-acre site with 32 touring pitches.

🔌 📻 ✳ 🏧 🦮 🛒 🐴

→ ∪ ▶ ♩ 🛒

Credit Cards 🏧 💳

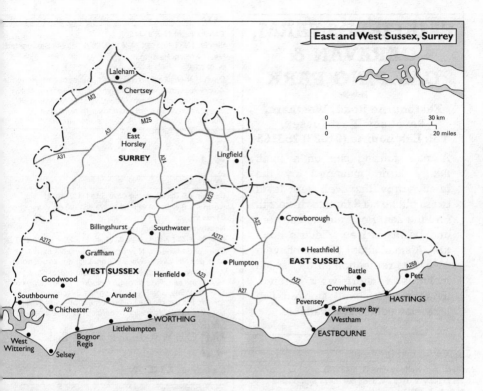

East and West Sussex, Surrey

Laleham
Chertsey
M3
M25
A3
East Horsley
A31
A24
SURREY
Lingfield
M23
Crowborough
Billingshurst
Southwater
A272
A22
A272
Heathfield
Graffham
EAST SUSSEX
WEST SUSSEX
Henfield
Plumpton
Battle
A259
A23
Goodwood
Crowhurst
Pett
Southbourne
Arundel
A27
A22
HASTINGS
Chichester
A27
Pevensey
WORTHING
Pevensey Bay
West Wittering
Bognor Regis
Littlehampton
Westham
EASTBOURNE
Selsey

0   30 km
0   20 miles

CROWBOROUGH

Camping & Caravanning Club Site (TQ520317)
Goldsmith Recreation Ground TN6 2TN
☎ 01892 664827 (in season) & 01203 694995
►►► ★ ⊕ £9.30-£10 ⊕ £9.30-£10 Å £9.30-£10
Open end Mar-end Oct Booking advisable bank hols &
peak periods Last arrival 21.00hrs Last departure noon
A spacious terraced site with stunning views of the
surrounding countryside. Situated next to an excellent
leisure centre. Please see the advertisement on page 27
for details of Club Members' benefits. A 13-acre site
with 60 touring pitches.

🕪 🌣 ⊙ 🖥 🚰 ✳ 🏔 🝙 🤟 🛒 ઉ
➔ ∪ ᛈ ⅄ 🍴 🎵
Credit Cards ▨ ▨▨ ▨▨

CROWHURST

Brakes Coppice Farm Park (TQ765134)
Forewood Ln TN33 0SJ ☎ 01424 830322 Signposted
Nearby town: Battle
►►► ★ ⊕ fr £6.50 ⊕ fr £6.50 Å fr £6.50
Open Mar-Oct Booking advisable public hols & Jul-Aug
Last arrival dusk Last departure noon
Secluded farm site in meadow surrounded by woodland
with small stream and fishing lake. Off A2100. A 3-acre
site with 30 touring pitches and 1 static.
Fishing.

🕪 🌣 ⊙ 🚰 ✳ 🏔 🝙 🤟 🖥 ⊤ ઉ 🛒 🐕 🛒
➔ ∪ ᛈ 🎵
🅳

EASTBOURNE

Bayview Caravan and Camping Park (TQ648028)
Old Martello Rd, Pevensey Bay BN24 6DX
☎ 01323 768688 Signposted
►►► ★ ⊕ fr £7.15 ⊕ fr £7.15 Å fr £6.65
Open Mar-Oct Booking advisable bank hols Last arrival
22.00hrs Last departure noon
A level and flat site two minutes' walk from the sea-
shore located E of the town centre of the A259 in an
area known as "The Crumbles". A 3.5-acre site with 49
touring pitches and 5 statics.

🕪 🌣 ⊙ 🖥 🚰 ✳ 🏔 🝙 🤟 🖥 ⊤ 🛒
➔ ᛈ 🍴 🎵
🅳

FAIRFIELDS FARM, CARAVAN & CAMPING PARK
▶▶▶

Eastbourne Road, Westham, Pevensey, East Sussex.
Tel: Eastbourne (01323) 763165

A quiet touring site on a small family farm, managed by the family, providing well kept level grass pitches, a 5 minute drive will find the sea. Hot water to showers and basins is free. Electric hook ups. A small shop. We also have a pleasant recreation area which includes a short walk through meadows to a well stocked fish lake. Day tickets are available.

HASTINGS & ST LEONARDS

Shearbarn Holiday Park (TQ842112)
TN35 5DX ☎ 01424 423583 & 716474 Signposted
▶ ▶ ▶ ▶ 🚐 🚐 Å
Open Mar-15 Jan (rs Mar-Etr, early May & mid Sep-15 Jan facilities may be closed or reduced) Booking advisable bank hols & Jun-Aug Last arrival 22.00hrs Last departure 10.00hrs
A large touring site with sea views. All entertainments are available at the static site nearby. A 16-acre site with 450 touring pitches and 250 statics.
Entertainment & amusements on site.
🔥 🏠 ⊙ 🅾 ◕ ☀ 🍴 🏔 🛡 🌊 ➕ T ✗ 📞 🚲 🏕
→ ∪ 🅿 🍴 🎵
💷
Credit Cards 🔲 🔲 🔲 🔲 🔲

HEATHFIELD

Greenview Caravan Park (TQ605223)
Broad Oak TN21 8RT ☎ 01435 863531 Signposted
▶ ▶ 🚐 🚐 Å
Open Apr-Oct Booking advisable Jul-Aug Last arrival 22.00hrs Last departure 10.30hrs ✍
Small, attractive site adjoining main A265 Broad Oak 1m E of Heathfield. A 3-acre site with 10 touring pitches and 51 statics.
🔥 🏠 ⊙ ☀ 🍴 🛡 🌊 T 📞

PETT

Carters Farm (TQ887145)
Elm Ln TN35 4JD ☎ 01424 813206 & 812244 Signposted
Nearby town: Hastings
▶ 🚐 🚐 Å
Open Mar-Oct Last arrival 21.00hrs Last departure noon
A very secluded, long-established working farm site in partly sloping meadow. The sea is only 15 mins walk away. From A259 from Hastings turn right after Guestling, signed Pett. A 12-acre site with 100 touring pitches and 85 statics.
🏠 ⊙ ◕ ☀ 🛡 🌊 ➕ T 📞 🏕
→ 🎵

PEVENSEY

Camping & Caravanning Club Site (TQ678054)
Normans Bay BN24 6PP ☎ 01323 761190 (in season) & 01203 694995
Nearby town: Eastbourne
▶ ▶ ▶ ★ 🚐 £9.40-£10.20 🚐 £9.40-£10.20 Å £9.40-£10.20
Open end Mar-early Nov Booking advisable bank hols & peak periods Last arrival 21.00hrs Last departure noon
A well-kept site with immaculate toilet block, right beside the sea. Pass through Elbourne, follow signs to Pevensey Bay, and take road signed Beachlands Only for 1m. Please see the advertisement on page 27 for details of Club Members' benefits. A 12-acre site with 200 touring pitches.
🔥 🏠 ⊙ 🅾 ◕ ◕ ☀ 🏔 🛡 🌊 📞 🐕 🚲 🏕 ♿
→ 🎵
Credit Cards 🔲 🔲 🔲

PEVENSEY BAY

Castle View Caravan Site (TQ648032)
Eastbourne Rd BN24 6DT ☎ 01323 763038 Signposted
Nearby town: Eastbourne
▶ ▶ ▶ ★ 🚐 £4.80-£10.80 🚐 £4-£10 Å £4.80-£10.80
Open Mar-Nov Booking advisable bank hols & Jul-Aug Last arrival 20.00hrs Last departure noon
A spacious touring site about .5 mile from the sea, overlooking meadows. Situated off A259 Eastbourne-Hastings road. A 10-acre site with 150 touring pitches and 40 statics.
Dishwashing facilities.
🔥 🍴 🏠 ⊙ 🅾 ◕ ▢ ☀ 🛡 🌊 ➕ 📞 🚲 🏕
→ 🍴 🎵
Credit Cards 🔲 🔲

PLUMPTON

Gallops Farm (TQ361155)
Streat Ln, Streat BN6 8SB ☎ 01273 890387 (1.75m NW)
Nearby town: Burgess Hill
▷ ★ 🚐 fr £1.50 🚐 fr £1.50 Å fr £1.50
Open all year Booking advisable bank hols Last arrival 23.00hrs Last departure 21.00hrs
A slightly sloping, partly shaded farm site, 2.5m E of Burgess Hill. Take B2113 at roundabout until signs for

Streat and Plumpton Green. A 3-acre site with 8 touring pitches.

🛒 🎍 🐕 🚻
→ ∪ � 🍴 ♪

WESTHAM

Fairfields Farm Caravan & Camping Site (TQ639039)

Eastbourne Rd BN24 5NG ☎ 01323 763165 Signposted

▶ ▶ ▶ 🚐 🚐 Å

Open Apr-Oct Booking advisable public & school hols
A well-maintained site away from beach with wildlife area and fishing lake. On the B2191, signposted from the east side of Eastbourne and off A27. Lorry park close by. A 3-acre site with 60 touring pitches.
Fishing, riding & clay pigeon shooting.

▇ 🐕 ⊙ ✳ 🎍 ∅ 🔲 🐕 🔥
→ ∪ � ◎ 🌿 🍴 ♪ 🔲

SUSSEX, WEST

For the map of this county, see Sussex, East

ARUNDEL

Maynards Caravan & Camping Park (TQ028061)

Crossbush BN18 9PQ ☎ 01903 882075 (0.5m E on A27) Signposted

▶ ▶ 🚐 £7.50 🚐 £7.50 Å £7.50

Open all year Booking advisable anytime Last arrival 21.30hrs
A busy site close to the main road and near to Arundel. From the A27 towards Brighton turn left into the car park of Howards Hotel, .75 mile from Arundel. A 2-acre site with 60 touring pitches.

🔲 🐕 ⊙ ❄ ✳ 🏔 🎍 ∅ 🔲 🐕 🛴
→ ∪ � 🌿 🍴 ♪ 🔲 🐕
🔁

Camping & Caravanning Club Site (SU957085)

Blindon Park BN18 0RG ☎ 01243 814387 (in season) & 01203 694995
Nearby town: Chichester

> ★ 🚐 £6.60-£7 Å £6.60-£7

Open end Mar-end Sep Booking advisable bank hols & peak periods Last arrival 21.00hrs Last departure noon
Beautiful former orchard, completely screened by NT trees and very quiet. Turn off A27 at Aldingbourne Nurseries, take second right into Britains Lane, and entrance is third on right. Please see the advertisement on page 27 for details of Club Members' benefits. A 2-acre site with 46 touring pitches.

🔲 ❄ 🎍 🐕 🛴
Credit Cards 🔲 🔲 🔲

BILLINGSHURST

Limeburner's Camping (TQ073255)

Newbridge RH14 9JA ☎ 01403 782311 Signposted

▶ ▶ 🚐 🚐 Å

Open Apr-Oct Booking advisable bank hols & Jul-Aug Last arrival 22.00hrs Last departure 14.00hrs
Secluded rural site alongside the attractive 'Limeburner's Arms' public house. Located a short distance from the village of Billingshurst on the A272 Midhurst road and the River Arun. A 3-acre site with 42 touring pitches.

🔲 🐕 ⊙ ❄ 🎍 🐕 ∅ 🔲 ✖ 🐕
→ ∪ ♪ 🛴

BOGNOR REGIS

Bognor Regis Caravan Club Site (SU939014)

PO22 9RP ☎ 01243 828515 (1.25m N)

▶ ▶ ▶ 🚴 🚐 🚐 Å

Open 26 Mar-1 Nov Booking advisable bank hols & Jul-Aug Last arrival 20.00hrs Last departure noon
Attractive site with a screen of trees and views of the Downs, about 1 m from beach. Turn R at first rndbt on dual carr on A29 opp Halfords. An 8-acre site with 120 touring pitches.
Veg prep area.

🔲 🐕 ⊙ 🔲 🚐 ❄ 🎍 🏔 ∅ 🔲 🐕 🔥
→ ♪ 🍴 ♪ 🛴

Credit Cards 🔲 🔲

CHICHESTER

Southern Leisure Lakeside Village (SU875032)

Vinnetrow Rd PO20 6LB ☎ 01243 787715 Signposted

▶ ▶ ▶ 🚐 🚐 Å

Open 25 May-mid Oct (rs Etr-24 May swimming pool not open) Booking advisable bank hols & Jul-Aug Last arrival 09.00hrs Last departure 16.00hrs
A large touring site in secluded rural setting surrounded by several lakes. Level, grassy and well laid out with modern toilets and good leisure facilities. Signed from A27. A 50-acre site with 400 touring pitches.
See advertisement on page 180.

🔲 🐕 ⊙ 🔲 🚴 ❄ 🎍 🏔 🎍 ∅ 🔲 🔲 ✖ 🐕 🛴
→ ∪ ♪ 🌿 🍴 ♪

GOODWOOD

Caravan Club Site (SU885111)

Goodwood Racecourse PO18 0PX ☎ 01243 774486 Signposted
Nearby town: Chichester

▶ ▶ ★ 🚐 £10.50-£11.50 🚐 £10.50-£11.50 Å £10-£11

Open Apr-Sep (rs during race meetings site is closed) Booking advisable public hols & Jul-Aug Last arrival 20.00hrs Last departure noon
A neat and tidy level grassy site on Goodwood Racecourse. Closed when race meetings are held. 5m N of Chichester. A 3-acre site with 70 touring pitches.

🔲 🐕 ⊙ 🏔 🎍 ∅ 🔲 🔲 🐕 🛴
→ ∪ ♪

Credit Cards 🔲 🔲 🔲

GRAFFHAM

Camping & Caravanning Club Site (SU941185)
Great Bury GU28 0QJ ☎ 01798 867476 (in season) &
01203 694995 (5m S Petworth on unclass rd off A285)
Nearby town: Petworth
▶▶▶♠★ 🚐 £9.30-£10 🚐 £9.30-£10 🅰 £9.30-£10
Open end Mar-early Nov Booking advisable bank hols &
peak periods Last arrival 21.00hrs Last departure noon
*A superb wooded site, with each pitch occupying its
own private, well-screened area. From A285 towards
Petworth turn first left after Duncton. Please see the
advertisement on page 27 for details of Club Members'
benefits. A 20-acre site with 90 touring pitches.*

🖭📻⊙🖥🏴❄🔌🖃🛒♿
➔ ∪ ▶

Credit Cards

HENFIELD

Harwoods Farm (TQ196153)
West End Ln BN5 9RF ☎ 01273 492820 Signposted
▷ 🚐 fr £4.50 🅰 fr £4.50
Open Etr-Oct Booking advisable bank hols Last arrival
mdnt Last departure eves
*A really unspoilt site down a rough, narrow lane in good
walking area. A 1.75-acre site with 35 touring pitches.*
➔ 🎵

LITTLEHAMPTON

White Rose Touring Park (TQ026041)
Mill Ln, Wick BN17 7PH ☎ 01903 716176
Signposted
▶▶▶★ 🚐 £9.70-£13.60 🚐 £6.75-£13.60
🅰 £6.75-£13.60
Open 15 Mar-15 Jan Booking advisable bank hols & Jul-
Aug Last departure noon
*A well-maintained family run site providing level, well-
drained ground surrounded by farmland. Located close
to Arundel and Littlehampton which provide good local
facilities. From A284 turn left into Mill Lane. A 7-acre site
with 127 touring pitches and 14 statics.*

🖭📻⊙🖥🏴❄🏔🖊✏🖃🆃🔌📻♿
➔ ∪ ▶ ⊙ 🔺 ⤴ 🎣 🎵
💷

Credit Cards

SELSEY

Warner Farm Touring Park (SZ845939)
Warner Ln, Selsey PO20 9EL ☎ 01243 604121
Signposted
Nearby town: Chichester
▶▶▶▶▶ ⊕ Holiday Centre 🚐 £6-£21 🚐 £6-£21
🅰 £6-£21
Open Mar-Oct Booking advisable 3 wks prior to arrival
Last arrival 22.00hrs Last departure 10.00hrs
*A new touring site adjoining three static sites under
same ownership. A courtesy bus runs around the
complex to entertainment and supermarkets. A 10-acre*

SOUTHERN LEISURE CENTRE ▶▶▶
TOURING CARAVAN PARK
Vinnetrow Road, Chichester, Sussex PO20 6LB
Tel: Chichester (01243) 787715 – 24 hour answering service

Ideally situated for visiting the many places of interest. Flat, grassy pitches. Electrical hook ups. Excellent free showers and toilet facilities. Ample mirrors and shaver points. Laundry room. Well stocked supermarket and off licence. Luxury lounge bar and separate family bar. Children's bar. Nightly free entertainment during high season. Heated swimming pool.

Windsurfing, water skiing and coarse fishing. Caravan sales area with wide selection of used vans. Dogs welcome on a lead. Family units only. Take away snack bar.

Free brochure on request.

site with 200 touring pitches and 150 statics.

🔌 🏠 ⊙ 🚽 ⛱ ⚡ 🔍 📷 ❄ ♀ 🏔 🅿 🖊 🖭 🇹

✕ 🔔 🏪 🏛 🎋 🐕 🐾 ♿

→ ∪ ↾ ⤳ 🎵

£

Credit Cards 🆎 💳 💳 💳

SOUTHBOURNE

Chichester Camping (SU774056)
343 Main Rd PO10 8JH ☎ 01243 373202
(6m W of Chichester, 3m E of Havant)
Nearby town: Chichester
▶ ▶ ▶ 🏕 ★ 🚐 £8-£10 🚗 £8-£10 🛖 £8-£10

Open Feb-Nov Booking advisable bank hols, wknds & mid
Jun-mid Sep Last arrival 22.00hrs Last departure 14.00hrs
*Situated in open meadow and orchard, a very pleasant
site with well looked after, clean facilities. Leave A27 at
roundabout signed Bosham and Funtington, site 5m
along A259. A 2-acre site with 60 touring pitches.*

🔌 🏠 ⊙ 🚽 🏳 ❄ ♿

→ ∪ ↾ 🎵 🐾

Credit Cards 🆎 💳 💳

SOUTHWATER

Raylands Park (TQ170265)
Jackrells Ln RH13 7DH ☎ 01403 730218 & 733598
Signposted
Nearby town: Horsham
▶ ▶ ▶ 🏕 ★ 🚐 £7.50-£8.50 🚗 £7.50-£8.50 🛖 £5-£7.50

Open Mar-Oct Booking advisable bank hols & high
season Last arrival 20.00hrs Last departure 14.00hrs
*A very well run site in an excellent setting. Reasonably
level ground, superb modern toilet blocks, a clubhouse
and children's play area. Well maintained access roads.
Signposted from the A24 in Southwater. A 6-acre site
with 40 touring pitches and 60 statics.*

🔌 🏠 ⊙ 🚽 🏳 ⚡ 🔍 ❄ ♀ 🏔 🅿 🖊 🇹 ✕ 🔔 🐕 ♿

→ ∪ ↾ ⛺ 🎳 🎵 🐾

£

WEST WITTERING

Wicks Farm Caravan Park (SZ796995)
Redlands Ln PO20 8QD ☎ 01243 513116 Signposted
Nearby town: Chichester
▶ ▶ ▶ ★ 🚐 £7-£9 🛖 £7-£9

Open 14 Mar-Oct Booking advisable peak periods Last
arrival 21.00hrs Last departure noon
*A pleasant rural site, well-screened by trees with good
walks nearby and 2m from coast. Signed from B2179. A
4-acre site with 40 touring pitches and 67 statics.
Bicycle hire.*

🔌 🏠 ⊙ 🚽 🏳 🔍 ❄ 🏔 🅿 🖊 🇹 🔔 🐕 🐾 ♿

→ ∪ ↾ ⤳ 🎵

£

WORTHING

Northbrook Farm Caravan Club Site (TQ106046)
Titnore Way BN12 6NY ☎ 01903 502962 (2.5m NW)
▶ ▶ ▶ ★ 🚐 £12-£13.50 🚗 £12-£13.50 ➡

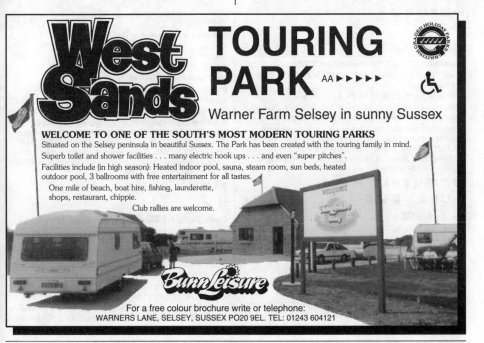

Open Mar-Nov Booking advisable bank hols & Jul-Aug Last arrival 20.00hrs Last departure noon
An attractively grassy site in open countryside, only 2m from the coast. Signed from A27 onto Titnore Lane. A 12.5-acre site with 120 touring pitches.
Veg prep area.

♨ ♠ ⊙ ❧ ⚒ ✳ ⚠ 🜚 ⌀ 🖅 🆃 ✆ ☈
→ ∪ ▶ 🛆 ⚓ 🥤 🖀 🖳

Credit Cards ▩ ▥

TYNE & WEAR

For the map of this county, see Northumberland

ROWLANDS GILL

Derwent Park Caravan Site (NZ168586)
NE39 1LG ☎ 01207 543383 Signposted
▶ ▶ ▶ ★ 🚲 £7.75-£8.50 🚲 £6.25-£7.25 ▲ £5-£7
Open Apr-Sep Booking advisable public hols & Jul-Aug Last arrival 22.30hrs Last departure noon
A very pleasant and well-maintained municipal site. Situated on edge of Rowlands Gill at junc of A694 and B6314. A 3-acre site with 47 touring pitches and 25 statics.
Fishing, crazy golf, giant draughts & chess, bowling.

♨ ♠ ⊙ 🖅 ❧ ⚒ ✳ ⚠ 🜚 ⌀ 🖅 ✆ 🛒 ⛪ 🏛 🖅
🖂 🖳 ♿
→ ∪ ▶ ◎ 🥤 🖀
£

SOUTH SHIELDS

Sandhaven Caravan & Camping Park (NZ376672)
Bents Park Rd NE33 2NL ☎ 0191 454 5594 & 0191 455 7411 Signposted
▶ ▶ ★ 🚲 £7.90-£9 🚲 £7.90-£9 ▲ £7.90-£9
Open Mar-Oct Booking advisable for complete wks Jul-5 Sep Last arrival anytime Last departure 11.00hrs
A spacious site adjoining the sea front, set in a well-screened and fenced area next to a public park. Situated on A183 .5 miles from the town centre with an entrance on Bents Park Road. A 3.5-acre site with 52 touring pitches and 46 statics.

♨ ♠ ⊙ ❧ 🜚 ⌀ ✆ 🏛 🖅 ♿
→ ∪ ▶ 🛆 ⚓ 🥤 🖀 🖳

Credit Cards ▥

Lizard Lane Caravan & Camping Site (NZ399648)
Lizard Ln NE34 7AB ☎ 0191 454 4982 & 0191 455 7411 Signposted
▶ ★ 🚲 £6.10-£6.90 🚲 £6.10-£6.90 ▲ £6.10-£6.90
Open Mar-Oct Booking advisable for complete wks Jul-5 Sep Last arrival anytime Last departure 11.00hrs
Sloping, grass site near beach, 2m S of town centre on

A183 Sunderland road. Well-kept and maintained. A 2-acre site with 45 touring pitches and 70 statics.

♠ ⊙ ❧ 🜚 ⌀ ✆ 🖅
→ ∪ ▶ 🛆 ⚓ 🥤 🖀 🖳 🖳

Credit Cards ▥

WARWICKSHIRE

For the map of this county, see Hereford & Worcester

ASTON CANTLOW

Island Meadow Caravan Park (SP137596)
The Mill House B95 6JP
☎ 01789 488273 Signposted
Nearby town: Stratford-upon-Avon
▶ ▶ ▶ ♣ 🏃 ★ 🚲 fr £7.75 🚲 fr £7.75 ▲ fr £3
Open Mar-Oct Booking advisable peak periods Last arrival 21.00hrs
A small well-kept site bordered by the River Alne and its mill stream. Mature willows line the banks. .25m W of Aston Cantlow on the road to Alcester. A 3-acre site with 24 touring pitches and 56 statics.
Free fishing for guests.

♨ ♠ ⊙ ✳ 🜚 ⌀ 🖅 🆃 ✆ 🖅 🖂 🖳 ♿
→ ∪ ▶ 🖀

QQQQQQQQQ

KINGSBURY

Camping & Caravanning Club Site (SP202968)
Kingsbury Water Park B76 0DY ☎ 01827 874101 (in season) & 01203 694995 (off unclass rd joining A4097 & A4091)
Nearby town: Sutton Coldfield
▶ ▶ ★ 🚲 £8.20-£8.80 🚲 £8.20-£8.80 ▲ £8.20-£8.80
Open end Mar-early Nov Booking advisable bank hols & Jul-Aug Last arrival 21.00hrs Last departure noon
A former gravel pit, now reclaimed and landscaped, the site is part of a level complex of lakes, canals, woods and marshland with good access roads. 2m SW on A5 take A4097 for 1m. Please see the advertisement on page 27 for details of Club Members' benefits. A 10-acre site with 60 touring pitches.

♨ ♠ ⊙ ❧ 🜚 ⌀ 🆃 ✆ 🖂 🖳 ♿
→ 🖀

Credit Cards ▩ ▥ ▦

Tame View Caravan Site (SP209979)
Cliff B78 2DR ☎ 01827 873853 (1m N A51) Signposted
Nearby town: Tamworth
▷ ★ 🚲 £3.50-£4 🚲 £3.50-£4 ▲ £3.50-£4
Open all year Booking advisable 1 month in advance Last arrival 23.00hrs Last departure 23.00hrs
Enclosed level small meadow on high bank overlooking River Tame. 400 yards off A51 Tamworth to Kingsbury road, 1m N of Kingsbury opposite restaurant. No

*through road sign. A 5-acre site with 55 touring pitches.
Fishing.*

🔳 🛠
→ ∪ ⸸ ◎ △ ⵜ ♨ ✈
£

WOLVEY

Wolvey Villa Farm Caravan & Camping Site (SP428869)
LE10 3HF ☎ 01455 220493 & 220630 Signposted
▶ ▶ ▶ ★ 🚐 £4.70-£4.90 🚐 £4.70-£4.90 🛆 £4.60-£4.80
Open all year Booking advisable Spring bank hol-mid
Aug Last arrival 23.15hrs Last departure noon
*Level, grass site with mature trees and bushes set in
meadowland. About 1m S of Wolvey. Ideally located to
explore the Midlands area. From M6 junc 2, take B4056
(signed Ansty) to Wolvey for 3m. A 7-acre site with 110
touring pitches.*
Fishing, putting green, off licence.

🔌 🐾 ⊙ 🔋 🖵 ☀ 🗑 🖉 🔁 🗂 📞 🐕 🛠
→ ∪ ⸸ ✈

WIGHT, ISLE OF

For the map, see
Hampshire

BEMBRIDGE
See **Whitecliff Bay**

NEWBRIDGE

**Orchards Holiday Caravan Park
(SZ411881)**
PO41 0TS ☎ 01983 531331
Signposted
Nearby town: Yarmouth
▶ ▶ ▶ ▶ ⚘ ♦♦ ★ 🚐 £6.20-£9.25 🚐 £6.20-£9.25 🛆 £6.20-
£9.25
Open 29 Mar-28 Oct (rs Etr-Apr & late Sep-Oct heated
pool mid May-mid Sep res shop hrs) Booking advisable
Etr, Spring bank hol & late Jun-Aug Last arrival 23.00hrs
Last departure 11.00hrs
*An excellent, well-managed site set in downs and
meadowland adjacent to B3401 and near the sea.
Signed left at Horse and Groom pub on A3054. An 8-
acre site with 175 touring pitches and 60 statics.*
Coarse fishing, petanque.
See advertisement on page 187.

🔌 🐾 🐾 ⊙ 🔋 🖵 ⤳ 🔴 🖵 ☀ 🗑 🗑 🖉 🔁 🗂
🖤 🐕 🛠 ⛄
→ ∪ ✈
£
Credit Cards 💳

NEWCHURCH

**Southland Camping Park
(SZ554852)**
PO36 0LZ ☎ 01983 865385
Signposted
Nearby town: Sandown
▶ ▶ ▶ ⚘ ♦♦ ★ 🚐 £8-£11 🚐 £8-£11 🛆 £8-£11
Open Etr-Sep Booking advisable Jul-Aug Last arrival
21.30hrs Last departure 11.00hrs
*Beautifully maintained site, peacefully located on the
outskirts of the village in the Arreton Valley off A3056. A
7-acre site with 100 touring pitches.*
12 volt transformers available.
See advertisement under SANDOWN

🔌 🐾 🐾 ⊙ 🔋 🔴 ☀ 🗑 🗑 🖉 🔁 🗂 📞 ⤳ 🗑 🐕
🖤 ⛄
→ ∪ ⸸ ⵜ ♨ ✈
Credit Cards 💳 ▭

PONDWELL

Pondwell Camp Site (SZ622911)
PO34 5AQ ☎ 01983 612330 Signposted
▶ ▶ ▶ ★ 🚐 fr £8 🚐 fr £8 🛆 fr £8
Open May-26 Sep Booking advisable Aug Last arrival
23.00hrs Last departure 11.00hrs ⚠
*A secluded site in quiet rural surroundings close to the
sea, slightly sloping with some level areas, and modern* ➡

toilet facilities. Signed from Ryde on B3330. A 9-acre site with 250 touring pitches.

🔌 🛒 📻 ☉ 🗑 🚩 🔍 ☐ ❄ ⛰ 🛢 🖉 🔋 📞 🛒
➜ �️ 🍴 🎣

Credit Cards 🖃 🚾

ST HELENS

Nodes Point Holiday Park (SZ636897)
Nodes Rd PO33 1YA ☎ 01983 872401 Signposted
▶ ▶ ▶ ▶ ▶ ⊕ Holiday Centre ★ ⚏ £8-£14.50
⚏ £8-£14.50 ⚐ £8-£14.50
Open May-Oct Booking advisable Jul-Aug Last departure 10.00hrs ⊘
Part of large holiday complex. Site on slight gradient with grass surface and near beach. The campsite entrance is off Duver Road. A 16-acre site with 240 touring pitches.
Free evening entertainment, amusements.

🔌 📻 ☉ 🗑 🔍 🍸 ⛰ ✖ 📞 🏬 🛒
➜ ⏍

SANDOWN

Adgestone Camping Park (SZ590855)
Lower Adgestone Rd PO36 OHL ☎ 01983 403432 & 403989 (2m NW) Signposted
▶ ▶ ▶ ▶ ♣ ★ ⚏ £6-£9.80 ⚏ £6-£9.80 ⚐ £6-£9.80
Open Etr-Sep (rs Off peak limited opening of takeaway) Booking advisable high season Last arrival dusk Last departure 11.00hrs
A well-managed site in a quiet location not far from the town. The slightly sloping pitches are surrounded by

flower beds and trees. 2m NW of Sandown. An 8-acre site with 200 touring pitches.
Free river fishing, football pitch, barbecue hire.

🔌 📻 ☉ 🗑 🚩 ⚡ 🔍 ❄ ⛰ 🛢 🖉 🔋 T 📞 🛒 🏬 🏛
🍴 🐴 🛒 ♿
➜ ⏍ ⏏️ ☉ ⚠️ 🍴 ⛱ 🎣

Credit Cards 🖃 🚾 🔵

Cheverton Farm Camping Park (SZ570834)
Newport Rd, Apse Heath PO36 9PJ ☎ 01983 866414 Signposted
▶ ▶ ▶ ★ ⚏ £4-£5.50 ⚏ £4-£5.50 ⚐ £4-£5.50
Open Mar-Oct Booking advisable school hols Last arrival 21.00hrs Last departure noon
A terraced site with good quality facilities, still in the process of becoming established. Off A3056 Newport Rd. A 5-acre site with 60 touring pitches.

🔌 📻 ☉ 🗑 🔍 ☐ ❄ 🛢 🖉 🔋 T 📞 🐕 🐴 🛒 ♿
➜ ⏍ ⏏️ ☉ ⚠️ 🍴 ⛱ 🎣

Credit Cards 🖃 🚾 🔵

SHANKLIN

Landguard Camping Park (SZ577825)
Landguard Manor Rd PO37 7PH ☎ 01983 867028 Signposted
▶ ▶ ▶ ▶ ★ ⚏ £5.90-£9 ⚏ £5.90-£9 ⚐ £5.90-£9
Open May-Sep Booking advisable school hols Last arrival 22.00hrs Last departure noon ⊘
Part of a holiday complex, the touring area is secluded

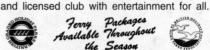

and surrounded by trees, in a rural setting. A 6-acre site
with 150 touring pitches.
Horse riding.

Credit Cards ▨ ▨ ▨

Camping & Caravanning Club Site (SZ579824)
Willow Brook, Ninham PO37 7PL ☎ 01983 866040
(in season) & 01203 694995 Signposted
► ► ★ ⊞ £7-£9.20 ⊞ £7-£9.20 ▲ £7-£9.20
Open end Mar-early Oct Booking advisable bank hols &
Jul-Aug Last arrival 21.00hrs Last departure noon
*A quiet site well away from roads, maintained to a high
standard. Use of adjoining swimming pool. Take A3056
to Shanklin, then first right after superstore roundabout
and follow signs. Please see the advertisement on page
27 for details of Club Members' benefits. A 6-acre site
with 75 touring pitches.*

Credit Cards ▨ ▨ ▨

THORNESS BAY

Thorness Bay Holiday Park (SZ448928)
PO31 8NJ ☎ 01983 523109 Signposted
Nearby town: Newport
► ► ► ► ★ ⊞ £8-£14.50 ⊞ £8-£14.50 ▲ £8-£14.50 ➡

Open 13 Apr-7 Oct Booking advisable mid Jun-Aug Last arrival mdnt Last departure noon

Situated in the centre of a holiday complex on level grass. 5m W of Cowes on rising ground with views of Thorness Bay and the Solent. A 5-acre site with 150 touring pitches and 275 statics.

Riding stables, table tennis, putting, pool tables.

🔣 icons

Credit Cards 🔳 🔳

WHITECLIFF BAY

Whitecliff Bay Holiday Park (SZ637862)
Hillway PO35 5PL ☎ 01983 872671 Signposted
► ► ► ► icons

Open May-Oct (rs Mar-Apr limited entertainments) Booking advisable Jul-Aug

A large seaside complex on two sites, with tourers and tents on one and tourers and statics on the other. Toilets of a very high standard. Many entertainments and easy access to beach. A 19-acre site with 450 touring pitches and 227 statics.

Leisure centre with fun pool, spa bath & sauna.

See advertisement under BEMBRIDGE

🔣 icons

Credit Cards 🔳 🔳

WROXALL

Appuldurcombe Gardens Caravan & Camping Park (SZ546804)
Appuldurcombe Rd PO38 3EP ☎ 01983 852597 Signposted
► ► ► ► icons

Open Spring bank hol-Aug bank hol (rs Mar-Spring bank hol & Aug bank hol-Oct pool & bar closed, shop restricted hrs) Booking advisable Jul-Aug Last arrival 23.00hrs Last departure noon

An attractive secluded site with a small stream running through it. Situated a few miles from Ventnor. A 12-acre site with 110 touring pitches and 42 statics.

Crazy golf & putting.

🔣 icons

See advertisement on page 185.

YARMOUTH

See **Newbridge**

WILTSHIRE

CALNE

Blackland Lakes Holiday & Leisure Centre (ST013687)
Knights Marsh Farm, Stockley Ln SN11 0NQ
☎ 01249 813672 Signposted
► ► ► ► ★ 🚐 £7-£7.60 🚐 £6.50-£6.75 ▲ £6-£6.50

Open all year (rs Nov-mid Mar bookings only) Booking advisable bank & school hols & Jul-Aug Last arrival 23.00hrs Last departure noon

A level, well-kept site in a rural area surrounded by Colstowe, and N and W Downs. Good outdoor facilities on site. A 17-acre site with 180 touring pitches.

Nature trail, wildfowl sanctuary, fishing facilities

🔣 icons

🖾

DEVIZES

Bell Caravan Park (SU054580)
Andover Rd, Lydeway SN10 3PS ☎ 01380 840230
► ► ► ★ 🚐 £6.50-£8.50 🚐 £6.50-£8.50 ▲ £6.50-£8.50

Open Etr or Apr-Sep Booking advisable bank hols & Jul-Aug

An attractive base for touring the area, with all level pitches. 3m S of Devizes on A342. A 3-acre site with 30 touring pitches.

🔣 icons

🖾

Credit Cards 🔳 🔳

Lakeside (SU992626)
Rowde SN10 2LX ☎ 01380 722767 Signposted
► ► ► ★ 🚐 fr £6.50 🚐 fr £6.50 ▲ fr £6.50

Open Apr-Oct Booking advisable bank hols & Jun-Aug Last arrival 22.00hrs Last departure noon

Pleasant level site on lakeside with attractive trees and shrubs within urban area. From Devizes take Calne rd, and site on right in 1m. A 4-acre site with 55 touring pitches.

Fishing.

🔣 icons

LACOCK

Piccadilly Caravan Site (ST913683)
Folly Ln SN15 2LP ☎ 01249 730260 Signposted
Nearby town: Chippenham
► ► ► 🚐 £7-£8 🚐 £7-£8 ▲ £7

Open Apr-Oct Booking advisable school & bank hols Last departure noon

A good family site, well-established and overlooking

➡

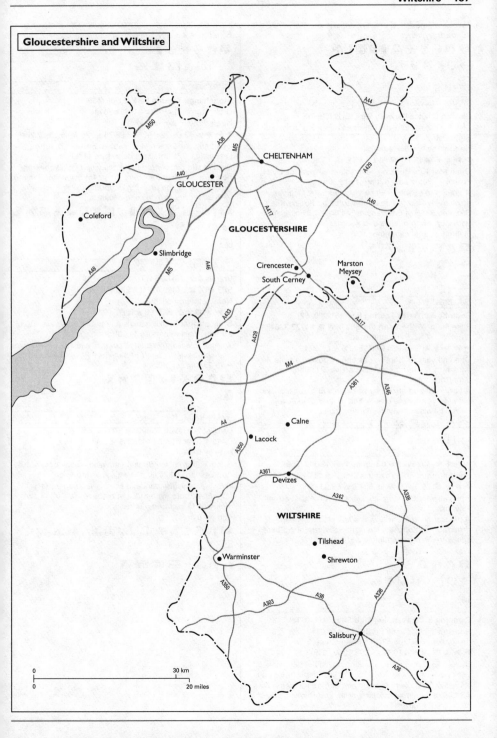

Gloucestershire and Wiltshire

CHELTENHAM

GLOUCESTER

Coleford

Slimbridge

GLOUCESTERSHIRE

Cirencester
South Cerney

Marston
Meysey

Calne

Lacock

Devizes

WILTSHIRE

Tilshead

Warminster

Shrewton

Salisbury

M50

A38

M5

A40

A44

A429

A40

A417

A48

M5

A46

A433

A429

A417

M4

A361

A345

A4

A350

A361

A342

A338

A350

A303

A36

A338

A36

0   30 km

0   20 miles

Lacock village. 4m S of Chippenham. A 2.5-acre site with 40 touring pitches.

MARSTON MEYSEY

Second Chance Caravan Park (SU140960)
SN6 6LG ☎ 01285 810675 (off A419,3m E of Cricklade) Signposted
Nearby town: Cricklade
► ► ♠ ★ ⊞ £5-£6 ⊞ £5-£6 ⅄ £5-£6
Open Mar-Nov Booking advisable peak periods Last arrival 21.30hrs Last departure 13.30hrs
A quiet and beautiful site with good toilet facilities, attractively situated near the source of the Thames. Situated 3m E of Cricklade off A419. A 1.75-acre site with 22 touring pitches and 4 statics.
Fishing on site, canoeing.

SALISBURY

Coombe Nurseries Touring Park (SU099282)
Race Plain, Netherhampton SP2 8PN ☎ 01722 328451 (2m SW off A3094) Signposted
► ► ► ★ ⊞ £7.50-£9 ⊞ £7.50-£9 ⅄ £7.50-£9
Open all year (rs Sep-Etr gas only) Booking advisable bank hols (by letter only) Last arrival 21.00hrs Last departure noon
A very neat and attractive site adjacent to racecourse with views over the downs and outstanding flower beds. A 3-acre site with 50 touring pitches.

Alderbury Caravan & Camping Park (SU197259)
Southampton Rd, Whaddon SP5 3HB ☎ 01722 710125
► ► ★ ⊞ £6.50-£8 ⊞ £6.50-£8 ⅄ £6.50-£8
Open all year Booking advisable anytime Last arrival 23.00hrs
A pleasant and friendly new site, set in the village of Whaddon just off A36, 3m from Salisbury. A 1.5-acre site with 39 touring pitches and 1 static.
Washing-up room.

Camping & Caravanning Club Site (SU140318)
Hudsons Field, Castle Rd SP1 3RR ☎ 01722 320713 (in season) & 01203 694995 Signposted
► ► ★ ⊞ £9.30-£10 ⊞ £9.30-£10 ⅄ £9.30-£10
Open end Mar-end Sep Booking advisable bank hols & peak periods Last arrival 21.00hrs Last departure noon
A well-kept site with friendly and helpful wardens. Take A345 Salisbury to Amesbury road, and Hudson's Field is close to Old Sarum Fort, 1m on L. Please see the

advertisement on page 27 for details of Club Members' benefits. A 4.5-acre site with 100 touring pitches.

Credit Cards 🖭 🖭 🖭

SHREWTON

Stonehenge Touring Park (SU061456)
Orcheston SP3 4SH ☎ 01980 620304
Nearby town: Amesbury
► ► ► ★ ⊞ £6.25-£7.25 ⊞ £6.25-£7.25 ⅄ £6.25-£7.25
Open all year Booking advisable bank hols & Jul-Aug Last arrival 22.00hrs Last departure 11.00hrs
A quiet site adjacent to the small village of Orcheston near the centre of Salisbury Plain. 4m from Stonehenge. Site maturing and growing in popularity. A 2-acre site with 30 touring pitches and 6 statics.

TILSHEAD

Brades Acre (SU035477)
SP3 4RX ☎ 01980 620402 Signposted
Nearby town: Salisbury
► ► ★ ⊞ fr £8 ⊞ fr £8 ⅄ fr £8
Open all year Booking advisable public hols Last arrival 21.00hrs Last departure 11.00hrs
A small, pleasantly situated country site set among trees and shrubs in the heart of Salisbury Plain. A 2-acre site with 25 touring pitches.

WARMINSTER

Longleat Caravan Club Site (ST806434)
BA12 7NL ☎ 01985 844663 (5m SW)
► ► ► ⊞ ⊞
Open 31 Mar-1 Nov Booking advisable bank hols & Jul-Aug Last arrival 20.00hrs Last departure noon
A lovely, peaceful parkland site in the middle of the Longleat estate, with miles of paths to walk. A 14-acre site with 150 touring pitches.
Veg prep area.

Credit Cards 🖭 🖭 🖭 🖭

YORKSHIRE, NORTH

See also Yorkshire, South, Yorkshire, West

ACASTER MALBIS

Chestnut Farm Caravan Park (SE589456)
YO2 1UQ ☎ 01904 704676 Signposted
Nearby town: York
▶▶▶ 🚐 Å
Open Apr-Oct Booking advisable public hols & Jul-Aug
Last arrival 23.00hrs Last departure noon
Level, grassy site with assorted trees and shrubs, adjacent to river. Leave A64 at Copmanthorpe, turning S signed Acaster Malbis. Site on unclass rd in 2m. A 2-acre site with 25 touring pitches and 56 statics.

🔌🚻🅿️⊙🗃⚡✻🛢️🔷🚾📞🔧🔋
➔∪▶⤴📺🎵

Moor End Farm (SE589457)
YO2 1UQ ☎ 01904 706727 Signposted
Nearby town: York
▶▶ ★ 🚐 fr £6.50 🚐 fr £6.50 Å fr £5.50
Open Etr or Apr-Oct Booking advisable bank hols & end
Jul-early Aug Last arrival 22.00hrs Last departure
14.00hrs
Level, grassy site with hedges, well-drained and maintained. Set in meadowland adjacent to road. Leave A64 at Copmanthorpe, turning S signed Acaster Malbis. Site on unclass rd in 2m. A 1-acre site with 10 touring pitches and 5 statics.
Dishwashing sink & fridge/freezer.

🔌🚻🅿️⊙🗃⚡✻🔷
➔▶⤴📺🎵🔧🔋
🔖

Yorkshire

ALLERSTON

Vale of Pickering Caravan Park (SE879808)
Carr House Farm YO18 7PQ
☎ 01723 859280 Signposted
▶▶▶ ♠ ♠ ♠ ⊕ ⊕ Å
Open Mar-Oct (rs Mar) Booking advisable anytime Last departure noon
A well-maintained modern site with good facilities set in rolling countryside, and convenient for North Yorkshire Moors and wolds. On the B1415, 1.75m off the main Pickering to Scarborough road. An 8-acre site with 120 touring pitches and 1 static.

🎪 🚐 ♠ ⊙ 🗖 🢂 ✳ ⚠ 🔒 ⌀ 🚽 Ⓣ 🦮 ★ 🐾 ♿
➔ ∪ ↾ ◎ ♪

ALLERTON PARK

Allerton Park Caravan Site (SE417576)
Allerton Mauleverer HG5 0SE ☎ 01423 330569
(0.25m E of A1 off the A59) Signposted
Nearby town: Knaresborough
▶▶▶ ♠ ★ ⊕ £8-£11 ⊕ £8-£11 Å £8-£11
Open Feb-3 Jan (rs Feb & Nov-Dec) Booking advisable bank hols
An immaculately maintained site set in parkland surrounded by mature trees, and offering peace and quiet. A 12-acre site with 45 touring pitches and 80 statics.

🎪 ⚡ ⊙ 🗖 🢂 ✳ ⚠ 🔒 🚽 Ⓣ 🦮 ★ 🐾
➔ ↾ ⤓ ♪
💷

ALLERTON PARK CARAVAN SITE

Allerton Mauleverer, Nr Knaresborough, North Yorkshire HG5 0SE

A lovely peaceful site ideally Placed for exploring the Yorkshire Dales Herriot Country, Vale of York and the North Yorkshire Moors.

Facilities for tourers, campervans and tents. Static caravans for sale with full mains services. Luxury caravans to let on site. Site amenities include toilets/shower blocks, launderette, children's play area, telephone, shop, Calor gas and electric hook-ups. Dogs welcome under strict control.

Telephone: (01423) 330569

AYSGARTH

Westholme Caravan Park (SE016882)
DL8 3SP ☎ 01969 663268 Signposted
Nearby town: Leyburn
▶▶▶ ♠ ★ ⊕ £6.50-£8.75 ⊕ £6.50-£8.75 Å £6.50-£8.75
Open Mar-Oct Booking advisable bank hols & Jul-Aug Last arrival 23.00hrs Last departure 14.00hrs
A beckside site with level grassy pitches in various paddocks set into the hillside. 1m E of Aysgarth on A684. A 4-acre site with 70 touring pitches and 44 statics.
Library, quiet room & fishing free on site.

🎪 ⚡ ⊙ 🗖 🢂 ♠ 🗖 ✳ ⚷ ⚠ 🔒 ⌀ 🚽 Ⓣ ✕ 🦮 ★
🐾
➔ ∪ ♪

BISHOP MONKTON

Church Farm Caravan Park (SE286658)
Knaresborough Rd HG3 3QQ ☎ 01765 677405 & 677297
Nearby town: Ripon
▶▶ ⊕ ⊕ Å
Open Apr-Oct Booking advisable peak periods
Mainly level tree-lined field, adjacent to farm in picturesque village. A 5-acre site with 30 touring pitches.

⚡ ⊙ ✳ 🔒 ⌀ 🚽 Ⓣ 🦮
➔ ∪ ↾ ⧖ ♪ 🐾

BOLTON ABBEY

Strid Wood Caravan Club Site (SE059564)
BD23 6AN ☎ 01756 710433
(1.75n NW)
Nearby town: Skipton
▶▶▶ ♠ ♠ ♠ ⊕ ⊕
Open 26 Mar-3 Jan Booking advisable all times
Pretty site set in an open glade surrounded by trees, with the River Strid on its boundaries and the Yorkshire Dales all around. Approach from N on B6160 is unsuitable for caravans. A 4-acre site with 57 touring pitches.
Veg prep area.

🎪 ⚡ ⊙ 🢂 ✳ 🔒 ⌀ 🚽 Ⓣ 🦮 ★
➔ ♪

Credit Cards 🔲 🔲 🔲 🔲

BOROUGHBRIDGE

Camping & Caravanning Club Site (SE384662)
Bar Ln, Roecliffe YO5 9LS ☎ 01423 322683 (in season) & 01203 694995
▶▶ ★ ⊕ £9.30-£10 ⊕ £9.30-£10 Å £9.30-£10
Open Mar-Oct (rs Nov-Feb all service pitches only) Booking advisable bank hols & Jul & Aug Last arrival 21.00hrs Last departure noon
A quiet, riverside site with boating and riding available. Close to the dales and the market town of Boroughbridge. Please see the advertisement on page

27 for details of Club Members' benefits. A 6-acre site
with 80 touring pitches.

🏪📶☀️☉📶🔍☀️🏔️🛈⌀🚿📞
➜🥄🎣

Credit Cards ▨ ▩ ▦

CAWOOD

**Cawood Holiday Park
(SE563385)**
Ryther Rd YO8 0TT
☎ 01757 268450 (0.5m NW on B1233) Signposted
Nearby town: York
▶ ▶ ▶ 🚽 ♨ ♨ £7.50-£9.50 ♨ £7.50-£9.50
🛖 £7.50-£9.50
Open Mar-Jan Booking advisable bank hols & Jul-Aug
Last arrival 23.00hrs Last departure noon
*A continually improving site with a very high level of
maintenance and excellent toilet facilities. 5m NW of
Cawood on B1223. A 4-acre site with 60 touring pitches
and 10 statics.*
Coarse & trout fishing, childrens boating.

🏪📶☀️☉📶🔍☀️🏔️🛈⌀📞🐕‍🦺🐕♿
➜∪🏴⛺🎣
💷

🔵🔵🔵🔵🔵🔵🔵🔵🔵🔵

CAYTON

Cayton Village Caravan Park (TA057837)
Mill Ln YO11 3NN ☎ 01723 583171 & 01904 624630
(in winter)
▶ ▶ ▶ ♨ ♨ 🛖
Open Etr/Apr-1 Oct
*A pleasant, landscaped site in an attractive rural area.
Situated off A165 Scarborough to Filey Rd, before
Cayton Village. An 11-acre site with 200 touring pitches.*

🏪📶☀️☉📶🔍🏔️🛈⌀📞🐕‍🦺🐕♿
➜∪🏴⛺🎣

CONEYSTHORPE (NEAR MALTON)

Castle Howard Caravan & Camping Site (SE705710)
YO6 7DD ☎ 01653 648366 & 648316 Signposted
▶ ▶ ▶ ♨ ♨ ♨ 🛖
Open Mar-Oct Booking advisable public hols Last arrival
19.00hrs Last departure 14.00hrs
*Tranquil grassy site adjacent to lake on Castle Howard
Estate. A superb touring centre. Well signed from A64. A
9-acre site with 40 touring pitches and 120 statics.*

🏪📶☀️☉📶🔍☀️🛈⌀Ⓣ📞🐕
➜∪🏴🎣

CONSTABLE BURTON

Constable Burton Hall Caravan Park (SE158907)
DL8 5LJ ☎ 01677 450428 Signposted
Nearby town: Leyburn
▶ ▶ ▶ ♨ ♨
Open Apr-Oct Booking advisable public hols Last arrival
22.00hrs Last departure noon

*A part-level, part-sloping site within parkland of
Constable Burton Hall in farmland at entrance to
Wensleydale. Located off A684 but screened behind old
deer park wall. A 10-acre site with 120 touring pitches.*

🏪📶☀️☉📶🔍☀️🛈⌀✛✖📞🐾
➜🎣

CROCKEY HILL

Swallow Hall Caravan Park (SE657463)
YO1 4SG ☎ 01904 448219 (E off A19)
Nearby town: York
▶ ▶ ★ ♨ £7-£9.50 ♨ £7-£9.50 🛖 £7-£9.50
Open Mar-Oct Booking advisable Etr & Spring bank hol
Last arrival 22.00hrs
*A quiet site on meadowland at the edge of a forest
within easy reach of the centre of York. A 5-acre site
with 30 touring pitches.*
Golf driving range & 18 hole course.

🏪📶☀️☉🔍☀️🏔️🛈✛Ⓣ📞
➜🏴🎣🐾

CROPTON

Spiers House Campsite (SE756918)
YO18 8ES ☎ 01751 417591 Signposted
Nearby town: Pickering
▶ ▶ ▶ ♨ ♨ ♨ 🛖
Open 25 Mar-2 Oct Booking advisable bank & school
hols Last arrival 21.00hrs
*Beautiful forest site in a clearing with good facilities and
peaceful surroundings. Walks are marked by Forestry
Commission. Approach by signs from A170. A 15-acre
site with 150 touring pitches.*

🏪📶☀️☉📶🔍☀️🏔️🛈⌀Ⓣ📞🐕‍🦺🐕♿
➜∪🎣

FILEY

Flower of May Holiday Park (TA085835)
Lebberston Cliff YO11 3NU ☎ 01723 584311
(Lebberston 2.5m NW off A165) Signposted
▶ ▶ ▶ ▶ ▶ 🌀 Holiday Centre ★ ♨ £6.25-£9.95 ♨ £6.25-
£9.95
🛖 £6.25-£9.95
Open Etr-Sep (rs early & late season) Booking advisable
Spring bank hol wk & Jul-Aug Last arrival 22.00hrs Last
departure noon
*A delightful family site with level grassy pitches,
excellent facilities and direct access to the beach.
Signed off A165 on Scarborough side of Filey. Winner of
the 1995 Campsite of the Year Award for the North of
England. A 13-acre site with 300 touring pitches and 179
statics.*
Squash, gymnasium, bowling & 9-hole golf.
See advertisement under SCARBOROUGH

🏪📶☀️☉📶🔍📡🔍🖥️☀️🏔️🛈⌀✛Ⓣ✖📞
🍴🍺🐾🐕‍🦺🐕♿
➜∪🏴☉⛺🥄🎱🎣
💷

FYLINGDALES ('FLASK' INN)

Grouse Hill Caravan Park (NZ928002)
Flask Bungalow Farm YO22 4QH ☎ 01947 880543
Signposted
Nearby town: Whitby
▶ ▶ ▶ ▶ ★ ⚏ £6-£7 ⚏ £6-£7 ▲ £6-£7
Open Spring bank hol-Sep (rs Etr-May shop & reception restricted) Booking advisable public hols
Set in the midst of spectacular scenery in North Yorkshire Moors National Park adjacent to A171 Whitby-Scarborough road. A 14-acre site with 175 touring pitches.

🔲 🍴 ⊙ ⚘ ✳ 🏔 🛈 ⌀ 🖃 🔲 🌣 🐕 🐾 & → ∪ ▶ 🅹

GRASSINGTON

See **Threshfield**

HARROGATE

High Moor Farm Park (SE242560)
Skipton Rd HG3 2LT ☎ 01423 563637 & 564955
Signposted
▶ ▶ ▶ ▶ ★ ⚏ £8.50-£10.50 ⚏ £8.50-£10.50
▲ £8.50-£10.50
Open Apr-Oct Booking advisable public hols Last arrival 23.30hrs Last departure 15.00hrs
An excellent site with first class facilities, set beside a small wood and surrounded by thorn hedges. On the A59, Harrogate-Skipton road. A 15-acre site with 320 touring pitches and 180 statics.

9 hole golf course.

🔲 🍴 🍴 ⊙ 🔲 🍴 ⚘ 🔦 ✳ 🍷 🏔 🛈 ⌀ 🖃 🔲 🌣 ✕ 🌣 🖥 🏠 🐕 🐾 → ∪ ▶ 🖥 ♪

                Rudding Holiday Park (SE333531)
Follifoot HG3 1JH
☎ 01423 870439 Signposted
▶ ▶ ▶ ▶ ♦ 🏃 ★ ⚏ £9.30-£18 ⚏ £9.30-£18 ▲ £6.50-£14
Open 22 Mar-3 Nov (rs 1-21 Mar no hot water no shop) Booking advisable bank hols Last arrival 22.30hrs Last departure 14.00hrs
A spacious site set in mature parkland and walled gardens, situated 3m SE of Harrogate signed off A661. A 25-acre site with 141 touring pitches and 95 statics.
Golf course, driving range & cycle hire.

🔲 🍴 🍴 🍴 ⊙ 🔲 🍴 ⚘ 🔦 ✳ 🍷 🏔 🛈 ⌀ 🖃 🔲 🌣 ✕ 🌣 🖥 🏠 🐕 🐾 & → ∪ ▶ 🍴 🖥 ♪ 🅹

Credit Cards 🖴 🖴 🖴 🖴

Caravan Club Site (SE328542)
Great Yorkshire Showground, Railway Road, off Wetherby Rd HG3 1TZ ☎ 01423 560470 (1m SE)
Signposted

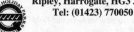

►►► ★ ⊞ £6-£9.50 ⊞ £6-£9.50 ⚐ fr £3.50
Open 31 Mar-10 Oct Booking advisable bank hols & Jul-Aug Last departure noon
A flat and pleasantly open site just off A661, close to Harrogate. An 8-acre site with 80 touring pitches.
Veg prep area.

🔧 📻 ⊙ 🗖 🏳 ✳ ⚏ 🛇 🖩 ⊕ Ⓣ 📞 ♿
→ ∪ ⍓ △ ⚲ 🏓 🎣 🐟

Credit Cards 🖪 ▭

Shaws Trailer Park (SE325557)
Knaresborough Rd HG2 7NE ☎ 01423 884432 & 883622
Signposted
►► ★ ⊞ £5.50-£6.50 ⊞ £5.50-£6.50 ⚐ £3-£4.50
Open all year Booking advisable public hols Last arrival 22.00hrs Last departure noon
A level, grassy site with mature trees. On A59 Harrogate-Knaresborough road. A 4-acre site with 43 touring pitches and 146 statics.

🔧 🛒 📻 ⊙ ⚏ 📞
→ ∪ ⍓ ⚲ 🏓 🎣 🖩 🐟

HAWES

Bainbridge Ings Caravan & Camping Site (SD879895)
DL8 3NU ☎ 01969 667354 Signposted
►► ⊞ ⊞ ⚐
Open Apr-Oct Booking advisable school hols Last arrival 22.00hrs Last departure 14.00hrs
A family run site in open countryside, close to Hawes in the heart of Upper Wensleydale. Off A684. A 5-acre site with 55 touring pitches and 14 statics.

🔧 📻 ⊙ ✳ 🛇 ⚏ ⊕ 🐟
→ 🎣
⊞

HELMSLEY

Golden Square Touring Caravan Park (SE604797)
Oswaldkirk YO6 5YQ ☎ 01439 788269 (2.5m S B1257 between Sproxton & Oswaldkirk) Signposted
►►►► ⚏⚏ ⊞ ⊞ ⚐
Open Mar-Oct Booking advisable bank hols Last arrival 23.30hrs Last departure noon
All-round excellent site with manicured grounds and first class toilets. Set in a quiet rural situation with lovely views over the N Yorks Moors. Off A170 on unclass road leading to B1257 near Ampleforth. An 8-acre site with 129 touring pitches.
Microwave oven.

🔧 🛒 📻 ⊙ 🗖 🏳 🔍 ✳ ⚏ 🛇 🖩 ⊕ Ⓣ 📞 🐎 🐟 ♿
→ ∪ ⍓ ◎ 🎣
⊞

Foxholme Caravan Park (SE658828)
Harome YO6 5JG ☎ 01439 770416 & 771241 (3m SE unclass between Harome & Nawton) Signposted
►►► ♦ ⊞ £6.50-£7 ⊞ £6.50-£7 ⚐ £6.50-£7
Open Etr-Oct Booking advisable bank & school hols Last ➥

arrival 23.00hrs Last departure noon
A quiet site with mostly individual pitches divided by mature trees. Set in superb wooded countryside 1m S of Beadlam on unclass road. A 6-acre site with 60 touring pitches.

Wombleton Caravan Park (SE670835)
Moorfield Ln, Wombleton, Kirkbymoorside YO6 5RY
☎ 01751 431684 Signposted
Nearby town: Kirkbymoorside
► ► ► ★ ⊞ £5-£6 ⊞ £5-£6 Å £5-£6
Open Mar-Oct Booking advisable bank hols Last arrival 23.00hrs Last departure noon
A rural grassy site maintained to a high standard. Situated off A170 on unclass road near Harome. Signed at Nawton. A 6-acre site with 78 touring pitches.

Wrens of Ryedale Caravan Site (SE656840)
Gale Ln, Nawton YO6 5SD ☎ 01439 771260
(Nawton 3m E A170, then S of village) Signposted
Nearby town: Kirkbymoorside
► ► ► ★ ⊞ £4.50-£6 ⊞ £4.50-£6 Å £3.50-£6
Open Apr-16 Oct Booking advisable bank hols Last arrival 22.00hrs Last departure noon
A level, grassy site with mature trees and bushes, and open views, .5m S of Beadlam village off A170. A 2.5-acre site with 30 touring pitches.
Bike, caravan & tent hire.

HIGH BENTHAM

Riverside Caravan Park (SD665688)
Wenning Av LA2 7HS ☎ 01524 261272 & 262163
Signposted
► ► ► ⊞ £6.70-£7.50 ⊞ £6.70-£7.50 Å fr £6
Open Mar-Oct Booking advisable bank hols Last arrival 20.00hrs Last departure 13.00hrs
This site is set on the banks of the River Wenning, in delightful countryside and screened by trees. Off B6480. A 12-acre site with 30 touring pitches and 170 statics.
Free fishing.

HUNMANBY

Orchard Farm Holiday Village (TA105779)
Stonegate YO14 0PU ☎ 01723 891582
► ► ► ⊞ ⊞ Å
A level grassy site with pitches around lake and model railway, close to Hunmanby village, with coarse fishing on site. Signed from A1039. A 14-acre site with 91 touring pitches and 6 statics.

Veg prep area, boating lake, fishing.

KNARESBOROUGH

Kingfisher Caravan Park (SE343603)
Low Moor Ln, Farnham HG5 9DQ ☎ 01423 869411
► ► ► ★ ⊞ £7.50-£9.50 ⊞ £7.50-£9.50 Å £7.50-£9.50
Open mid Mar/Etr-Oct Booking advisable bank hols & 15 Jul-1 Sep Last arrival 23.00hrs Last departure 16.00hrs
A large grassy site with open spaces set in wooded area in rural countryside. From Knaresborough take A6055, after 1m turn L towards Farnham, and L again in village, signed Scotton. Site 1m on L. A 4-acre site with 35 touring pitches and 30 statics.

LOTHERSDALE

Springs Caravan Park (SD944451)
Springs Farm BD20 8HH ☎ 01535 632533 Signposted
Nearby town: Skipton
► ► ⊞
Open May-Sep (rs Apr & Oct weather conditions) Booking advisable at all times Last arrival 19.00hrs Last departure noon ⊘ no cars by tents
On rising ground in rural setting overlooking a small trout lake on edge of Yorkshire Dales and moors. Well-signposted from A6068 at Cross Hills. A 3.5-acre site with 17 touring pitches.
Qualified first aider. Fly fishing.

NORTH STAINLEY

Sleningford Water Mill Caravan Site (SE280783)
HG4 3HQ ☎ 01765 635201 Signposted
Nearby town: Ripon
► ► ► ♣ ★ ⊞ £6.50-£10.50 ⊞ £6.50-£10.50
Å £6.50-£10.50
Open Etr & Apr-Oct Booking advisable bank hols & school holidays Last arrival 22.00hrs Last departure 12.30hrs
Level, grassy site with mature trees set in woods and meadowland adjacent to River Ure and A6108. A 14-acre site with 80 touring pitches.
Off-licence, canoe access, fly fishing.

OSMOTHERLEY

Cote Ghyll Caravan Park (SE461983)
DL6 3AH ☎ 01609 883425 Signposted
Nearby town: Northallerton
► ► ★ ⊞ fr £6 ⊞ fr £5.50 Å fr £5.25
Open Apr-Oct Booking advisable bank hols & Jul-Aug Last arrival 23.00hrs Last departure noon
Quiet site in pleasant valley on edge of moors. Situated

off A19. A 4-acre site with 77 touring pitches and 17 statics.

🔫 📻 ☉ 🗄 ✳ 🔌 🥗 ⬆ 🐕

➔ 🛁

💷

Upper Carr Touring Park (SE804816)
Upper Carr Ln, Malton Rd YO18 7JP ☎ 01751 473115
▶ ▶ ▶ ★ 🚐 £5.50-£7 🚐 £5.50-£7 ▲ £5.50-£7
Open Mar-Oct
Attractive and well-maintained rural touring park set amongst mature trees and hedges, with adjacent 9-hole golf course. A 4-acre site with 80 touring pitches.
Off-licence.

🔫 📻 ☉ 🗄 🍴 ⚓ 🔌 🐕 🛁 ♿

➔ ▶

Wayside Caravan Park (SE764859)
Wrelton YO18 8PG ☎ 01751 472608 Signposted
▶ ▶ ▶ 🚐 fr £7.50 🚐 fr £6.50 ▲ fr £6.50
Open Etr-early Oct Booking advisable Etr, Spring bank hol & Jul-Aug Last arrival 23.00hrs Last departure noon
A level, grassy, well-maintained site divided up by mature hedges into small areas off the A170 at Wrelton village. A 5-acre site with 75 touring pitches and 80 statics.

🔫 📻 ☉ 🗄 🍴 ✳ 🔌 🥗 ⬆ T 📞 🛁 ♿

➔ ∪ ▶ ⚽ 🎣

Brompton-on-Swale Caravan Park (NZ199002)
Brompton-on-Swale DL10 7EZ ☎ 01748 824629 (1.5m SE B6271 towards Brompton-on Swale) Signposted
▶ ▶ ▶ ▶ 👤 ★ 🚐 fr £5.85 🚐 fr £5.65 ▲ £4.70-£5.85
Open Etr or Apr-Oct Booking advisable school & bank hols Last arrival 22.00hrs Last departure 14.00hrs
A riverside site on former meadowland with mature trees and other natural features. Very well-equipped and maintained, adjacent to main road on the banks of the River Swale. A 7-acre site with 150 touring pitches and 23 statics.
Fishing & canoeing on site.

🔫 📻 ☉ 🗄 🍴 ⬜ ✳ 🏔 🔌 🥗 ⬆ T 📞 🐕 🛁 ♿

➔ ∪ ▶ 🎣

💷

Swale View Caravan Site (NZ134013)
Reeth Rd DL10 4SF ☎ 01748 823106 Signposted
▶ ▶ ▶ ★ 🚐 £4.10-£6.20 🚐 £3.80-£5.90 ▲ £2.50-£6.20
Open Mar-Oct Booking advisable bank hols & summer hols Last arrival 21.00hrs Last departure noon
A level, grassy site shaded by trees, lying on the banks of the River Swale in picturesque country. On A6108, 1.5m W of Richmond. A 4-acre site with 60 touring pitches and 100 statics.

🔫 📻 ☉ 🗄 ⚓ ✳ 🏔 🔌 🥗 ⬆ T 📞 🛁

➔ ▶ 🎣

Ripley Caravan Park (SE289610)
Knaresborough Rd HG3 3AU
☎ 01423 770050 Signposted
Nearby town: Harrogate
▶ ▶ ▶ 👤 👥 ★ 🚐 £5.50-£6.50 🚐 £5.50-£6.50 ▲ £5-£6.50
Open Etr-Oct Booking advisable bank hols Last arrival 21.00hrs Last departure noon
A well-run rural site with easy access on B6165 .75m S of Ripley. An 18-acre site with 100 touring pitches.
Nursery playroom, sauna, sunbed, tennis net, football.
See advertisement under HARROGATE

🔫 📻 ☉ 🗄 🍴 🍸 ⚓ ✳ 🏔 🔌 🥗 ⬆ T 📞 🐕 🛁 ♿

➔ ∪ ▶ ☉ 🌴 ⚽ 🎣

◎◎◎◎◎◎◎◎◎◎◎◎◎

Ure Bank Caravan Park (SE317726)
Ure Bank Top HG4 1JD ☎ 01765 602964 & 607764 Signposted
▶ ▶ ▶ 🚐 🚐 ▲
Open May-Oct (rs Mar-Apr bar open wknds only) Last departure noon
This pleasant and well-maintained site stands on high ground overlooking the River Ure, 1 mile from town centre. There is no access to the river from the site. A 10-acre site with 200 touring pitches and 200 statics.

🔫 📻 ☉ 🗄 🍴 ⚓ ⬜ ✳ 🍸 🏔 🔌 🥗 ⬆ T ✖ 📞 ✋

🐕 🛁

➔ ∪ ▶ 🎣

SAWLEY

Hallgates Farm (SE256671)
HG4 3EE ☎ 01765 620275 & 620472
Nearby town: Ripon
▷ ★ ⊕ fr £2 ⊕ fr £2 ▲ fr £2
Open Apr-Oct Booking advisable holiday periods
A basic farm site in a mainly level field on south-side of road out of Sawley towards Fountain Abbey. A 1-acre site with 30 touring pitches.

⊟ ⊩

→ ∪ ⅃

SCARBOROUGH

Jacobs Mount Caravan Park (TA021868)
Jacobs Mount, Stepney Rd YO12 5NL ☎ 01723 361178
(2m in W on A170 Thirsk Road) Signposted
▶ ▶ ▶ ★ ⊕ £5.75-£8.50 ⊕ £5.75-£8.50 ▲ £5.75-£8.50
Open Mar-Oct (rs Mar-May & Oct limited shop hours)
Booking advisable bank hols & late Jun-early Sep Last arrival 21.00hrs Last departure noon
A gently sloping site situated in attractive countryside 2m from the coast, with direct access from A170. A 2.5-acre site with 56 touring pitches and 44 statics.
Dish wash & food preparation area.

🎮 📶 🐾 ⊙ 📷 ⅃ 🖵 ✳ ⊻ 🗚 🔒 🛢 ⊞ T ✕ 🍴 🛒 ⊩
⅃

→ ∪ 🇵 ◎ △ ⅄ 🏓 🎣

💷

Scalby Close Park (TA018925)
Burniston Rd YO13 0DA ☎ 01723 365908 Signposted
▶ ▶ ▶ ★ ⊕ £3.95-£7.95 ⊕ £3.95-£7.95 ▲ £3.95-£7.95
Open Mar-Oct Booking advisable bank hols & high season Last arrival 22.00hrs Last departure noon
A small family-run site situated 2m N of Scarborough on the A165. A 3-acre site with 42 touring pitches and 5 statics.

🎮 📶 🐾 ⊙ 📷 ✳ 🔒 🛢 ⊞ T ⅃ ⅃
→ ∪ 🇵 ⅄ 🏓 🎣
💷

Credit Cards

SCOTCH CORNER

Scotch Corner Caravan Park (NS210054)
DL10 6NS ☎ 01748 822530 & 826272 (winter)
Signposted
Nearby town: Richmond
▶ ▶ ▶ ★ ⊕ £5-£9 ⊕ £5-£9 ▲ £5-£9
Open Etr-mid Oct Booking advisable public hols & Jul-Aug Last arrival 22.30hrs Last departure noon
A well-maintained site with excellent facilities. Off A6108, approach from Scotch Corner is towards Richmond for approx 200yds then make U-turn, crossing central reservation and proceed approx 160yds back towards Scotch Corner for site entrance. A 7-acre site with 96 touring pitches.

🎮 📶 🐾 ⊙ 📷 ⅃ ✳ ⊻ 🗚 🔒 🛢 ⊞ T ✕ 🍴 🐕 ⅃ ⅃ 🚿
→ ∪ 🇵 🎣
💷

Credit Cards

BEST CHOICE FOR CARAVAN TOURING AND CAMPING

**In the North York Moors National Park -
Heritage countryside so close to Moors and Coast.**
An idyllic setting with every facility
for a wonderful holiday.

- **Free Baths and Showers**
- **Baby Care Units** ●**Launderette**
- **Late Arrivals Park with Hook-ups**
- **Information Room** ●**Ladies' Hair Care Units**
- **Games Room** ●**Takeaway... and lots more!**

<u>AA CAMPSITE OF THE YEAR 1994</u> National Winner
Open for winter touring (limited facilities)
Fishing and Boating facilities now available

AA CAMPSITE OF THE YEAR 1994 NATIONAL WINNER

BRITISH GRADED HOLIDAY PARKS
EXCELLENT

S~t Helens in the Park

**WYKEHAM, SCARBOROUGH
NORTH YORKSHIRE Y013 9QD
TELEPHONE & FAX
01723 862771**

AROSA
Caravan and Camping Park

Nestled in the pretty village of Seamer, the Arosa benefits from its close proximity to both Scarboro's Heritage coastline and the beautiful North Yorkshire Moors with its forestry, moorland and spacious tranquility.

Along with the parks excellent facilities including a fully licensed bar and superior toilet/shower block, the Arosa excells itself with its warm and friendly welcome and personal service to all its customers.
"Definitely the place to stay!"

Please phone anytime for further details:
Arosa, Ratten Row, Scarborough,
North Yorkshire YO12 4QB
Tel/Fax (01723) 862166

SEAMER

Arosa Caravan & Camping Park (TA011830)
YO12 4QB ☎ 01723 862166
► ► ► ⚞ ⚞ Å
Open Mar-4 Jan
A very well laid out site with screening from mature trees, approx 4m from Scarborough. From junc with unclass rd and A64 S of Seamer, travel N into village. Site 250yards along Ratten Road. A 3.5-acre site with 92 touring pitches.

SHERIFF HUTTON

Camping & Caravanning Club Site (SE638652)
Bracken Hill YO6 1QG ☎ 01347 878660 (in season) & 01203 694995 Signposted
Nearby town: York
► ► ► ⚭⚭ ★ ⚞ £9.30-£10 ⚞ £9.30-£10 Å £9.30-£10
Open end Mar-early Nov Booking advisable bank hols & peak periods Last arrival 21.00hrs Last departure noon
The site is within easy reach of York in a quiet rural setting. From A1237 (York northern ring road) take unclass rd signed Strensall and Sheriff Hutton, through Strensall turn left on unclass rd signed Sheriff Hutton and site 2m on right. Please see the advertisement on page 27 for details of Club Members' benefits. A 6-acre site with 90 touring pitches.

Credit Cards 🖪 🖾 🖪

SLINGSBY

Robin Hood Caravan & Camping Park (SE701748)
Green Dyke Ln YO6 7AU ☎ 01653 628391 Signposted
► ► ► ★ ⚞ £7.50-£9 ⚞ £7.50-£9 Å £7.50-£9

Open Mar-Oct Booking advisable bank hols & 15 Jul-1 Sep Last arrival 22.00hrs Last departure 16.00hrs
A pleasant, well-maintained grassy site, well-situated for touring Yorks Dales. Situated on B1257. A 2-acre site with 39 touring pitches and 7 statics.
Caravan hire, washing up area. Off-license.

🖾 🖪 ⊙ 🖥 ⚲ ✳ 🅐 🛉 ∅ 🔃 T ↻ 🛏 🛖 🐕 🦮 🐾 ⚹
→ ∪ ♪
🆓

Camping & Caravanning Club Site (SE699755)
Railway St YO6 7AA ☎ 01653 628335 (in season) & 01203 694995 Signposted
► ► ★ ⚞ £8.40-£9 ⚞ £8.40-£9 Å £8.40-£9
Open end Mar-early Nov Booking advisable bank hols & peak periods Last arrival 21.00hrs Last departure noon
A part-grassy, part-hardstanding site near village centre, signed from B1257. Please see the advertisement on page 27 for details of Club Members' benefits. A 3-acre site with 60 touring pitches.

🖾 🖪 ⊙ 🖥 ⚲ ✳ 🛉 ∅ 🔃 T ↻ 🛖 ⚹
→ ∪

Credit Cards 🖪 🖾 🖪

SNAINTON

Jasmine Caravan Park (SE928813)
Cross Ln YO13 9BE ☎ 01723 859240 Signposted
Nearby town: Scarborough
► ► ⚭ ⚞ £5.50-£7.50 ⚞ £5.50-£7.50 Å £5.50-£7.50
Open Mar-Dec Booking advisable 3 wks in advance for bank hols Last arrival 22.00hrs Last departure noon
A well-screened rural site on edge of the village, 1m off A170 Pickering-Scarborough road; turn off opposite school into Barker Lane. A 5-acre site with 90 touring pitches and 10 statics.

🖾 🖪 ⊙ 🖥 ⚲ ✳ 🛉 ∅ 🔃 T ↻ 🛖
→ ∪ ► ♪
🆓

SNEATON

Low Moor Caravan Club Site (NZ893038)
Redgates YO22 5JE ☎ 01947 810505
▷ ⚭ ⚭
Open Apr-Oct Booking advisable bank hols & wknds in Jul-Aug Last arrival 20.00hrs Last departure noon no cars by tents
A pleasant, open site with pitching areas divided up by established trees which shelter the site. Spectacular moorland views from lower end. Care required on steep hills each side of Ruswarp. Route from S also includes 1 in 5 gradient downhill approaching Sleights. A 12-acre site with 100 touring pitches.

🖾 ✳ 🛉 🔃 T ↻ 🛖 ⚹
→ ► 🦮 ♪

Credit Cards 🖪 🖾

STAINFORTH

Knight Stainforth Hall Caravan & Campsite (SD816672)
BD24 0DP ☎ 01729 822200 Signposted
Nearby town: Settle
▶▶▶ ★ 🚐 fr £7.50 🚐 fr £7.50 🛆 fr £7.50
Open May-Oct Booking advisable bank hols & Jul-Aug
Last arrival 22.00hrs Last departure noon
*A very well-maintained site located near a river in the
Yorkshire Dales National Park. Approach only possible
from B6479 at Giggleswick. A 6-acre site with 100
touring pitches and 60 statics.*
Fishing on site.

🖪 🏕 ⊙ 🗓 🦐 🦐 ⛉ 🕸 🛈 🖉 🖃 🔲 📞 🛋 🌄
→ ∪ ▶ 🎵
🖾

Credit Cards

STAXTON

Spring Willows Touring Caravan Park (TA026794)
Main Rd, Staxton Roundabout YO12 4SB
☎ 01723 891505 (jct A64/A1039) Signposted
Nearby town: Scarborough
▶▶▶▶ ★ 🚐 £5-£12 🚐 £5-£12 🛆 £5-£12
Open Mar-Dec (rs Mar & Oct-Dec bar, pool & take-away
restricted) Booking advisable bank hols, Etr & Aug Last
arrival 19.00hrs Last departure 11.00hrs
*A sheltered grassy site in a former sandpit, 6m from
Scar at junct of A64 and A1039. A 10-acre site with 184
touring pitches.*
Washing-up facilities, sauna, solarium, coffee lounge
See advertisement under SCARBOROUGH

🖪 🏕 ⊙ 🗓 🦐 🦐 🦐 📞 🞰 ⛉ 🖉 🕸 🛈 🖃 🔲 🞽 📞
🞙 🝫 🝬 🛏 🛋 ⛐
→ ∪ ▶
🖾

SUTTON-ON-THE-FOREST

**Goosewood Caravan Park
(SE595636)**
YO6 1ET ☎ 01347 810829
(From A1237 outer York ring rd, take B1363 signed
Helmsley North, pass Haxby/Wigginton jct & take next
right) Signposted
Nearby town: York
▶▶▶▶ 🞿 🕊🕊 🚐 £7.50-£9 🚐 £7.50-£9
Open 22 Mar-Oct Booking advisable bank hols Last
arrival 20.00hrs Last departure noon
*An immaculately maintained site with its own lake and
seasonal fishing, set in attractive woodland within the
Vale of York. From A1237 (York northern ring road) take
B1363, in 1.5m take unclass rd signed Farlington, and
turn right in .25m. Take right turn in .5m, and site on
right. A 12-acre site with 75 touring pitches.*
Fishing lake.

🖪 🏕 ⊙ 🗓 🦐 ⛉ 🕸 🛈 🖉 🖃 🔲 📞 🞙 🛏 🛋 🌄
→ ∪ ▶ 🝫 🎵

THIRSK

Sowerby Caravan Park (SE437801)
Sowerby YO7 3AG ☎ 01845 522753 (0.5m S off A168)
Signposted
▶▶▶ 🚐 £5.75-£6.25 🚐 £5.75-£6.25 🛆 £5.75-£6.25
Open Mar-Oct Booking advisable bank hols Last arrival
23.00hrs
*A level grassy site, 1m from town on the Sowerby Road,
with a tree-lined river bank. A 1-acre site with 25 touring
pitches and 85 statics.*

🖪 🏕 ⊙ 🗓 🦐 ⛉ 🕸 🛈 🖉 🖃 🔲 📞 🛋 ⛐
→ ∪ 🝫 🎵
🖾

THRESHFIELD

AWARD
**Wood Nook Caravan Park
(SD974641)**
Skirethorns BD23 5NU
☎ 01756 752412 Signposted
Nearby town: Grassington
▶▶▶ 🞿 🕊🕊 ★ 🚐 £7-£9.50 🚐 £7-£9.50 🛆 £7-£8.50
Open Mar-Oct Booking advisable bank hols & peak
periods Last arrival 22.00hrs Last departure noon
*Gently sloping site in a rural setting, completely hidden
by natural features of surrounding hills and woodland.
Site on unclass rd 1m NW of Threshfield, W of B6160. A
2-acre site with 48 touring pitches and 10 statics.*

🖪 🏕 ⊙ 🗓 🦐 ⛉ 🕸 🛈 🖉 🖃 🔲 📞 🛏 🌄
→ ∪ 🎵
🖾

Credit Cards

🔘🔘🔘🔘🔘🔘🔘🔘🔘

UGTHORPE

Burnt House Holiday Park (NZ784112)
YO21 2BG ☎ 01947 840448 Signposted
Nearby town: Whitby
▶▶▶ 🚐 🚐 🛆
Open Mar-Oct Booking advisable bank hols & Jul-Aug
Last arrival 21.00hrs
*Level grass site with trees and bushes set in moorland.
4.5m from sea and beach and 9m W of Whitby off A171
Teeside road. A 7.5-acre site with 99 touring pitches and
41 statics.*

🖪 🏕 ⊙ 🗓 🦐 ⛉ 🕸 🛈 🖉 🖃 📞
→ ∪ ▶ 🝪 🎵
🖾

WHITBY

Northcliffe Holiday Park (TA930076)
YO22 4LL ☎ 01947 880477 (3.5m S, off A171)
Signposted
▶▶▶ 🕊🕊 🚐 £4-£13 🚐 £4-£13 🛆 £4-£8.50
Open Etr or end Mar-Oct Booking advisable school &
bank hols & Jul-Aug Last arrival 21.00hrs Last departure
11.00hrs 🞰
*A lovely little site in a peaceful position on the outskirts
of Whitby, with clifftop views and country walks, and* ➡

excellent sanitary facilities. Situated 3.5m S off A171. A 2-acre site with 30 touring pitches and 171 statics.
Barbecue hire, off-licence.

🎪 📻 ☉ 🗄 🍳 🔍 ☀ ⚲ 🛆 🍴 ⊞ Ⓣ ✕ 🔌 ➡ 🛄 🚤 ♿

➜ ∪ ◎ ↳ ⌇ 🎵

Credit Cards 💳 💳 💳

Rigg Farm Caravan Park (NZ915061)
Stainsacre YO22 4LP ☎ 01947 880430 (3.5m S on unclass off A171 at High Hawsker)
▶ ▶ ▶ ★ 🚐 £6-£8 🚐 £6-£8 ▲ £6-£8
Open Mar-Oct Booking advisable bank hols & Jul-Aug Last arrival 21.00hrs Last departure 13.00hrs
A neat rural site with good views in peaceful surroundings. Site is off B1416 on unclass road. From A171 Scarborough rd turn L onto B1416 signed Ruswarp. In 3.25m turn R onto unclass road signed Sneatonthorpe-Hawsker-Stainsacre. In 1.25m turn L signed Hawsker-Robin Hoods Bay-Scarborough, site in .5m. A 2-acre site with 14 touring pitches and 15 statics.

🎪 📻 ☉ 🔍 ☀ ⚲ 🛆 ⊞ 🔔

➜ ∪ ▶ ↳ ⚽ 🎵 🚤

York House Caravan Park (NZ926071)
YO22 4LW ☎ 01947 880354 (3.5m S, off A171) Signposted
▶ ▶ ▶ 🚐 🚐 ▲
Open Mar-Oct Booking advisable Spring bank hol & mid Jul-Aug Last arrival 23.00hrs Last departure noon
A very well-kept site in an undulating position located south of Whitby, close to local attractions. Just off A171 at Hawkser and signed. A 3-acre site with 59 touring pitches and 41 statics.
Open area for games.

🎪 📻 ☉ 🗄 🍳 ☀ ⚲ 🛆 🍴 ⊞ 🔔 ⌂ 🐕 🚤

➜ ∪ ▶ ⚠ ↳ ⚽ 🎵

YORK

Rawcliffe Manor Caravan Site (SE583553)
Manor Lane, Shipton Rd YO3 6TZ
☎ 01904 624422 Signposted
►►►► ♣ ♠ ♣ ⚐ £7.40-£10.40 Å £4.20-£10.40
Open all year Booking advisable all times Last arrival
20.00hrs Last departure noon
*A level site divided into hedged paddocks, with
immaculate landscaping incorporating rose trees
throughout. A 4.5-acre site with 120 touring pitches.
Petanque pitches & satellite TV.*

🔥 🚿 🏕 ⊙ 🖸 🐎 🔍 🍴 ⌷ ☼ ⚡ 🗜 🛢 🧼 🖲 ✕ 🔌
🛒 ♿

→ ∪ ⊳ ◎ ⅄ ☎ 🥄 🔩

Credit Cards 🔲 🔳

─────────────────────

Rowntree Park Caravan Club Site (SE604509)
Terry Av YO2 1JQ ☎ 01904 658997
►►► ♣ ⚐ 🚐 Å
Open all year Booking advisable all times
*A popular level site on the banks of the Ouse, within
easy walking distance of the city. Follow city centre
signs to inner ring road S of river, then site signs to
Terry Avenue. A 4-acre site with 103 touring pitches.*

🛢

→ ⊳ 🔺 🥄

YORKSHIRE, SOUTH

For the map of this county, see
Yorkshire, North

BARNSLEY

Greensprings Touring Park (SE330020)
Rockley Abbey Farm, Rockley Ln, Worsbrough S75 3DS
☎ 01226 288298 Signposted
►► ★ ⚐ fr £5.50 🚐 fr £5.50 Å fr £5.50
Open Apr-Oct Booking advisable when hook up is
required Last arrival 21.00hrs Last departure noon
*Part-level, part-sloping, grass site with young trees and
bushes, set in woods and meadowland with access to
river. From exit 36 off M1 turn along A61 to Barnsley,
then signposted. A 4-acre site with 65 touring pitches.
Cycle hire.*

🔥 🏕 ⊙ ☼ 🛢 🧼 🐎 🦅
→ ∪ ⊳ ☎ 🥄 🖸 🔩
💷

DONCASTER

See **Hatfield**

HATFIELD

Hatfield Marina Water Sports Centre (SE670098)
DN7 6EQ ☎ 01302 841572 & 737343 Signposted
Nearby town: Doncaster
►► ★ ⚐ fr £6 🚐 fr £6 Å fr £6
Open all year Booking advisable bank hols Last arrival
19.00hrs Last departure noon
*A clean, well-run site with fishing and good supervised
marina facilities. Signed from Hatfield off A18. A 10-acre
site with 38 touring pitches.
Canoeing, rowing, sailing, windsurfing & fishing.*

🔥 🏕 ⊙ ☼ ✕ 🐎 🦅 🔩
→ ∪ ⊳ 🔺 ⅄ 🥄

SHEFFIELD

See **Barnsley**

YORKSHIRE, WEST

For the map of this county, see
Yorkshire, North

BARDSEY

Moor Lodge Park (SE352423)
Blackmoor Ln LS17 9DZ ☎ 01937 572424 Signposted
Nearby town: Leeds
►► ⚐ fr £7 🚐 fr £7
Open all year Booking advisable Jul-Aug
*A neat, well-kept site in a peaceful and pleasant rural
location convenient to Leeds and surrounds. From
Harewood to Scarecroft Rd turn left to Bardsey into
Blackmoor Lane. Signed. A 2-acre site with 12 touring
pitches and 60 statics.*

🔥 🏕 ⊙ ☼ 🗜 🛢 🧼 🖲 🔌
→ ∪ ⊳ 🥄 🔩
💷

LEEDS

Roundhay Park Site (SK339376)
Roundhay Park, Elmete Ln, off Wetherby Rd LS8 2LG
☎ 0113 2652354 (in season) & 2661850 Signposted
►►► ★ ⚐ £7.50-£8 🚐 £7.50-£8 Å £2.50-£3
Open Mar-26 Nov Booking advisable Spring bank hol &
Jul-Aug Last arrival 21.00hrs Last departure noon
*On a south-facing hillside, adjacent to Roundhay Park,
3.5m from city centre. A very well-maintained site. An 8-
acre site with 60 touring pitches.*

🔥 🏕 ⊙ 🔍 ☼ 🗜 🛢 🧼 🖲 🔌 🍴 🪑 🐎 🦅 ♿
→ ∪ ⊳ ⅄ 🥄 🖸
💷

MYTHOLMROYD

Lower Clough Foot Caravan Club Site (SE007248)
Cragg Vale HX7 5RU ☎ 01422 882531
▷ ⚐ 🚐
Open 26 Mar-8 Nov Booking advisable bank hols & Aug
A well-screened site on a gentle slope, terraced for level ➡

pitching, and bordered by a stream. Do not leave M62 at junc 22 with towed caravans as awkward corner at A672/A58 junc. A 2.5-acre site with 50 touring pitches.

🔒

→ U 🍴 🏕

SILSDEN

Dales Bank Holiday Park (SE036483)
Low Ln BD20 9JH ☎ 01535 653321 & 652323
(1m NW on unclass rd) Signposted
▶ ★ 🚐 fr £5.50 🚐 fr £5.50 ▲ fr £5.50
Open Apr-Oct (rs Mar) Booking advisable public hols
Last arrival 22.00hrs Last departure 16.00hrs
A pleasant farm site with very good facilities in open countryside of typical Dales scenery. A 3-acre site with 40 touring pitches and 12 statics.

🔌 🐾 ☺ 🖥 🎣 ◀ ※ ⛾ 🏔 🏮 🌿 🔲 ✕ 📞 🏕
→ U ▶ 🥄 🍴 🖥
💷

CHANNEL ISLANDS

There is no map of the Channel Islands

GUERNSEY

CATEL (CASTEL)

Fauxquets Valley Farm
CC GY5 7QA ☎ 01481 55460 Signposted
Nearby town: St Peter Port
▶ ▶ ▶ ♣ ★ 🚐 ▲ £7.40-£8.40
Open Etr-mid Sep Booking advisable last 2 wks Jul-1st 3 wks Aug
Beautiful, quiet farm site in a hidden valley yet close to the sea. Friendly, helpful owners who understan campers' needs. 3m W of St Peter Port, near German Underground Hospital. A 3-acre site with 90 touring pitches.

🔌 🐾 ☺ 🖥 🎣 ⚡ ◀ 🗻 ※ 🏔 🏮 🌿 🔲 ✕ 📞 🚲 🐕
🏕
→ U ▶ ◎ 🍷 🐟 🍴
💷
Credit Cards 🔳 🔳 🔳 🔲

VALE

La Bailloterie Camping
GY3 5HA ☎ 01481 43636 Signposted
▶ ▶ ▶ ★ 🚐 £6-£7.50 🚐 £6-£7.50 ▲ £6-£7.50
Open 15 May-15 Sep Booking advisable Jul-Aug Last arrival 23.00hrs
Pretty little site with one large touring field and a few small, well-screened paddocks. 3m N of St Peter Port, and .75m W of St Sampsons. An 8-acre site with 100

touring pitches.
Volleyball net & boules pitch.
🔌 🐾 ☺ 🖥 🎣 ◀ 🗻 ※ 🏔 🏮 🌿 🔲 ✕ 📞 🚲 🚏
🚗 🐕 🏕
→ U ▶ ◎ 🍷 🐟 🍴

JERSEY

ST BRELADE

Rose Farm
Route Des Genets JE3 8DE ☎ 01534 41231 Signposted
Nearby town: St Aubin
▶ ▶ ▶ ▶ ★ ▲ £3-£9
Open May-Sep Booking advisable as early as possible
An attractive site set in a valley close to St Aubins, with friendly owners and secluded pitches. Facilities are of a very good standard. Located 1m W of St Aubin's village on A13. A 5-acre site with 150 touring pitches.

🔌 🐾 ☺ 🖥 🍷 ⚡ ◀ 🗻 ※ 🏔 🏮 🌿 ✕ 📞 🏕 ♿
→ U ▶ ◎ 🐟 🍷 🍴

ST MARTIN

Rozel Camping Park
Summerville Farm JE3 6AX ☎ 01534 856797
Nearby town: St Helier
▶ ▶ ▶ ♣ ★ ▲ £6.60-£10.40
Open Jun-Aug (rs end Apr-May snack bar closed)
Booking advisable Jul-Aug Last departure noon 🐕✕
An attractive and well-maintained secluded holiday site offering very good amenities. From St Helier follow Bagatelle Road (A6) or St Saviour's Road (A7) then B38. Last arrival and departure time as soon as possible after car ferry docks. A 4-acre site with 70 touring pitches and 20 statics.

🔌 🐾 ☺ 🖥 🎣 ⚡ ◀ 🗻 ※ 🏔 🏮 🌿 🅃 ✕ 📞 🚲
🏕 ♿
→ U ▶ 🐟 🍴

ISLE OF MAN

For the map, see
Cumbria

KIRK MICHAEL

Glen Wyllin Campsite (SC302901)
IM6 1AL ☎ 01624 878231 & 878836
Nearby town: Peel
▶ ▶ ▶ ★ 🚐 fr £6 ▲ fr £6
Open mid May-mid Sep Booking advisable end May-mid Jun

Caravans are not allowed on the Island. This tree-lined glen is divided by a tarmac road leading down to the beach. Just off A3 TT course at Kirk Michael, clearly signed on edge of village. A 9-acre site with 70 touring pitches.

LAXEY

Laxey Commissioners Campsite (SC438841)
Quarry Rd, (off Minorca Hill) ☎ 01624 861241 & 861816
Signposted
► ★ ⊞ fr £5 Å fr £5
Open Apr-Sep Booking advisable Apr-May Last arrival anytime
Level grassy site in hilly country with access to sea, beach and hills. A 2-acre site with 50 touring pitches.

SCOTLAND

BORDERS

BONCHESTER BRIDGE

Bonchester Bridge Caravan Park (NT586123)
Fernbank TD9 8JN ☎ 01450 86676
► ► ► 🚐 🚐 Å
Open Apr-Oct Booking advisable Jul-Aug Last arrival 22.00hrs Last departure noon
Neat little country village site close to Bure Water, on A6088 N of village centre.. A 3-acre site with 25 touring pitches.

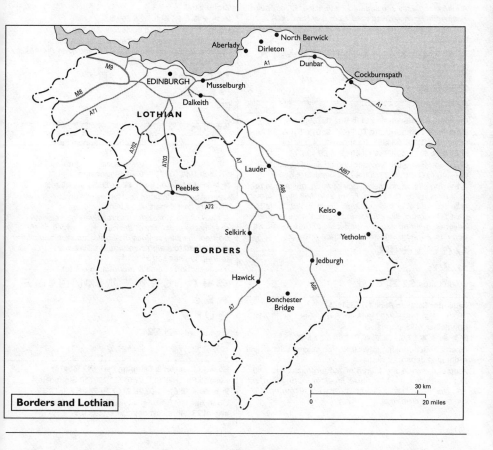

Borders and Lothian

COCKBURNSPATH

Chesterfield Caravan Site (NT772701)
Neuk Farm TD13 5YH ☎ 01368 830459 & 830226
Signposted
Nearby town: Dunbar
▶ ▶ ▶ ★ ♠ fr £5.50 ♠ fr £5.50 Å fr £5.50
Open Apr-Sep Booking advisable Jul-Aug Last arrival
21.00hrs Last departure noon
Secluded grass site set in Border country, screened by
gorse-covered hills. Situated approx .5m from the
village and within 3m of the sea. A 5-acre site with 33
touring pitches and 40 statics.
🔌 🐾 ⊙ 🗟 ❋ 🏔 🔒 📷 ❗
→ 🧺 🈸
💷

HAWICK

Riverside Caravan Park (NT537169)
TD9 8SY ☎ 01450 373785 Signposted
▶ ▶ ▶ ★ ♠ fr £6 ♠ fr £6 Å fr £6
Open Apr-10 Sep (rs 11 Sep-Nov) Booking advisable
May bank hol & Jul-Aug Last arrival 20.30hrs Last
departure noon 🐾
A pleasant grassy site situated on banks of River Teviot.
Near A698 Hawick-Kelso road 2.5m E of Hawick. A 2-
acre site with 25 touring pitches and 54 statics.
Fishing.
🔌 🐾 ⊙ 🗟 🖵 ❋ 🏔 🔒 ∅ 🈸 🆃 ✕ 🔔 🏧 📷 🐕
🈸
→ ∪ ▶ 🧺

JEDBURGH

Camping & Caravanning Club Site (NT658218)
Elliot Park, Edinburgh Rd TD8 6ED ☎ 01835 863393 (in
season) & 01203 694995 Signposted
▶ ▶ ▶ ★ ♠ £8.40-£9 ♠ £8.40-£9 Å £8.40-£9
Open end Mar-early Nov Booking advisable bank hols &
Jul-Aug Last arrival 21.00hrs Last departure noon
A touring site on northern edge of town, nestling at foot
of cliffs close to Jed Water. From S on A68 bypass town,
take 1st right over bailey bridge. From N A68, 1st left
past "Welcome" sign, following signs. Please see the
advertisement on page 27 for details of Club Members'
benefits. A 2-acre site with 60 touring pitches.
🔌 🐾 ⊙ 🗟 ❋ 🈸 🔔
→ 🧺 🈸
Credit Cards 💳 💳 💳

Jedwater Caravan Park (NT665160)
TD8 6QS ☎ 01835 840219 (4.5m S of Jedburgh off A68
on unclass rd) Signposted
▶ ▶ ▶ ★ ♠ £7.50-£8.50 ♠ £7.50-£8.50 Å £7-£8
Open Etr-Oct Booking advisable high season Last arrival
mdnt Last departure noon
A quiet riverside site 4.5m S of Jedburgh, close to A68
but unaffected by traffic noise. Ideal for touring Borders
and Northumberland. A 3-acre site with 30 touring
pitches and 60 statics.

Pitch/putt, bike hire, trampoline, football field.
🔌 🐾 ⊙ 🗟 🖵 🔍 ❋ 🏔 ∅ 🈸 🔔 🏧 🛒 🐕 🧺
→ ∪ ▶ 🧺
🈸

KELSO

Springwood Caravan Park (NT720334)
TD5 8LS ☎ 01573 224596 Signposted
▶ ▶ ▶ ♠ £7-£11 ♠ £7-£10 Å £6-£10
Open end Mar-Oct Booking advisable bank hols & Jul-
Aug Last arrival 23.00hrs
A very well-maintained site with a pleasant atmosphere.
Set in a secluded position close to the tree-lined River
Teviot about 1m W of town. A 4-acre site with 50 touring
pitches and 260 statics.
🔌 🐾 ⊙ 🗟 🖵 🔍 🏔 🔒 🔔
→ ∪ ▶ 🍼 🧺 🈸
💷

LAUDER

Thirlestane Castle Caravan & Camping Site (NT536473)
Thirlestane Castle TD2 6RU ☎ 01578 722542 & 722254
Signposted
▶ ▶ ★ ♠ fr £6 ♠ fr £6 Å £5-£6
Open Etr-Oct Booking advisable Jul-Aug
Mainly level grass site set in the grounds of the
impressive Thirlestane Castle. The site is off the A697. A
5-acre site with 60 touring pitches.
🔌 🐾 ⊙ 🗟 🔔
→ ▶ 🧺 🈸
💷

PEEBLES

Crossburn Caravan Park (NT248417)
The Glades, 95 Edinburgh Rd
EH45 8ED ☎ 01721 720501 Signposted
▶ ▶ ▶ ♦ 👫 ★ ♠ £8-£10 ♠ £7-£8.50 Å £4.50-£9
Open Apr-Oct Booking advisable Jul-Aug Last arrival
23.00hrs Last departure 14.00hrs
A level site in a peaceful and relatively quiet location,
despite the proximity of the main road which partly
borders the site, as does the Eddleston Water. Facilities
maintained to a high standard. A 6-acre site with 35
touring pitches and 95 statics.
9 hole putting course & mountain bikes for hire.
🔌 🛒 🐾 ⊙ 🗟 🔍 🔍 ❋ 🏔 🔒 ∅ 🈸 🆃 🔔 📷 🏧
🐕 🧺 ♿
→ ∪ ▶ 🧺
Credit Cards 💳 💳

Rosetta Caravan & Camping Park (NT245415)
Rosetta Rd EH45 8PG ☎ 01721 720770 Signposted
▶ ▶ ▶ ★ ♠ £7.75-£8.25 ♠ £7.75-£8.25 Å fr £3.25
Open Apr-Oct Booking advisable public & bank hols Last
arrival 23.00hrs Last departure 15.00hrs

A pleasant parkland site set in hilly woodland country. .5m from town centre off A72. A 25-acre site with 160 touring pitches and 29 statics.

Bowling & putting greens.

SELKIRK

Victoria Park Caravan & Camping Park (NT465287)

Victoria Park, Buccleuch Rd TD7 5DN ☎ 01750 20897 Signposted

▶ ▶ ★ ⊕ £5.50-£6.50 ⊕ £5.50-£6.50 ▲ £5.50-£6.50

Open Apr-Oct (rs 10-18 Jun site closed) Booking advisable Jul-Aug Last arrival 21.00hrs Last departure 14.00hrs

A consistently well-maintained site with good basic facilities forming part of public park and swimming pool complex close to River Ettrick. From A707/A708 N of town, cross river bridge, take first left then left again. A 3-acre site with 60 touring pitches.

Mini gymnasium, sauna, sunbed.

YETHOLM

Kirkfield Caravan Park (NT821281)

TD5 8RU ☎ 01573 420346 & 420201 Signposted

▶ ▶ ⊕ ⊕

Open Apr-Oct Booking advisable public hols & Jul-Aug Last arrival 20.00hrs Last departure noon

Small, mainly sloping site (southwards). Set on edge of village overlooking a valley. 7m S of Kelso on B6352. A 1-acre site with 15 touring pitches and 15 statics.

CENTRAL

ABERFOYLE

Trossachs Holiday Park (NS544976)

FK8 3SA ☎ 01877 382614 (access on E side of A81 1m S of junc A821) Signposted

▶ ▶ ▶ ⊕ ⊕ £6.50-£9.50 ⊕ £6.50-£9.50 ▲ £6.50-£9.50

Open 15 Mar-Oct Booking advisable anytime Last arrival 22.00hrs Last departure noon   ➥

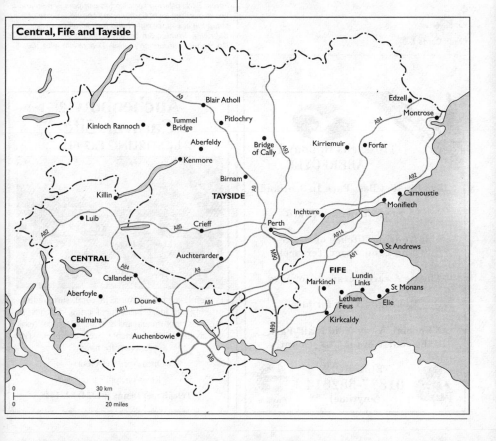

Central, Fife and Tayside

Edzell
Montrose
Blair Atholl
Pitlochry
Kinloch Rannoch
Tummel Bridge
Aberfeldy
Kirriemuir
Forfar
Bridge of Cally
Kenmore
Birnam
Carnoustie
Monifieth
TAYSIDE
Killin
Inchture
Perth
Luib
Crieff
St Andrews
CENTRAL
Auchterarder
Callander
FIFE
Lundin Links
Aberfoyle
Markinch
Doune
St Monans
Letham Feus
Elie
Balmaha
Kirkcaldy
Auchenbowie

0   30 km
0   20 miles

An imaginatively designed terraced site offering a high degree of quality all round, with fine views across Flanders Moss. Sited off A81, 3m S of Aberfoyle. A 15-acre site with 45 touring pitches and 38 statics. Cycle hire.

🔌 🐾 ☉ 🗑 🔧 🔍 ♿ ❊ 🏔 ⓘ ⊘ 🏧 Ⓣ 🔔 🐕 🐈 🦵 → ▶ ⌇ 🍴

🖾

Credit Cards 🖃 🖾 🖾

Cobleland Campsite (NS531989)
FK8 3UX ☎ 01877 382392
(access on E side of A81 1m S of junc A821) Signposted
▶ ▶ 🚐 🚍 🛆
Open 26 Mar-29 Oct Booking advisable bank hols & May-Aug Last arrival 20.00hrs Last departure noon
Set within the Queen Elizabeth Forest Park, this grass and tree-studded site offers seclusion, views, forest walks and free fishing on the River Forth which borders the camping area. Signed on unclass road off A81 approx 1.5 miles S of Aberfoyle. An 8-acre site with 100 touring pitches and 27 statics.
Fishing & swimming in river.

🔌 🐾 ☉ 🗑 🔧 ❊ 🏔 ⊘ 🏧 Ⓣ 🔔 🚲 🏕 🛋 🐕 🦵
♿
→ ▶ ⌇ 🍴
Credit Cards 🖃

AUCHENBOWIE
Auchenbowie Caravan & Camping Site (NS795880)
FK7 8HE ☎ 01324 822141
Nearby town: Stirling
▶ ▶ 🚐 £7 🚍 £7 🛆 £5.50-£7
Open Apr-Oct Booking advisable mid Jul-mid Aug Last departure noon
A mainly level, grassy site in quiet rural location .5m S of junction 9 of M9. Turn right off A872 for half a mile, signposted. A 3.5-acre site with 60 touring pitches and 7 statics.

🔌 🐾 ☉ 🔧 🏔 ⓘ ⊘ 🔔 🛋 🖾
→ ∪ ▶ 🚻 🍴 🗑 🦵
Credit Cards 🖃

BALMAHA
Cashel Caravan & Camping Site (NS396939)
G63 0AW ☎ 01360 870234
Nearby town: Drymen
▶ ▶ ▶ 🚐 🚍 🛆
Open 26 Mar-30 Oct Booking advisable public hols & Jul-Aug Last arrival 20.00hrs Last departure noon
An attractive and well-wooded site, lying on the eastern shores of Loch Lomond within the Queen Elizabeth Forest Park, offering seclusion to campers and splendid views over the loch. Caravanners should beware of a steep hill at a quick right hand turn when leaving Balmaha. Situated 3m beyond Balmaha village on A837 Drymen-Rowardennan road. A 12-acre site with 100

touring pitches and 65 statics.
Boating on Loch Lomond.

🔌📶☉▣🍳✳🏠🚿Ⓜ️🅿️🚿⬆️🛖🐕🐶♿

➔⛵🦆🛶🎣

Credit Cards 🔲 🔲

CALLANDER

Callander Holiday Park (NN615073)
Invertrossachs Rd FK17 8HW ☎ 01877 330265
Signposted
▶▶▶ 🚐 £10 🚃 £10
Open 15 Mar-Oct Booking advisable Jun-Aug Last
arrival 22.00hrs Last departure noon
An attractive terraced park with glorious views over the
surrounding countryside. From A84 in centre of
Callander take A81 Glasgow road over bridge, then turn
right in 200 yards towards Invertrossachs road, and site
in .5 mile. A 10-acre site with 54 touring pitches and 110
statics.
Fishing on site.

🔌📶☉▣✳Ⓜ️🅿️🔋🚿♿

➔∪🅿️🎣🛶🚲

Gart Caravan Park (NN643070)
The Gart FK17 8LE ☎ 01877 330002 Signposted
▶▶▶ 🚐 £10.50-£11 🚃 £10.50-£11
Open Etr or Apr-15 Oct Booking advisable Last arrival
22.00hrs Last departure noon
A well-screened site bordered by trees and shrubs and
with helpful owners. 1m E of Callander on A84. A 25-

acre site with 122 touring pitches and 66 statics.
Fishing on site.

🔌📶☉▣✳Ⓜ️🅿️🔋🚿🐕🚿♿

➔∪🅿️🎣🛶🚲

DOUNE

**Blair Drummond Caravan Club Site
(NS727991)**
Cuthill Brae FK9 4UX
☎ 01786 841208 (1.5m S) Signposted
▶▶▶ 🚶🚶‍♀️ 🚐🚃
Open end Mar-6 Jan Booking advisable all times
An attractive site set in and around a walled garden, and
sheltered by mature trees and flowering shrubs. An 8.5-
acre site with 100 touring pitches.

🔌📶☉▣🍳Ⓜ️🅿️🔋🚿🏧🔋🚿♿

➔∪🅿️🎣🛶

Credit Cards 🔲 🔲 🔲

KILLIN

Maragowan Caravan Club Site (NN571337)
Aberfeldy Rd FK21 8TN ☎ 01567 820245
▶▶▶ 🚐🚃
Open 26 Mar-18 Oct Booking advisable bank hols &
Jun-Sep
An ideal family holiday base set on the banks of the

River Lochay, and within walking distance of Killin. An 8.5-acre site with 118 touring pitches.
Veg prep area.

DUMFRIES & GALLOWAY

LUIB

Glendochart Caravan Park (NN477278)
FK20 8QT ☎ 01567 2637 Signposted

Open Etr-Oct (rs Mar-Etr no showers) Booking advisable Jul & Aug Last arrival 22.00hrs Last departure noon
A small, well-maintained site with imaginative landscaping. Set on hillside in Glendochart with glorious mountain and hill-country views, 5m E of Crianlarich on the A85. A 7-acre site with 45 touring pitches and 40 statics.

STIRLING

See **Auchenbowie**

ANNAN

Galabank Caravan Park (NY192676)
North St DG12 5BQ ☎ 01461 203311 Signposted

Open Etr-Sep
A tidy, well-maintained grassy little site close to the centre of town but with pleasant rural views, and skirted by River Annan. Follow B721 into town centre, turn rt at traffic lights into Lady St and site 500yds on left. A 1-acre site with 30 touring pitches.

AUCHENMALG

Cock Inn Caravan Park (NX238518)
DG8 0JT ☎ 01581 500227 Signposted
Nearby town: Stranraer
► ► ► ⛺ £6.50-£10 ⛺ £6.50-£10 ▲ £5
Open Mar-Oct Booking advisable bank hols & Jul-Aug

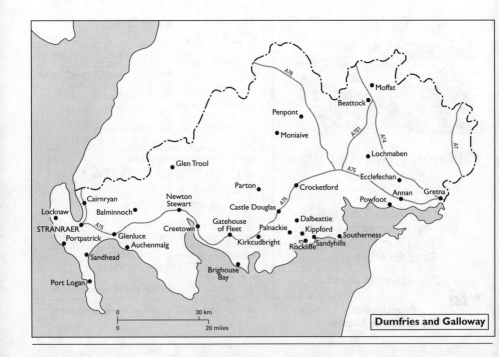

Dumfries and Galloway

Last departure 11.00hrs
*A grassy site in meadowland, close to sea, beach and
main (A747 Glenluce-Fort William) road. Overlooks Luce
Bay. A 2-acre site with 40 touring pitches and 80 statics.*

BALMINNOCH

Three Lochs Holiday Park (NX272655)
DG8 OEP ☎ 01671 830304
Nearby town: Newton Stewart
► ► ► ♦ ★ ₩ £8-£9.50 ₩ £8-£9.50 ▲ £5-£9.50
Open Etr-mid Oct Booking advisable bank hols & Jul-
Aug Last arrival 22.00hrs Last departure 11.00hrs
*A spacious, well-maintained site in moorland close to
lochs, N off A75, with lovely views. Signed off B7027 on
an unclass road in Glenluce direction. . A 15-acre site
with 45 touring pitches and 90 statics.*
Games room & snooker.

BEATTOCK

Beattock House Hotel Caravan Park (NT079027)
DG10 9QB ☎ 01683 300403 & 300402 Signposted
Nearby town: Moffat
► ► ₩ fr £6.50 ₩ fr £6.50 ▲ fr £6
Open Mar-Oct (rs winter parking limited) Booking
advisable
*Pleasant, well-maintained level touring site set amongst
trees in the grounds of a country house, adjacent to
A74. A 2-acre site with 15 touring pitches.*
Fishing.

BRIGHOUSE BAY

**Brighouse Bay Holiday Park
(NX628453)**
DG6 4TS ☎ 01557 870267
Signposted
Nearby town: Kirkcudbright
► ► ► ► ♦ ᶭᶭ ⊕ Holiday Centre ★ ₩ £7.95-£10.75
₩ £7.95-£10.75
▲ £7.95-£10.75
Open Apr-Sep (rs Oct-Mar) Booking advisable Etr,
Spring bank hol & Jul-Aug Last arrival 21.30hrs Last
departure 11.30hrs
*This grassy site enjoys a marvellous coastal setting
adjacent to the beach and with superb sea views.
Pitches have been imaginatively sculpted into the
meadowland with stone walls and hedges blending in
with the site's mature trees. These features together
with the large range of leisure activities available make
this an excellent holliday centre. Winner of the 1994* ➥

Campsite of the Year Award for Scotland. A 30-acre site with 190 touring pitches and 120 statics.
All weather family leisure centre. 9 hole golf.
See advertisement under KIRKCUDBRIGHT

🔌 🛒 📻 ⊙ 🗑 🍳 🥤 ⚓ ☀ 🍴 🎮 🏪 🛢 🌀 ⊞ 🚽 ✕ 📞
🐷 🚿 🎣 🐕 🐾 🚻 ♿
➜ 🎵

○○○○○○○○○○○

Cairnryan Caravan & Chalet Park (NX075673)
DG9 8QX ☎ 01581 200231 Signposted
Nearby town: Stranraer
▶ ▶ ▶ 🚐 fr £8 🚛 fr £8 ▲ fr £5
Open 22 May-Oct (rs Apr-21 May restricted pub hours)
Booking advisable Jul-Aug Last arrival 23.00hrs Last departure noon
Mainly static site immediately opposite ferry terminal for N Ireland (Larne). Ideal stopover site with good views of Loch Ryan. A 7.5-acre site with 15 touring pitches and 83 statics.
Snooker & pool tables.

🔌 📻 ⊙ 🗑 🥤 ⚓ ☀ 🍴 🎮 🏪 🛢 ⊞ 🚽 ✕ 📞 🐷 🚻
➜ ∪ ▶ 🎵
🔢

Lochside Caravan & Camping Site (NX766618)
Lochside Park DG7 1EZ ☎ 01556 502949 & 01557 330291 ext 320 Signposted
▶ ▶ ▶ ★ 🚐 £6.50-£8 🚛 £6.50-£8 ▲ £6.50-£8
Open Etr-mid Oct Last departure noon
Municipal touring site incorporating park with recreational facilities, on southern edge of town in attractive setting adjacent to Carlingwark Loch. Situated off B736 Auchencairn road. A 5.5-acre site with 161 touring pitches.
Putting, rowing boats (wknds & high season)

🔌 📻 ⊙ 🗑 ☀ 🎮 📞 ♿
➜ ▶ 🍴 🎵 🚻

Castle Cary Holiday Park (NX475576)
DG8 7DQ ☎ 01671 820264
Signposted
▶ ▶ ▶ ▶ ♦ 🕴 ⊕ ★ 🚐 £7.80-£10 🚛 £7.80-£10 ▲ £7.80-£10
Open Mar-Jan (rs Oct-Mar reception/shop, no heated outdoor pool) Last arrival anytime Last departure noon
This attractive site in the grounds of Cassencarie House is sheltered by woodlands, and faces south towards Wigtown Bay. The park's secluded location, beautiful landscaping and excellent facilities have earned it this year's nomination as Winner for Scotland of the AA's 1996 Campsite of the Year award. For full details of the award winners, see the colour section at the front of the book. A 6-acre site with 50 touring pitches and 26 statics.
Mountain bike hire, crazy golf, snooker & fishing.

See advertisement under Colour Section

🔌 🛒 📻 ⊙ 🗑 🍳 🥤 ⚓ ☀ 🍴 🎮 🏪 🛢 🌀 ⊞
🚽 ✕ 📞 🐷 🚿 🎣 🐕 🐾 🚻 ♿
➜ ▶ ◎ 🎵
🔢
Credit Cards 💳 💳 💳

○○○○○○○○○○○

Park of Brandedleys (NX830725)
DG2 8RG ☎ 01556 690250
Signposted
Nearby town: Dumfries
▶ ▶ ▶ ▶ ♦ 🕴 ⊕ ★ 🚐 £12 🚛 £8-£12 ▲ £8-£12
Open Etr-Oct (rs Mar-Etr some facilities restricted)
Booking advisable public hols & Jul-Aug Last arrival 22.00hrs Last departure noon
A well-maintained site in an elevated position off the A75, with fine views of Auchenreoch Loch and beyond. Excellent on-site amenities. A 9-acre site with 80 touring pitches and 27 statics.
Putting, badminton court & outdoor draughts.

🔌 🛒 📻 ⊙ 🗑 🍳 🥤 ⚓ ☀ 🍴 🎮 🏪 🛢 🌀
⊞ 🚽 ✕ 📞 🐷 🚿 🐕 🐾 🚻 ♿
➜ ◎ 🎵
Credit Cards 💳 💳

○○○○○○○○○○○

DALBEATTIE

Islecroft Caravan & Camping Site (NX837615)
Colliston Park, Mill St DG5 4HE ☎ 01556 610012 &
01557 330291 ext 323 Signposted
► ► ★ ⊞ £5-£6 ⊞ £5-£6 ⚠ £5-£6
Open Etr-Sep Last departure noon
*A neat site in two sections tucked away to rear of town,
close to local park. Access is via Mill Street. A 3.5-acre
site with 74 touring pitches.*

🔌 ⌕ ⊙ ℃
→ ⊩ ⌇ ⌇ ⚒

ECCLEFECHAN

Hoddom Castle Caravan Park (SE154729)
Hoddom DG11 1AS ☎ 01576 300251 Signposted
Nearby town: Lockerbie
► ► ► ► ♦ ⊞ £6.50-£10 ⊞ £6.50-£10 ⚠ £6.50-£10
Open Etr or Apr-Oct (rs early season cafeteria closed)
Booking advisable bank hols & Jul-Aug Last arrival
21.00hrs Last departure 15.30hrs
*A beautiful site within the grounds of Hoddom Castle,
with amenities housed in the keep and outhouses. 2m
SW of Hoddom Bridge which carries B725 over River
Annan. A 12-acre site with 170 touring pitches and 29
statics.*
Nature trails, visitor centre & 9 hole golf course.
See advertisement under LOCKERBIE

🔌 ⌕ ⊙ 🗗 🗨 ⚲ ⚡ ☀ ⚺ ⛰ ⚓ ⊕ Ⓣ ✕ ℃ ⛪
⛲ ⏢ ⚑ ⚒ ⚷
→ ⊩ ◎ ⌇

Cressfield Caravan Park (NY196744)
DG11 3RD ☎ 01576 300702 Signposted
Nearby town: Lockerbie
► ► ► ⊞ £6-£7.50 ⊞ £6-£7.50 ⚠ £6-£7.50
Open all year Last arrival 23.00hrs Last departure
11.00hrs
*An open, spacious park with views to the hills, ideal as a
stopover or for touring the area. Take loop service road
from A74(M) to Ecclefechan, and site is at S end of
town. A 12-acre site with 65 touring pitches and 48
statics.*
Sports enclosure, golf nets, petanque, giant chess.

🔌 ⌕ ⊙ 🗗 🗨 ☀ ⛰ ⚡ ℃ ⚓ ⊞ ⚒ ⚷
→ ⊩ ⌇
£⃣

GATEHOUSE OF FLEET

Anwoth Caravan Site (NX595563)
DG7 2JU ☎ 01557 814333 Signposted
► ► ► ⊞ ⊞
Open 26 Mar-1 Oct Booking advisable Jul-Aug Last
arrival 22.00hrs Last departure noon
*A sheltered touring site close to the town centre, signed
from town centre, on right towards Stranraer direction.
A 2-acre site with 28 touring pitches and 38 statics.*

🔌 ⌕ ⊙ 🗗 ⚡ ☀ ⚡ ⊞
→ ⊩ ⌇ ⚒

GLENLUCE

Glenluce Caravan & Camping Park (NX201576)
DG8 0QR ☎ 01581 300412 Signposted
Nearby town: Stranraer
► ► ► ⊞ £7-£8.50 ⊞ £7-£8.50 ⚠ £6-£7.50
Open Mar-Oct Booking advisable Jul-Aug Last arrival
22.00hrs Last departure noon
*A neat, well-maintained site situated beside a small river
close to the village centre. Off A75 Stranraer road.
Concealed entrance at telephone kiosk in centre of main
street. A 3-acre site with 30 touring pitches and 30
statics.*

🔌 ⌕ ⊙ 🗗 🗨 ☀ ⛰ ⚡ ⚡ ⊕ Ⓣ ℃ ⛲ ⏢ ⚑ ⚷
→ ∪ ⊩ ⌇ ⚒
£⃣

Whitecairn Farm Caravan Park (NX225599)
DG8 0NZ ☎ 01581 300267 Signposted
Nearby town: Stranraer
► ► ►
Open Mar-Oct Booking advisable all times Last arrival
22.00hrs Last departure 11.00hrs
*A well-maintained farmland site, in open countryside
with extensive views. 1.5m N of Glenluce village on
Glenluce-Glassnock Bridge Rd. A 3-acre site .*

🔌 ⌕ ⊙ 🗨 ☀ ⚡ ⚡ ℃ ⏢
→ ∪ ⊩

GLEN TROOL

Caldons Campsite (NX400790)
DG8 6SU ☎ 01671 840218
► ► ► ♦ ⊞ ⊞ ⚠
Open Etr-Sep Booking advisable Etr, Spring bank hol &
Jul-Aug
*Secluded Forestry Commission site amidst fine hill, loch
and woodland scenery in Galloway Forest Park. 13m N
of Newton Stewart. A 25-acre site with 160 touring
pitches.*

🔌 ⚒
→ ⌇

Glen Trool Holiday Park (NX400790)
DG8 6RN ☎ 01671 840280 Signposted
Nearby town: Newton Stewart
► ► ► ★ ⊞ £6.50-£8 ⊞ £6.50-£8 ⚠ £6.50-£8
Open Mar-Oct Booking advisable Jul-Aug Last arrival
22.30hrs Last departure noon
*A small compact site close to the village of Glen Trool
and bordered by the Galloway National Park. 9m N of
Newton Stewart. A 1-acre site with 14 touring pitches
and 26 statics.*
Trout pond for fly fishing, bikes for hire.

🔌 ⌕ ⊙ 🗨 ⚡ ☀ ⚡ ⚡ ⊕ ℃ ⚒ ⚷
→ ∪ ⌇
£⃣

Credit Cards 📇 📇

GRETNA

Braids Caravan Park (NT313674)
Annan Rd DG16 5DQ ☎ 01461 337409 Signposted
Nearby town: Annan
▶ ▶ ▶ ⊕ £6-£7 ⊕ £6-£7 ▲ £5
Open all year Booking advisable Jul-Sep Last arrival
22.00hrs Last departure noon
*A well-maintained grassy site in centre of the village just
inside Scotland. Situated on B721 .5m from village on
right, towards Annan. A 4-acre site with 70 touring
pitches and 8 statics.*

🔧🐾☉🏴⚡✳🅿📶🛈⊘📋🍽️📞🔋♿
➜▶🧦
🅰️

KIPPFORD

Kippford Caravan Park (NX844564)
Kippford Caravan Park DG5 4LF ☎ 01556 620636
Signposted
Nearby town: Dalbeattie
▶ ▶ ▶ ★ ⊕ £7-£9 ⊕ £7-£9 ▲ £2-£9
Open Mar-Oct Booking advisable Last arrival 21.00hrs
Last departure 21.00hrs
*Part-level, part-sloping grass site surrounded by trees
and bushes, set in hilly country adjacent to Urr Water
estuary and stony beach. On A710. A 4-acre site with 45
touring pitches and 119 statics.*
Childrens adventure playground.

🔧🐾☉🖥️🏴📶🛈🔋📞🐕🔋
➜∪▶⛴🧦

KIRKCUDBRIGHT

**Seaward Caravan Park
(NX662494)**
Dhoon Bay DG6 4TJ
☎ 01557 870267 & 01557 331079 (2m SW off B727
Borgue Road) Signposted
▶ ▶ ▶ ⬥♦⃰ ★ ⊕ £6.95-£9.50 ⊕ £6.95-£9.50 ▲ £6.95-£9.50
Open Apr-Oct (rs Mar-mid May & mid Sep-Oct swimming
pool closed) Booking advisable Spring bank hols & Jun-
Aug Last arrival 21.30hrs Last departure 11.30hrs
*This very attractive elevated site has outstanding views
over the Dee estuary. Facilities are well organised and
neatly kept. On B727 from Kirkcudbright towards Borgue.
An 8-acre site with 26 touring pitches and 30 statics.*
TV aerial hook-up, mini golf. Dishwashing.

🔧🛒🐾☉🖥️🏴🥄🔌☎🛒✳🏴📶🛈⊘📋📞🐕
🔋♿
➜∪▶🧦

Silvercraigs Caravan & Camping Site (NX686508)
Silvercraigs Rd DG6 4BT ☎ 01557 330123 & 330291
Signposted
▶ ▶ ★ ⊕ £6-£7.50 ⊕ £6-£7.50 ▲ £6-£7.50
Open Etr-mid Oct Last departure noon
*A well-maintained municipal site overlooking town and
harbour, just a short stroll to the town centre. A 6-acre
site with 50 touring pitches.*

🔧🐾☉✳🏴📞
➜∪▶⛴🧦🔋

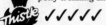

LOCHMABEN

Halleaths Caravan Site (NY098818)
DG11 1NA ☎ 01387 810630 Signposted
Nearby town: Lockerbie
▶ ▶ ▶ 🚐 £7 🚐 £7 ▲ £7
Open Mar-Nov Booking advisable bank hols & Jul-Aug
Last arrival 22.00hrs Last departure noon
*Level, grassy site in a sheltered position with a wood on
one side and a high hedge on the other. From Lockerbie
on A74(M) take A709 to Lochmaben - .5m on right after
crossing River Annan. An 8-acre site with 70 touring
pitches and 12 statics.*
Fishing (charged).

Kirkloch Brae Caravan Site (NY082825)

☎01461 203311 Signposted
▶ ▶ 🚐 🚐 ▲
Open Etr-Oct
*A grassy lochside site with superb views and well-
maintained facilities. Signed from centre of town. 30
touring pitches.*

LOCHNAW

Drumlochart Caravan Park (NW997634)
DG9 0RN ☎ 01776 870232 Signposted
Nearby town: Stranraer
▶ ▶ ▶ 🚐 £7.50-£9.50 🚐 £7.50-£9.50
Open Mar-Oct Booking advisable bank hols & Jul-Aug
Last arrival 22.00hrs Last departure noon
*A peaceful rural site in hilly woodland, adjacent to Loch
Ryan and Luce Bay. 5m NW of Stranraer on B7043. A 9-
acre site with 30 touring pitches and 96 statics.*
Fly-fishing on stocked trout loch.

LOCKERBIE

See Ecclefechan

MOFFAT

Camping & Caravanning Club Site (NT085050)
Hammerlands Farm DG10 9QL ☎ 01683 20436
(in season) & 01203 694995 Signposted
▶ ▶ ▶ ★ 🚐 £9.30-£10 🚐 £9.30-£10 ▲ £9.30-£10
Open end Mar-early Nov Booking advisable Spring bank
hol & peak periods Last arrival 21.00hrs Last departure
noon
*Well-maintained level grass touring site. Leave A74 onto
A701 to Moffat centre, take A708 and site is signed. Please
see the advertisement on page 27 for details of Club
Members' benefits. A 12-acre site with 200 touring pitches.*

Credit Cards 🔲 🔲 🔲

MONIAIVE

Woodlea Hotel (NX767895)
DG3 4EN ☎ 01848 200209
▶ ▶ 🚐 🚐
Open Apr-Oct Booking advisable anytime Last arrival
23.00hrs Last departure noon
*A small site in hotel grounds with bays amongst shrubs
and trees. It lies 1.5m W of Moniaive on A702. A 1-acre
site with 8 touring pitches.*
Badminton, bowls, croquet, putting, sauna & solarium.

NEWTON STEWART

Creebridge Caravan Park (NX415656)
Minnigaff DG8 6AJ ☎ 01671 402324 Signposted
▶ ▶ ▶ ★ 🚐 fr £3.50 🚐 £3-£3.50 ▲ £2-£3.50
Open Apr-Oct (rs Mar only one toilet block open)
Booking advisable Jul-Aug Last arrival 20.00hrs Last
departure noon
*A level urban site a short walk from the amenities of
town. .25m E of Newton Stewart on A75. A 2-acre site
with 36 touring pitches and 50 statics.*
Security street lighting.

Talnotry Campsite (NX492719)
Queens Way DG8 7BL ☎ 01671 402420 (7m NE off A712)
Signposted
▷ ★ ⊞ £5-£6 ⊞ £5-£6 ▲ £5-£6
Open 22 Mar-Sep Booking advisable
*An attractive open grassy site set amidst the superb
scenery of Galloway Forest Park close to A712 and the
picturesque Queens Way. A 15-acre site with 60 touring
pitches.*

✳ ⚠ ⓐ ✗ ⓛ ⊟ ⓗ ⓩ ⓑ
➔ ∪ ⓟ ⓔⓔ ⌿ ⓞ

Credit Cards ◪

PALNACKIE

Barlochan Caravan Park (NX819572)
DG7 1PF ☎ 01556 600256 Signposted
Nearby town: Dalbeattie
▶ ▶ ▶ ⊞ ⊞ ▲
Open Apr-Oct (rs Apr-mid May & mid Sep-end Oct
swimming pool) Booking advisable Spring bank hol &
Jul-Aug Last arrival 21.30hrs Last departure 11.30hrs
*An attractive terraced site in a sheltered position but
with fine, open views. On A711. A 9-acre site with 20
touring pitches and 40 statics.*
Fishing, pitch & putt. Dishwashing facilities.

ⓞ ⓝ ⊙ ⓞ ⓠ ⓥ ◖ ⊟ ✳ ⚠ ⓐ ⌀ ⊞ ⓣ ⓛ ⊟
ⓗ ⓩ ⓗ
➔ ⓟ ⌿

PARTON

Loch Ken Holiday Park (NX687702)
DG7 3NE ☎ 01644 470282 Signposted
Nearby town: Castle Douglas
▶ ▶ ▶ ◆ ⊞ ⊞ ▲
Open mid Mar-mid Nov Booking advisable Etr, Spring
bank hol & Jun-Aug Last arrival 21.00hrs Last departure
noon
*An attractive touring site on eastern shores of Loch Ken,
with superb views. Off A713. A 5-acre site with 52
touring pitches and 33 statics.*
Bike, boat & canoe hire, fishing on loch.

ⓞ ⓝ ⊙ ⓞ ⓠ ✳ ⚠ ⓐ ⌀ ⓣ ⓛ ⓗ ⊟ ⓗ ⓩ ⓗ
➔ ⓐ ⌄ ⌿

PENPONT

Penpont Caravan and Camping Park (NX852947)
DG3 4BH ☎ 01848 330470 Signposted
▶ ▶ ⊞ £6.50-£8 ⊞ £5.50-£7 ▲ £5-£8
Open Etr or Apr-Oct Booking advisable Jul-Aug Last
arrival 23.00hrs Last departure 14.00hrs
*Quiet, grassy, slightly sloping site by roadside.
Excellently situated for touring. On the A702 from
Thornhill on left before Penpont village. A 1.5-acre site
with 20 touring pitches and 20 statics.*

ⓞ ⓝ ⊙ ✳ ⓐ ⌀ ⊞ ⓛ ⓗ
➔ ⓟ ⌿

PORT LOGAN

New England Bay Caravan Club Site (NX120420)
DG9 9NX ☎ 01776 860275 Signposted
Nearby town: Stranraer
▶ ▶ ◆ ⊞ ⊞ ▲
Open 26 Mar-28 Sep Booking advisable bank hols & Jul-
Aug Last arrival 20.00hrs Last departure noon
*A very spacious and attractive seaside holiday site with
level pitches leading directly onto a sandy beach, ideal
for swimming, sailing and canoeing. Superb sea and
country views from all pitches, and plenty of natural
screening. From Stranraer on A77 continue onto A716
signed Drummore, and site on left in 10miles about 1m
past B7065 junc. A 17-acre site with 150 touring pitches.*
Veg prep & dishwashing area.

ⓞ ⓝ ⊙ ⓞ ⓠ ✳ ⚠ ⓐ ⌀ ⊞ ⓣ ⓛ ⓗ
➔ ∪ ⓟ ⓐ ⌿ ⓩ

Credit Cards ◪ ▦

PORTPATRICK

Galloway Point Holiday Park (NX005537)
Portree Farm DG9 9AA ☎ 01776 810561 Signposted
Nearby town: Stranraer
▶ ▶ ◆ ⊞ £9-£12 ⊞ £9-£12 ▲ £7-£10
Open Mar-Oct Booking advisable Mar, & May-Oct Last
arrival 23.00hrs Last departure 14.00hrs
*Strung out along gorse-clad downland, the holiday park
looks out on the North Channel 1m S of town. A 10-acre
site with 100 touring pitches and 60 statics.*

ⓞ ⓝ ⊙ ⓞ ✳ ⓨ ⚠ ⓐ ⌀ ⊞ ⓣ ✗ ⓛ ⓗ ⓗ ⓩ
➔ ∪ ⓟ ⌄ ⌿
⊞

POWFOOT

Queensberry Bay Caravan Park (NY135653)
DG12 5PU ☎ 01461 700205 Signposted
Nearby town: Annan
▶ ▶ ▶ ⊞ ⊞ ▲
Open Etr-Oct Booking advisable Jul-Aug Last arrival
20.00hrs Last departure noon
*A flat, mainly grassy site in a quiet location on the
shores of the Solway Firth with views across the estuary
to Cumbrian hills. Follow sign to Powfoot off B724 and
drive through village past golf club on single track road
on shore edge to site in .75m. A 5-acre site with 100
touring pitches and 60 statics.*
See advertisement under ANNAN

ⓞ ⓝ ⊙ ⓞ ⓐ ⌀ ⊞ ⓛ ⓩ
➔ ⓟ ⓔⓔ ⌿

ROCKCLIFFE

Castle Point Caravan Park (NX851539)
DG5 4QL ☎ 01556 630248 Signposted
Nearby town: Dalbeattie
▶ ▶ ⊞ £6.50-£8.50 ⊞ £6.50-£8.50 ▲ £6.50-£8.50
Open Etr-Sep (rs Mar-Etr & 1-30 Oct limited supervision)
Booking advisable Whit wk & Jul-Aug Last arrival
23.00hrs Last departure 11.00hrs

A level, grassy site with superb views across the estuary and surrounding hilly countryside. A 3-acre site with 29 touring pitches and 8 statics.

SANDHEAD

Sands of Luce Caravan Park (NX103510)
D69 9JR ☎ 01776 830456 Signposted
Nearby town: Stranraer
► ► ► 🚗 £6-£7.50 🚐 £5.50-£7 ▲ £6-£7.50
Open mid Mar-Oct Booking advisable Jul-Aug Last arrival 22.00hrs Last departure noon
A friendly site on a beautiful sandy beach, with lovely views across Luce Bay. Facilities are well-maintained and clean. Turn left off A75 onto B7084 2m from Glenluce, signed Sandhead and Drunmore, and site signed on left in 5m. A 5-acre site with 26 touring pitches and 34 statics.
Boat launching, dishwashing sinks.

SANDYHILLS

Sandyhills Bay Leisure Park (NX892552)
DG5 4NY ☎ 01557 870267 & 01387 780257
(7m from Dalbeattie, 6.5m from Kirkbean) Signposted
Nearby town: Dalbeattie
► ► ► ♣ ★ 🚗 £6.50-£9.51 🚐 £6.50-£9.51 ▲ £6.50-£9.51
Open Apr-Oct Booking advisable Spring bank hol & Jun-Aug Last arrival 21.30hrs Last departure 11.30hrs
A flat, grassy site adjacent and with access to south-facing Sandyhills Bay and beach, sheltered by woods and hills with superb views. A 6-acre site with 26 touring pitches and 34 statics.
Dishwashing facilities.

SOUTHERNESS

Southerness Holiday Village (NX976545)
DG2 8AZ ☎ 01387 880256 & 880281 Signposted
Nearby town: Dumfries
► ► ► 🚗 £6.50-£8 🚐 £6.50-£8 ▲ £6.50-£8
Open Mar-Oct Last departure 16.00hrs
A large family campsite with plenty of on-site entertainment situated in close proximity to sandy beach. An 8-acre site with 200 touring pitches and 350 statics.
Amusement centre, disco, videos.

STRANRAER

Aird Donald Caravan Park (NX075605)
DG9 8RN ☎ 01776 702025 Signposted
► ► ► ► ★ 🚗 fr £8 🚐 fr £8 ▲ £3.50-£8
Open all year Booking advisable Last departure 16.00hrs
A spacious touring site, mainly grass but with tarmac hard-standing area. On the fringe of town screened by mature shrubs and trees. Ideal stopover en route to N.I. ferry ports. A 12-acre site with 100 touring pitches and 8 statics.

FIFE

For the map of this county, see Central

ELIE

Shell Bay Caravan Park (NO465005)
KY9 1AR ☎ 01333 330283 Signposted
► ► ► ★ 🚗 fr £8 🚐 fr £8
Open 21 Mar-Oct Booking advisable Jul-Aug Last arrival 20.00hrs Last departure noon
Large, mainly static holiday site utilizing natural coastal area of a secluded bay. 1.5m NW of Elie off A917, signed off unclass road, with direct access to beach. A 5-acre ➤

site with 120 touring pitches and 250 statics.

🔌📻☉🔲🔍🗲☀🍷🏔🔥🖉⊞✗📞♿🏕🎠

🛠

→∪🅿🖌♒🎵

KIRKCALDY

Dunnikier Caravan Park (NT283940)
Dunnikier Way KY1 3ND ☎ 01592 267563 Signposted
▶▶▶🚤🚐🚐⚠
Open Mar-Jan Booking advisable peak periods Last
arrival 19.00hrs Last departure noon
*A level site set in mature parkland adjacent to the B981
but screened by trees. An 8-acre site with 60 touring
pitches.*
🔌📻☉🔲🗲☀🍷🖉⊞T📞♿🏕🐕🎠♿🛠&

→∪🅿◎♒🖉🎵

LETHAM FEUS

Letham Feus Caravan Park (NO369048)
KY8 5NT ☎ 01333 350323 Signposted
Nearby town: Leven
▶▶▶🚤🚐 fr £8 🚐 fr £6
Open Apr-Sep Booking advisable Jul-Aug Last arrival
22.00hrs Last departure noon
*A peaceful spacious site within a walled garden
sheltered by woodland and overlooking farmland, with
fine views across Firth of Forth. On A916 2m NE of
Kennoway. A 1-acre site with 21 touring pitches and 90
statics.*
🔌📻☉🔲🗲🍷🔲🏔🖉⊞T📞🛠

→🅿🖉🎵

LUNDIN LINKS

**Woodland Gardens Caravan & Camping Site
(NO418031)**
Blindwell Rd KY8 5QG ☎ 01333 360319 Signposted
Nearby town: Leven
▶▶▶🚐 £6 🚐 £6 ⚠ £6
Open Mar-Oct Booking advisable Jul-Aug Last arrival
22.00hrs Last departure noon
*A secluded and sheltered site off the A917 coast road at
Largo. Approach along narrow, well signed road. A 1-
acre site with 20 touring pitches and 5 statics.*
🔌📻☉🗲🍷🔲☀🏔🖉⊞📞🏕🛠

→∪🅿🎵

MARKINCH

Balbirnie Park Caravan Club Site (NO293018)
KY7 6NR ☎ 01592 759130 Signposted
▶▶▶🚐🚐⚠
Open 31 Mar-9 Oct Booking advisable bank hols & Jul-
Aug Last arrival 20.00hrs
*Attractive parkland site with pitches grouped in open
areas, bordered by mature trees. An 8-acre site with 110
touring pitches.*
🔌📻☉🔲🗲☀🏔🖉⊞T📞🐕🛠

→∪🅿♒🎵

Credit Cards 📇 💳

ST ANDREWS

**Craigtoun Meadows Holiday Park
(NO482150)**
Mount Melville KY16 8PQ
☎ 01334 475959 Signposted
▶▶▶▶🚤♦🚣★🚐 £10.75-£12.75 🚐 £10.75-£12.75
⚠ £8.50-£12.75
Open Mar-Oct Booking advisable bank hols & Jun-Aug
Last arrival 21.00hrs Last departure 13.00hrs
*An attractive site set unobtrusively in mature woodlands
with large pitches in hedged paddocks, 2m from sea and
sandy beaches. 2m from St Andrews on the Craigtoun
road. A 10-acre site with 98 touring pitches and 143 statics.*
Adult mini-gymnasium.
🔌📻☉🔲🗲🔍🔍☀🏔🖉⊞T✗📞🏕🚿

🏕🐕🛠&

→∪🅿♒🖉🎵

Credit Cards 📇 💳 💳 💳

〰〰〰〰〰〰〰〰〰

Kinkell Braes Caravan Site (NO522156)
KY16 8PX ☎ 01334 74250
▶▶▶🚐🚐
Open 21 Mar-Oct Booking advisable Jun-Aug Last
departure noon no cars by tents
*A mainly static site with touring area giving views
across St Andrews and the Eden estuary. On A917 1m S
of St Andrews. A 4-acre site with 110 touring pitches
and 370 statics.*
🔌📻☉🔍☀🍷🏔🖉🖉✗📞🛠&

→🅿♒♒🖉🎵📻

KINKELL BRAES CARAVAN PARK

ST ANDREWS, FIFE, KY16 8PX
Telephone:
St Andrews (01334) 474250

▶ ▶ ▶

A beautiful location overlooking the sea, the beaches and the spires of St Andrews. Ideal for families and of course the home of Golf. Facilities include a Lounge Bar with Fast Food Service, Free Entertainment, Laundry, Free Hot Showers, Electric Hook-ups, Games Room and a Bus Service to the site entrance. The Beautiful Harbours of Crail, Anstruther, St Monans and Elie are close by.
New Leisure Complex nearby.
Hire caravans also available.

St Monans Caravan Park (NO529019)
KY10 2DN ☎ 01333 730778 & 310185 Signposted
Nearby town: St Andrews
▶ ▶ ★ ⊞ £8 ⊞ £8 ▲ £5-£8
Open 21 Mar-Oct Booking advisable Jul-Aug Last arrival 22.00hrs Last departure noon
Mainly static site on fringe of coastal village adjacent to main road and public park. On A917, 100yds E of St Monans. A 1-acre site with 18 touring pitches and 112 statics.

🎮 🦮 ☉ ⊡ 🗓 🌢 ☎ 🖃 🍴
→ ∪ 🏴 ◎ △ ⅄ ☕ 🎣

GRAMPIAN

Aboyne Loch Caravan Park (NO538998)
AB34 5BR ☎ 013398 86244 (1m E of Aboyne off A93) Signposted
▶ ▶ ▶ ★ ⊞ £8.50-£9.50 ⊞ £8.50-£9.50 ▲ £6-£8.50
Open 31 Mar-Oct Booking advisable Jul-Aug Last arrival 20.00hrs Last departure 11.00hrs
Attractively-sited caravan park set amidst woodland beside Aboyne Loch in scenic Deeside. A 4-acre site ➡

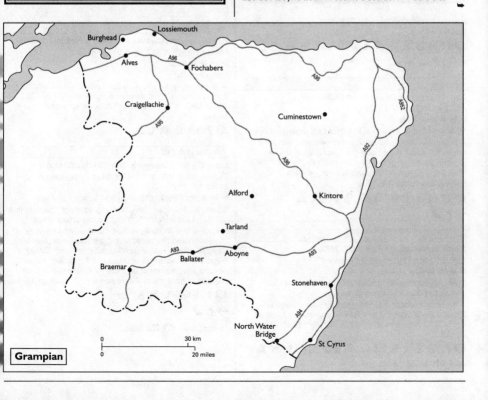

Grampian

Haughton House
Caravan Park
Alford Aberdeenshire

Sheltered woodland site located within Haughton Country Park. Open April-September. 135 grass and hard standing sites for touring caravans/motor vans & tents. Electricity hook-up available. No advance bookings accepted. Modern toilet blocks. Hot showers. Chemical disposal points. Fully equipped laundry. Dish washing facilities. Colour TV Room. Calor gas. Games rooms, Putting Green. Children's play area. Woodland walks. Ranger service and visitor centre. Approximately 25 miles from Aberdeen.

For further details please contact: The Warden, Haughton Caravan Park, Alford AB33 8NA or telephone Alford (019755) 62107. ▶ ▶ ▶

with 55 touring pitches and 40 statics.
Coarse fishing.

🔌 📞 ☉ 📺 🍳 ✳ 🛗 🅿 🌿 🖸 📞 ⛲ 🐕 🏊
→ ∪ ▶ △ 𝌭 ♪

ALFORD

Haughton House Caravan Site (NJ583169)
AB33 8NA ☎ 019755 62107
▶ ▶ ▶ ♠ 🚐 🚙 🅰
Open Apr-Sep Last arrival 21.00hrs Last departure noon
A first class site for all ages, set in beautiful parkland amongst woodland beside the River Don, within a country park approximately .5m NW of Alford. An 18-acre site with 135 touring pitches and 40 statics.
Putting & outdoor draughts.

🔌 📞 ☉ 📺 🍳 🍷 ☐ ✳ 🛗 🅿 ☐ 📞 🏊
→ ▶ ♪

ALVES

North Alves Caravan Park (NJ122633)
IV30 3XD ☎ 01343 85223 Signposted
▶ ▶ ▶ 🚐 🚙 🅰
Open Apr-Oct Booking advisable peak periods Last arrival 23.00hrs Last departure noon
A quiet rural site in attractive rolling countryside within 3m of a good beach. From A96 take unclass rd signed Alves. A 10-acre site with 45 touring pitches and 12 statics.

🔌 📞 ☉ 📺 🍳 🍷 ☐ ✳ 🛗 🅰 🌿 ⊞ ☐ 📞 🐕 🏊
→ ∪ ▶ 𝌭 ♨ ♪

BALLATER

Anderson Road Caravan Site (NO371955)
Anderson Rd AB3 5QW ☎ 013397 55727 (in season) & 01569 762001 Signposted
▶ ▶ ▶ ★ 🚐 £6.50-£8.50 🚙 £6.50-£8.50 🅰 £2-£2.50
Open Apr-mid Oct Booking advisable anytime Last arrival 20.00hrs Last departure 10.00hrs
This site is in a beautiful setting bordered by the River Dee with wooded hills behind. A 5-acre site with 66 touring pitches and 93 statics.
See advertisement under STONEHAVEN

🔌 📞 ☉ 📺 🍷 🍳 🌿 🛗 ✳ 🛗 📞 🏊 ♿
→ ∪ ▶ 𝌭 ♨ ♪

BRAEMAR

The Invercauld Caravan Club Site (NO153910)
Glenshee Rd AB3 5YQ
☎ 01339 741373
▶ ▶ ▶ ♠ 👫 🚐 🚙 🅰
Open all year Booking advisable all times
Attractive well screened site, landscaped into separate areas and surrounded by magnificent scenery. A 9.5-acre site with 100 touring pitches.
Veg prep area.

🛗 🍴
→ ▶ ♪ 🏊

BURGHEAD

Red Craig Hotel Caravan & Camping Park (NJ124689)
Mason Haugh IV30 2XX ☎ 01343 835663
▶ ▶ ▶ 🚐 🚙 🅰
Open Apr-Oct
A slightly sloping site with level pitches, overlooking the Moray Forth. On outskirts of Burghead at junc of B9012 and B9040. A 3-acre site with 30 touring pitches and 8 statics.

🔌 📞 ☉ 🍷 🛗 📞 🏊

CRAIGELLACHIE

Camping & Caravanning Club Site (NJ257449)
Elchies AB38 9SD ☎ 01340 810414 (in season) & 01203 694995
▶ ▶ ▶ ★ 🚐 £9.30-£10 🚙 £9.30-£10 🅰 £9.30-£10
Open end Mar-early Nov Booking advisable bank hols & Jul-Aug Last arrival 21.00hrs Last departure noon
A rural site with views across meadowland towards Speyside, and the usual high Club standards. From Craigellachie travel N on A941, turn left onto B9102 (signed Archiestown), and site is 2.5m on left. Please see the advertisement on page 27 for details of Club Members' benefits. A 7-acre site with 75 touring pitches.

🔌 📞 ☉ ✳ 📞 🐕 ♿
→ ▶ ♪

Credit Cards 🟦 💳 🟥

CUMINESTOWN

East Balthangie Caravan Park (NJ841516)
East Balthangie AB53 7XY ☎ 01888 544261
▶ ⊞ ⊞ Å
Open Mar-Oct
A small farm site with level pitches, sheltered by trees to N and with extensive views to the S. A remote rural setting. From N leave A98 to head S on A9027 to New Byth, then unclass rd signed New Deer to junc with farm rd in 2.25m. A 2-acre site with 12 touring pitches and 7 statics.

🖂 🏕 ☉ 🔧 ⚞

FOCHABERS

Burnside Caravan Site (NJ350580)
Keith Rd IV32 7PF ☎ 01343 820511 & 820362 Signposted
Nearby town: Elgin
▶ ▶ ▶ ★ ⊞ £6.75-£8.25 ⊞ £6.75-£8.25 Å £4.25-£8.25
Open Apr-Oct Booking advisable Jul-Aug Last departure noon
Attractive site in tree-lined sheltered valley with footpath to the village. .5m E of town off the A96. A 5-acre site with 110 touring pitches and 60 statics.

🖂 🏕 ☉ 🔧 ⚞ 🖵 ⚞ ⚞ ⚞ ⚞
→ ∪ ▶ ✈ 🛒
£

KINTORE

Hillhead Caravan Park (NJ777163)
AB51 0YX ☎ 01467 632809 Signposted
Nearby town: Inverurie
▶ ▶ ▶ ⊞ £5.75-£7.25 ⊞ £5.75-£7.25 Å £5.75-£7.25
Open 31 Mar-Oct Booking advisable at all times Last arrival 22.00hrs Last departure 13.00hrs
An attractive, peaceful site in the R Don Valley, about 1m from the village and A96. A 1.5-acre site with 24 touring pitches and 5 statics.
Caravan repair service & caravan storage, shop.

🖂 🏕 ☉ ⚞ ✳ ⚞ ⚞ ⚞ ⚞ ⚞ ⚞ ⚞ ⚞
→ ▶ 🍴 ✈
£

Credit Cards 🟦 🟥

LOSSIEMOUTH

Silver Sands Leisure Park (NJ205710)
Covesea, West Beach IV31 6SP ☎ 01343 813262 (2m W B9040) Signposted
▶ ▶ ▶ ▶ ★ ⊞ £7.25-£9.65 ⊞ £7.25-£9.65 Å £7.25-£9.65
Open Jun-Sep (rs Apr, May & Oct shops & entertainment restricted) Booking advisable Jul-Aug Last arrival 23.00hrs Last departure noon
A holiday park with entertainment for all during the peak season. From Lossiemouth follow B9040 to site. A 7-acre site with 140 touring pitches and 180 statics.
Childrens entertainment.

🖂 🏕 ☉ ⚞ ⚞ ⚞ 🖵 🍺 ⚞ ⚞ ⚞ ⚞ ⚞ ⚞ ✖ ⚞ ⚞ ⚞
→ ∪ ▶ ◎ ⚞ ✈ 🛒

NORTH WATER BRIDGE

Dovecot Caravan Park (NO648663)
AB30 1QL ☎ 01674 840630 Signposted
▶ ▶ ▶ ⊞ £6.50-£7.50 ⊞ £6.50-£7.50 Å £6.50-£7.50
Open Apr-Oct Booking advisable Jul & Aug for hook up Last arrival 20.00hrs Last departure noon
A level grassy site in a country area close to the A94, with mature trees screening one side and the R North Esk on the other. A handy overnight stop in a good touring area. A 6-acre site with 25 touring pitches and 44 statics.

🖂 🏕 ☉ ⚞ ⚞ 🖵 ✳ ⚞ ⚞ 🆃 ⚞ ⚞ ⚞ ⚞ ⚞

ST CYRUS

East Bowstrips Caravan Park (NO745654)
DD10 0DE ☎ 01674 850328 Signposted
Nearby town: Montrose
▶ ▶ ▶ ⚞ ⊞ £6-£7 ⊞ £6-£7 Å £5-£7
Open Etr or Apr-Oct Booking advisable at all times Last arrival 22.00hrs Last departure noon
A quiet, rural site close to seaside village, with thoughtfully modernised facilities and a particular welcome for the disabled. From A92 travelling N turn left after post office and hotel, follow unclass road, then take first L and second R. A 2-acre site with 30 touring pitches and 18 statics.

🖂 🏕 ☉ ⚞ ⚞ ✳ ⚞ ⚞ 🆃 ⚞ ⚞ ⚞ ⚞ ⚞
→ ✈
£

STONEHAVEN

Queen Elizabeth Caravan Site (NO875866)
AB3 2RD ☎ 01569 764041(in season) & 762001
Signposted
► ► ★ ⊞ £6.50-£8.50 ⊞ £6.50-£8.50
Open Apr-mid Oct Booking advisable anytime Last
arrival 20.00hrs Last departure 10.00hrs
*A gently sloping grass site offering a good range of
recreational facilities, situated between a main road and
seafront adjoining a public park. Situated at junc of A90
and B979. A 4.5-acre site with 35 touring pitches and 76
statics.*

🔧 📞 ⊙ 🔲 🔫 ⓘ ⊘ 🔳 ⊞ 🔲
➔ ∪ ⏁ ⅄ ♫ 🏋

See advertisement on page 219

TARLAND

Drummie Hill Caravan Park (NJ474045)
AB34 4UP ☎ 013398 81388 & 81264 Signposted
Nearby town: Aboyne
► ► ► ⊞ £7-£8 ⊞ £7-£8 Å £4-£6
Open Apr-mid Oct Booking advisable Jul-Aug Last
arrival 23.00hrs Last departure noon
*Landscaped site on edge of village amidst hill and
farmland. Enter Tarland on B9119, bear left before
bridge and continue for 600yds. Site is on left. A 4-acre
site with 45 touring pitches and 80 statics.*

🔧 📞 ⊙ 🔲 🔍 ✳ 🏔 ⓘ ⊘ 🔳 ⓝ � 🏋
➔ ∪ ⏁ ♫
🔞

HIGHLAND

APPLECROSS

Applecross Campsite (NG714443)
IV54 8ND ☎ 01520 744268 & 744284 Signposted
► ► ► ⊞ ⊞ Å
Open Etr-Oct (rs Apr, May, Sep & Oct only 1 toilet block
open) Last arrival 22.00hrs
*A quiet site in a lovely remote area close to mountains,
moorland and beach. Caravans should approach via
Shieldaig. On unclass rd off A896, 300yds from village. A
6-acre site with 60 touring pitches and 4 statics.
Bakery.*

🔧 📞 ⊙ ✳ ⓘ ⊘ 🔳 🔲 🗙 🏋
➔ ♫

Credit Cards 💳

ARDMAIR

Ardmair Point Caravan Park (NH108983)
IV26 2TN ☎ 01854 612054 Signposted
Nearby town: Ullapool
► ► ► ⅍⅍ ★ ⊞ £6-£7.50 ⊞ £6-£7.50 Å £6-£7.50
Open May-Sep Booking advisable Jul-Aug Last arrival
22.00hrs Last departure noon
*An excellent touring site on small peninsula 3.5m
N of Ullapool on A835, with superb views of*
*surrounding mountains and sea lochs. A 4-acre
site with 45 touring pitches.*
Boats, fishing, canoes, windsurfers for hire.

🔧 📞 ⊙ 🔲 🔫 ✳ ⓘ ⊘ 🔳 ⊞ 🔲 🗙 � 🏋 ⅙
➔ ∪ ⏁ 🛆 ⅄ ♫

ARISAIG

Gorten Sands Caravan Site (NM640879)
Gorten Farm PH39 4NS ☎ 01687 450283 Signposted
Nearby town: Mallaig
► ► ► ⊞ fr £7.50 ⊞ £6-£7.50 Å £6-£7.50
Open Etr-Sep Booking advisable Jul-Aug Last arrival
23.00hrs Last departure 13.00hrs
*A well-run site with mainly modern facilities. 2m NW of
Arisaig on A830, turn left at sign "Back of Keppoch" and
follow to end of road. A 6-acre site with 41 touring
pitches and 4 statics.*

🔧 📞 ⊙ 🔲 🔫 ✳ ⓘ ⊘ 🔳 🔲 � 🏠 🐕
➔ ⏁ ♫ 🏋
🔞

Portnadoran Caravan Site (NM651892)
PH39 4NT ☎ 01687 450267 Signposted
Nearby town: Mallaig
► ► ► ⊞ £5-£8 ⊞ £4.50-£7 Å £4-£6
Open Apr-Oct Booking advisable Jul-Aug Last arrival
23.00hrs Last departure noon
Small, level, grassy site situated close to sandy beach

Highland

Scourie

John O'Groats
Dunnet
Thurso
Reay
A836
Wick
A895
A897
A9

Ardmair
Ullapool
Laide
Lairg
Brora

Poolewe
Gairloch
A835
Dornoch
Tain

Kinlochewe
Dingwall
Rosemarkie

Edinbane
Dunvegan
Nairn
Culloden Moor
Applecross
Daviot
Scaniport
Grantown-on-Spey
Balmacara
Cannich
A82
Boat of Garten
Shiel Bridge
Aviemore
A87
Invergarry
A86
A9
Arisaig
A830
Corpach
Fort William
Resipole
Strontian
Onich
Glencoe
Lochaline

0   30 km
0   20 miles

overlooking the Islands of Eigg, Rhum and Skye. Very
welcoming. Signed .25m off A380, 1.5m N of Arisaig. A
2-acre site with 55 touring pitches and 9 statics.

▶ ▶ ▶ ★ 🚐 £6.50-£10.50 🚐 £6.50-£10.50 ▲ £6.50-£10.50
Open all year Booking advisable Jul-Aug Last arrival
22.00hrs Last departure 11.00hrs no cars by tents
*A secluded site in tree-studded undulating ground off
approach road to the Cairngorm Mountains. An
attractive natural site offering good facilities. A 4-acre
site with 39 touring pitches and 50 statics.*

AVIEMORE

Campgrounds of Scotland (NH916108)
Coylumbridge PH22 1QU ☎ 01479 810120
(1.5m E on A951) Signposted

Dalraddy Holiday Park (NH859083)
PH22 1QB ☎ 01479 810330 Signposted
▶ ▶ ▶ 🚐 🚑 ▲
Booking advisable Jul-Aug Last arrival 19.00hrs Last departure noon
A secluded site off the A9, 3.5m S of Aviemore, set amidst heather and young birch trees, with mountain views. A 25-acre site with 30 touring pitches and 94 statics.

🔫 ⁿ 💿 ▤ ▨ ✳ 🅰 🖊 🖋 ⬆ Ⓣ ☎ 🛒
➔ ∪ ⬥ ⅍ 🍽 ✒

Credit Cards

Glenmore Forest Camping & Caravan Park (NH975097)
Glenmore PH22 1QU ☎ 01479 861271 & 01463 791575 Signposted
▶ ▶ ▶ ♦ 🚑 🚐 ▲
Open 6 Dec-Oct Booking advisable New year, Etr & Jul-Aug Last arrival 20.00hrs Last departure noon
An attractive forest site with grassy areas, landscaped with mature trees, and close to the eastern end of Loch Morlich at the head of Glenmore. There are sandy beaches close by. Signed off B970 on Cairngorms rd. A 17-acre site with 220 touring pitches.

🔫 ⁿ 💿 ✳ 🅰 🖊 🖋 Ⓣ ✕ ☎ 🛒 ♿
➔ ⬥ ⅍ ✒ ✒

Credit Cards 🟦 🟦 🟦 💿

Reraig Caravan Site (NG815272)
IV40 8DH ☎ 01599 566215 Signposted
Nearby town: Kyle
▶ ▶ ▶ 👫 🚐 £6.20 🚑 £6.20 ▲ £6.20
Open mid Apr-Sep Last arrival 22.00hrs Last departure noon
Set on level, grassy ground surrounded by trees, the site looks south towards Loch Alsh and Skye. Very nicely organised with a high standard of maintenance. On A87 at rear of Balmacara Hotel. A 2-acre site with 45 touring pitches.
Hard standings available & dish washing sinks.

🔫 ⁿ 💿 ▨ 🖊 🖋 ⬆
➔ 🛒

Credit Cards 🟦 🟦 🟦

Balmacara Woodland Campsite (NG802279)
IV40 8DN ☎ 01599 566321 Signposted
Nearby town: Kyle of Lochalsh
▶ ♦ ★ 🚐 £3.50-£4.50 🚑 £3.50-£4.50 ▲ £3.50-£4.50
Open Etr-Sep Last arrival 22.00hrs Last departure noon
An attractive and sheltered wooded site situated 3.5m E of Kyle of Lochalsh, off the A87 (signposted Balmacara Square). A 7-acre site with 58 touring pitches.
Forest walks & orienteering.

🔫 ☎ 🎋 🐕
➔ ∪ ▶ ⅍ ✒

BOAT OF GARTEN

Campgrounds of Scotland (NH939191)
PH24 3BN ☎ 01479 831652 Signposted
Nearby town: Aviemore
▶▶▶ ⊞ ⊞ ⚲
Open all year Booking advisable 26 Dec-2 Jan & 25 Jul-7
Aug Last arrival 22.00hrs Last departure 11.00hrs
*Level, grass site with young trees and bushes set in
mountainous woodland in the village itself, near the
River Spey and Loch Garten, off A95. A 3.5-acre site with
37 touring pitches and 60 statics.*
🔌📶⊙🗑🍳✳🏧🚰🛅⊞✕📞🛒👤
➜🏄⚓

BRORA

Dalchalm Caravan Club Site (NC912059)
KW9 6LP ☎ 01408 621479 (1.5m N) Signposted
▶▶▶ ⊞ ⊞ ⚲
Open 26 Mar-4 Oct Booking advisable Jun-Aug Last
arrival 20.00hrs Last departure noon
*Sheltered site on the east coast of Sutherland close to a
safe, sandy beach. An 8-acre site with 90 touring
pitches.*
Veg prep area.
🔌📶⊙🗑🍳🚰🛅⊞T📞
➜🏄⚓👤

Credit Cards 🔲 💳

CANNICH

Cannich Caravan and Camping Park (NH345317)
IV4 7LN ☎ 01456 415364 & 415263 Signposted
Nearby town: Inverness
▶▶▶ ⊞ £4.50-£7.50 ⊞ £4.50-£7.50 ▲ £3-£5.50
Open Apr-Oct Booking advisable Jul & Aug Last arrival
23.00hrs Last departure noon
*A well-run site with plenty of potential, situated on A831
200 yards SE of Cannich Bridge. A 6.5-acre site with 140
touring pitches and 79 statics.*
Mountain bike hire & fishing.
🔌📶⊙🗑🍳🔍🛒✳🏧🚰🛅⊞T📞🚲🏕
♿
➜🏄🏪⛱⚓👤
🖼

CORPACH

                    **Linnhe Caravan Park
                    (NN074771)**
                    PH33 7NL ☎ 01397 772376
Signposted
Nearby town: Fort William
▶▶▶ ⚑ ♿ ⊞ £7.50-£12 ⊞ £7.50-£12 ▲ £6-£7.50
Open Etr-Oct (rs 15 Dec-Etr shop & main toilet block
closed) Booking advisable school hols & peak periods
Last arrival 21.00hrs Last departure 11.00hrs
*An excellently maintained site in a beautiful setting.
Situated 1m W of Corpach on A830 on shores of Loch
Eil with Ben Nevis to E and mountains to Sunart to W. A
5.5-acre site with 95 touring pitches and 85 statics.*
Launching slipway, private beach, free fishing.

See advertisement under FORT WILLIAM
🔌🚤📶⊙🗑🍳✳🏧🚰🛅⊞T📞🏕🏪🐕
🛅
➜🏄🏪⛴🎥⚓
🖼

Credit Cards 🔲 💳

CULLODEN MOOR

Culloden Moor Caravan Club Site (NH769459)
Newlands IV1 2EF ☎ 01463 790625 Signposted
Nearby town: Inverness
▶▶▶ ⊞ ⊞
Open 26 Mar-11 Oct Booking advisable bank hols & Jun-
Aug Last arrival 20.00hrs Last departure noon
*A gently sloping site, sheltered on one side by a belt of
trees, and facing a glorious view over the Nairn Valley.
Approx 1m from Culloden battlefield, on B9006 and
signed. A 7-acre site with 90 touring pitches.*
Veg prep area.
🔌📶🗑🍳🏧🚰🛅⊞T📞🐕♿
➜🏄⚓👤

Credit Cards 🔲 💳

DAVIOT

Auchnahillin Caravan Park (NH742386)
IV1 2XQ ☎ 01463 772286 Signposted
Nearby town: Inverness
▶▶▶ ⊞ £6.75-£8.50 ⊞ £6.75-£8.50 ▲ £5.50-£7.50
Open 15 Mar-Oct Booking advisable Jun-Aug Last
arrival 22.00hrs Last departure noon
*Level grassy site with clean and spacious facilities,
surrounded by hills and forest. Situated 7m SE of
Inverness on B9154 off A9; follow Daviot East signs. A 5-
acre site with 65 touring pitches and 35 statics.*
🔌📶⊙🗑🍳🔍✳🍷🏧🚰🛅⊞T✕📞🐕👤
♿
➜⚓
🖼

DINGWALL

Camping & Caravanning Club Site (NH557588)
Jubilee Park IV15 9QZ ☎ 01349 862236 (in season) &
01203 694995 Signposted
▶▶▶ ♦♦ ★ ⊞ £9.30-£10 ⊞ £9.30-£10 ▲ £9.30-£10
Open end Mar-early Nov Booking advisable bank hols &
Jul-Aug Last arrival 21.00hrs Last departure noon
*An attractive site with well-equipped facilities and a high
standard of maintenance, close to the town centre.
Cross bridge at Dingwall rlwy stn then turn L past
football ground. Please see the advertisement on page
27 for details of Club Members' benefits. A 6-acre site
with 90 touring pitches.*
🔌📶⊙🍳✳🏧🚰🛅⊞T📞👤♿
➜⚓

Credit Cards 🔲 💳 💳

DORNOCH

Grannie's Heilan Hame (NH818924)
IV25 3QD ☎ 01862 810383 Signposted
▶ ▶ ▶ ★ ⚑ £7.50-£14.50 ⚑ £7.50-£14.50 ▲ £5.50-£12.50
Open all year (rs 31 Oct-Mar shop, pool, & restaurant
complex) Booking advisable Jul-Aug for electric hook-
up Last arrival 23.30hrs Last departure 14.00hrs
*An ideal Highland touring centre set on the beach.
Signed off unclass rd at Embo. A 32-acre site with 324
touring pitches and 100 statics.*
Spa bath, sauna & solarium.

🅐 🌂 ⊙ 🖃 🖳 🥄 🔍 🕯 ⚹ ⊻ ⚠ 🔋 🖉 🎦 T ✕ ☎
🖤 🕇 🐾
→ ▶ 🎣

Credit Cards 🖃 ▨

DUNNET

Dunnet Bay Caravan Club Site (ND219703)
KW14 8XD ☎ 01847 821319 Signposted
Nearby town: Thurso
▶ ▶ ⚑ £5-£7 ⚑ £5-£7 ▲ fr £2.20
Open mid Apr-mid Sep Booking advisable Jul-Aug & for
electric hook-ups Last arrival 20.00hrs Last departure noon
*This is a mainly level grassy site with gravel driveways,
set alongside 3 miles of white-shell sands. Access is
directly onto A836 approx 8m E of Thurso, immediately
W of the village of Dunnet. A 5-acre site with 45 touring
pitches.*

🅐 🌂 ⊙ 🖳 ⚹ 🔋 🖉 🎦 T 🕇
→ ∪ ▶ 🎣 🐾

Credit Cards 🖃 ▨

FORT WILLIAM

Glen Nevis Caravan & Camping Park (NN124722)
Glen Nevis PH33 6SX ☎ 01397 702191 & 705181
Signposted
▶ ▶ ▶ ▶ ⚓ ★ ⚑ £6.90-£9.10 ⚑ £6.60-£8.80
▲ £4.60-£8.80
Open 15 Mar-Oct (rs Mar & mid Oct-mid Nov limited
shop & restaurant facilities) Booking advisable Jul-Aug
Last arrival 22.00hrs Last departure noon
*A tasteful site with well-screened enclosures, at the foot
of Ben Nevis, in the midst of some of the Highlands'
most spectacular scenery. On A82 Glen Nevis rd. A 19-
acre site with 380 touring pitches and 30 statics.*

🅐 🌂 ⊙ 🖃 🖳 ⚹ ⊻ ⚠ 🔋 🖉 🎦 T ✕ ☎ 🖤 🎏 🍴
🕇 🐾 ♿
→ ▶ 💈 🎣
£

Credit Cards 🖃 ▨ ▨ 🦪

GAIRLOCH

Sands Holiday Centre (NG758784)
IV21 2DL ☎ 01445 712152 Signposted
▶ ▶ ▶ ⚑ £7-£8.50 ⚑ £7-£8.50
Open 20 May-10 Sep (rs Apr-19 May & 11 Sep-mid Oct no
shop or laundry some toilets closed) Booking advisable
Jul-Aug Last arrival 22.00hrs Last departure noon

Part-level site close to sandy beach with a panoramic outlook towards Skye. 3m W of Gairloch on B8021. A 51-acre site with 360 touring pitches and 20 statics. Boat slipway.

🐕🏕️☉回🥄❄️⚠️🔥⚿🛗🚻📞🛒
→🌙

Credit Cards 🔲 🔳

Gairloch Caravan & Camping Park (NG798773)
Strath IV21 2BT ☎ 01505 614343 Signposted
▶▶★🚐£7-£8 🚐£6-£7 🛖£3-£5
Open Apr-15 Oct Booking advisable bank hols & Jul-Aug Last arrival 21.30hrs Last departure noon
A clean, well-maintained site on flat coastal grassland close to Loch Gairloch, signed off A832. A 6-acre site with 70 touring pitches and 3 statics.
Adjacent cafe, restaurant, activity centre & bar.

🐕🏕️☉回🔧🛒🍽️⚿🛗🚻🛒
→▶🍴🌙

💷

Credit Cards 🔲 🔳

GLENCOE

Invercoe Caravan Site (NN098594)
PA39 4HP ☎ 01855 811210 Signposted
▶▶▶🚐£6-£8 🚐£6-£8 🛖£5-£8
Open Etr-mid Oct Booking advisable Jul-Aug for electric hook ups Last departure 13.00hrs

Level, grass site set on the shore of Loch Lever with excellent mountain views. Located on the Kinlochleven road on the edge of Glencoe village. A 5-acre site with 60 touring pitches and 5 statics.

🐕🏕️☉回🥄❄️⚠️🔥⚿🛗🚻📞🛒♿
→🍴🌙

Glencoe Campsite (NN111578)
Carnoch PA39 4LA ☎ 01855 811397
▶▶🚐🚐🛖🍴
Open Etr-Sep Booking advisable Jul-Aug Last arrival 22.00hrs Last departure 17.00hrs
Part-level, part-sloping, grass, gravel and sand site with young trees and bushes in mountainous woodland. Direct access to river and main A82 road. A 40-acre site with 150 touring pitches.

🐕🏕️☉回🥄⚠️⚿🚻📞🛒♿
→⛵🍴🌙

GRANTOWN-ON-SPEY

Grantown on Spey Caravan Park (NJ028283)
Seafield Avenue, PH26 3JQ ☎ 01479 872474 Signposted
▶▶▶★🚐£7-£11.75 🚐£7-£11.75 🛖£4.50-£8.50
Open Etr-Sep Booking advisable Etr, Whitsun & Jul-Aug Last arrival 22.00hrs
Attractive site with mature trees and bushes near river, and set amidst hills, mountains, moors and woodland. Good standards and personal attention. .5m from town. A 15-acre site with 100 touring pitches and 45 statics.
➡️

Picnic tables, football pitch. Free dishwashing.

Credit Cards

INVERGARRY

Faichem Park (NH285023)
Ardgarry Farm, Faichem PH35 4HG
☎ 01809 501226
Nearby town: Fort Augustus
▶► ♣ ♦♦ ♣ £5.50-£6 ♣ £5.50-£6 ▲ £5.50-£6
Open 15 Apr-15 Oct Booking advisable Jul-Aug Last
arrival 22.00hrs Last departure noon
*Small, quiet touring site with good, clean facilities and
panoramic views. Meticulously maintained. The site is
located just off the A87 about 1m W of Invergarry,
signed Faichem. A 2-acre site with 30 touring pitches.*

JOHN O'GROATS

John O'Groats Caravan Site (ND382733)
KW1 4YS ☎ 01955 611329 Signposted
▶► ▶► ♣ £6-£7 ♣ £6-£7 ▲ £6-£7
Open Apr-Oct Booking advisable Last arrival 22.00hrs
Last departure noon
*Good clean and attractive site in open position above
the seashore and looking out towards the Orkney
Islands, at the end of A9. Passenger ferry nearby. A 4-
acre site with 90 touring pitches.*

Stroma View Site (NO362730)
Huna KW1 4YL ☎ 01955 611313 Signposted
▶► ▶ ♣♣ ▲
Open Apr-Oct Booking advisable Last arrival 23.00hrs
Last departure 11.00hrs
*Simple roadside site forming grassy area in front of
owner's house. Open views across to Stroma and
Orkney Islands. 1.5m W of John O'Groats. A 1-acre site
with 30 touring pitches and 2 statics.*
Sea angling & sea cruises.

KINLOCHEWE

Kinlochewe Caravan Club Site (NH025620)
IV22 2PA ☎ 01445 84239
▶► ▶ ♣♣
Open 2 Apr-4 Oct Booking advisable bank hols & Jun-
Aug Last arrival 20.00hrs Last departure noon

*A small site with stone hardstandings, in a peaceful
position at the foot of Ben Eighe, at the end of a
beautiful drive along the valley from Achnasheen. Care
is needed on final approach from Achnasheen as road is
single track with passing places. On A832 in village
100yds past junc with A896. A 5-acre site with 60 touring
pitches.*
Veg prep area & drying room.

Credit Cards

LAIDE

Gruinard Bay Caravan & Camping Park (NG906908)
Laide, By Achnasheen IV22 2ND ☎ 01445 731225
Signposted
Nearby town: Aultbea
▶► ▶► ♣ £5-£9.50 ♣ £5-£9.50 ▲ £5-£9.50
Open Apr-Sep Booking advisable Jul-Aug Last arrival
22.00hrs Last departure noon
*Campers receive a warm welcome at this spotless,
lovingly managed site on the outskirts of Laide. On
A832, 300yds N of village. A 3.25-acre site with 43
touring pitches and 14 statics.*
Dishwashing sinks/free hot water. Laundry service.

LAIRG

Dunroamin Caravan Park (NC585062)
Main St IV27 4AR ☎ 01549 402447 Signposted
▶ ▶ ▶ ★ ⊞ £5.50-£6.50 ⊞ £5.50-£6.50 ▲ £4-£6.50
Open Apr-Oct Booking advisable anytime Last arrival
23.00hrs Last departure noon
*A small, attractive and well laid out site on A839 in
village. A 3-acre site with 50 touring pitches and 10
statics.*

🏤 📞 ☉ 🗗 🍃 🌣 🔒 🗑 ⊡ 🅃 ✕ 📞 🖳 🖳
➔ 🛆 ⌇ 🎣

Credit Cards 🖸

Woodend Caravan & Camping Site (NC551127)
Achnairn IV27 4DN ☎ 01549 402248 Signposted
▶ ▶ ▶ ⊞ £5-£6 ⊞ £5-£6 ▲ £5
Open Apr-Sep Booking advisable Last arrival 23.00hrs
*A clean, fresh site set in hilly moors and woodland with
access to sea, beach, river and Loch Shin. 4m N of Lairg
off A838, signed at Achnairn. A 4-acre site with 60
touring pitches and 5 statics.*

🏤 📞 ☉ 🗗 🍃 🌣 🜨 🔒 🗑 ⊡ 📞 🖳
➔ ⌇ 🎣
💷

LOCHALINE

Fiunary Camping & Caravanning Park (NM614467)
Morvern PA34 5XX ☎ 01967 421225 Signposted
▶ ▶ ★ ⊞ £5-£6.50 ⊞ £5-£6.50 ▲ £5-£6.50
Open May-Oct (rs Apr hot water & showers not
available) Booking advisable Last arrival 22.00hrs Last
departure noon
*A small, carefully maintained site with beautiful lochside
views, quiet and secluded and in an area of great
interest to naturalists. Signed 5m W of Lochaline and
ferry on Loch Shore at Fiunary. A 3-acre site with 25
touring pitches and 2 statics.*

🏤 📞 ☉ 🌣 ⊡ 📞 🎡 🗛 🐕 🖽
➔ 🎣
💷

NAIRN

Nairn Lochloy Holiday Park (NH895574)
IV12 4PH ☎ 01667 453764 Signposted
▶ ▶ ▶ ⊞ ⊞ ▲
Open 15 Mar-30 Oct (rs 31 Oct-mid Mar shop/pool &
restaurant complex) Booking advisable end Jun-Jul Last
arrival 22.00hrs Last departure 14.00hrs
*A level site bordered by the beach, the River Nairn and
golf course. Signed off A96 in Nairn close to town
centre. A 3-acre site with 100 touring pitches and 290
statics.*
Holiday units. Discount on adjacent golf course.

🏤 📞 ☉ 🗗 🍃 🍴 ❤ ✕ 🍷 🗑 🔒 🗑 ⊡ 🅃 ✕ 📞 🖳
🖳
➔ ∪ ▶ ⌇ 🎣
Credit Cards 🖸 📇 📇 📇 𝓢

Delnies Woods Caravan Park (NH852552)
Delnies Wood IV12 5NX ☎ 01667 455281 Signposted
▶ ▶ ★ ⊞ £7.50-£9.50 ⊞ £7.50-£9.50 ▲ £7.50-£9.50
Open Etr-Oct Booking advisable end Jun-early Aug Last
arrival 22.00hrs Last departure noon
*An attractive site amongst pine trees. Situated about 3m
W of Nairn on the A96. A 7-acre site with 50 touring
pitches and 16 statics.*

🏤 📞 ☉ 🗗 🍃 ❤ 🌣 🜨 🔒 🗑 ⊡ 🅃 📞 🎡 🗛 🐕
➔ ∪ ▶ ⌇ 🎣 🖳
💷

Credit Cards 🖸 📇

Spindrift Caravan & Camping Site (NH863537)
Little Kildrummie IV12 5QU ☎ 01667 453992
▶ ▶ ▶ ♦ ⊞ £5.50-£7.50 ⊞ £5.50-£7.50 ▲ £5.50-£7.50
Open Apr-Oct Booking advisable Jul-Aug Last arrival
22.00hrs Last departure noon
*An informal site in attractive setting with good facilities
and first class maintenance. Signed off B9090, 2m S of
Nairn. A 3-acre site with 40 touring pitches.*
Fishing permits available from reception.

🏤 📞 ☉ 🗗 🍃 🌣 🔒 🜨 📞 🖳
➔ ∪ ▶ 🛆 ⌇ 🎣
💷

ONICH

Bunree Caravan Club Site (NN019626)
PH33 5SE ☎ 01855 821283 (1m N)
Signposted
Nearby town: Fort William
▶▶▶ ♠ ♣♣ ⊞ ⊞

Open 26 Mar-Oct Booking advisable all times Last arrival 20.00hrs Last departure noon
A secluded lochside site with panoramic mountain views and modern, well-arranged facilities. .25m off A82 and signed, or 3.25m N of Ballachulish Bridge and .5m S of ferry. A 7-acre site with 110 touring pitches.
Veg prep area.

🔌 ⋔ ⊙ 🗄 🥄 ※ ⚠ 🏧 ⊘ 🚻 Ⓣ 🐾 🕯 🛒 ♿
➔ ⤙ 🛒

Credit Cards 🔲 💳 💳

POOLEWE

Camping & Caravanning Club Site (NG862812)
Inverewe Gardens IV22 2LE ☎ 01445 781249 (in season) & 01203 694995 Signposted
▶▶▶ ★ ⊞ £9.30-£10 ⊞ £9.30-£10 ▲ £9.30-£10

Open end Mar-early Nov Booking advisable bank hols & Jul-Aug Last arrival 21.00hrs
A well-run site located in Loch Ewe Bay, not far from Inverewe Gardens. On A832, .25m N of Poolewe village. Please see the advertisement on page 27 for details of Club Members' benefits. A 3-acre site with 60 touring pitches.

🔌 ⋔ ⊙ 🏧 ⊘

Credit Cards 🔲 💳 💳

REAY

Dunvegan Euro Campsite (NC960644)
KW14 7RQ ☎ 01847 81405 Signposted
▶ ⊞ ⊞ ▲

Open May-Oct Booking advisable at anytime Last arrival 22.00hrs Last departure noon
A lovingly maintained site with immaculate facilities. The site is adjacent to the A836 in the centre of the village. A 1-acre site with 20 touring pitches.

⋔ ⊙ 🗄 ※ ⚠ ⊞ 🕯
➔ ▶ ⤙ ⤙ 🛒

RESIPOLE (LOCH SUNART)

Resipole Farm (NM725639)
PH36 4HX ☎ 01967 431617 &
431235 Signposted
Nearby town: Ardnamurchan
▶▶▶ ♠ ♣♣ ★ ⊞ £7.50-£8.50 ⊞ £7.50-£8.50 ▲ £7.50-£8.50

Open Apr-Sep (rs Oct shop closed) Booking advisable bank hols Last arrival 22.00hrs Last departure 11.00hrs
A well-managed site in beautiful surroundings, with deer frequently sighted. On A861 5m W of Strontian and 2m E of Salen. An 8-acre site with 45 touring pitches and 15 statics.

Private slipway, 9 hold golf.

🔌 ⋔ ⊙ 🗄 🥄 ♦ ※ ⚑ 🏧 ⊘ ⊞ Ⓣ 🗡 🕯 🐾 🛒 ♿
➔ ⤙ ⤙

Credit Cards 🔲 💳 💳

ROSEMARKIE

Camping & Caravanning Club Site (NH739569)
IV10 8UW ☎ 01381 621117 (in season) & 01203 694995
Nearby town: Fortrose
▶▶ ★ ⊞ £8.40-£9 ⊞ £8.40-£9 ▲ £8.40-£9

Open end Mar-early Oct Booking advisable bank hols & Jul-Aug Last arrival 21.00hrs Last departure noon
A very clean and well-maintained site. At Rosemarkie turn right onto Promenade, and site is in 100 yards, or turn right at Fortrose police station and follow signs. Please see the advertisement on page 27 for details of Club Members' benefits. A 5-acre site with 60 touring pitches.

⋔ ⊙ ※ 🐾 ♿
➔ ⤙ ⤙ 🛒

Credit Cards 🔲 💳 💳

SCANIPORT

Scaniport Caravan & Camping Park (NH628398)
IV1 2DL ☎ 01463 751351
Nearby town: Inverness
▶ ⊞ £4.50-£5 ⊞ £4.50-£5 ▲ £4.50-£5

Open Etr-Sep Last arrival 23.45hrs Last departure 17.00hrs
A simple, pleasant site with some trees, set in hills, woods and moorland near canal. On B862 Inverness-Foyers road about 5m S of Inverness. Entrance to site is opposite shop at Scaniport. A 2-acre site with 30 touring pitches.

⋔ ⊙ ※ 🏧 ⊘ 🕯 🛒

SCOURIE

Scourie Caravan & Camping Park (NC153446)
Harbour Rd IV27 4TG ☎ 01971 502060 & 502061
Signposted
▶▶▶ ⊞ fr £8 ⊞ fr £8 ▲ fr £8

Open Etr-Sep Last arrival 22.00hrs Last departure noon
An attractive and well-equipped site adjacent to beach and sea in centre of village off the Ullapool-Durness road A894. A 4-acre site with 60 touring pitches.

🔌 ⋔ ⊙ 🗄 🥄 ※ ⚑ ⊞ 🗡 🕯 ⚙ 🛒 ♿
➔ ⤙ ⤙

SHIEL BRIDGE

Morvich Caravan Club Site (NG964210)
IV40 8HQ ☎ 01599 81354 (3m N) Signposted
Nearby town: Kyle of Lochalsh
▶▶▶ ⊞ ⊞ ▲

Open mid May-mid Oct Booking advisable bank hols & Jun-Aug Last arrival 20.00hrs Last departure noon

Broomfield ▶ Holiday Park

Ullapool, Ross & Cromarty
Telephone: (01854) 612020 & 612664

This is the only caravan and camping park in Ullapool

Situated on the sea front at the West End of Ullapool and extends to some 12 acres of level grass overlooking the Summer Isles, famous for marvellous sunsets. The site has 2 large toilet blocks with flush toilets and hot & cold wash basins, shaving points, hairdryers and hand dryers, hot & cold showers, coin operated, and coin operated washing machines and tumble dryers. Power hook-ups. Children's playground. Within 5 minutes walk from the park entrance are supermarkets, bars, restaurants, cafes, bus stops, post office, telephone and boat hire. Also 9-hole golf course, tennis courts, leisure centre and covered swimming pool.

Hospitable and well-maintained site on level valley floor surrounded by hills and mountains offering dazzling scenery. On loop road off A87 at head of Loch Duich. A 7-acre site with 106 touring pitches.
Veg prep area & drying room.

Credit Cards

STRONTIAN
Glenview Caravan Park (NM818619)
PH36 4JD ☎ 01967 402123 Signposted
Nearby town: Fort William
▶ ▶ ▶ 🚐 £8.50-£9.50 🚐 £8.50-£9.50 🛆 £6-£7
Open Mar-Jan Booking advisable Jul-Aug Last arrival 23.00hrs Last departure 14.00hrs no cars by tents
An attractive, quiet site in an area of interest to naturalists, constantly being upgraded and improved. 100yds off A861 at village. A 2.5-acre site with 30 touring pitches and 6 statics.

TAIN
Meikle Ferry Caravan & Camping Park (NH748844)
IV19 1JX ☎ 01862 892292 Signposted
▶ ▶ ▶ 🚐🚐🛆
Open all year Booking advisable Jul-Aug Last arrival 22.00hrs Last departure noon
A pleasant family site with meticulously maintained

facilities, on A9 N of Tain. A 2-acre site with 30 touring pitches and 15 statics.

THURSO
Thurso Caravan & Camping Site (ND111688)
Smith Ter, Scrabster Rd KW14 7JY ☎ 01847 894545 & 01955 603761 Signposted
▶ ▶ ★ 🚐 £4.85-£5.60 🚐 £4.85-£5.60 🛆 £3.10-£5
Open May-Sep Booking advisable 14 days in advance Last arrival 22.00hrs Last departure noon
Exposed grassy site, set high above the coast on the W side of town with panoramic views out to sea. A 4.5-acre site with 117 touring pitches and 10 statics.

ULLAPOOL
Broomfield Holiday Park (NH123939)
West Shore St IV26 2UR ☎ 01854 612020 & 612664 Signposted
▶ ▶ 🚐🚐🛆
Open Apr-Oct
A level grass site by the shore of Loch Broom close to the harbour and town centre. A 10-acre site with 120 touring pitches.

WICK
Riverside Caravan Club Site (ND361509)
Janetstown KW1 5SR ☎ 01955 605420 Signposted
▶ ▶ ▶ 🚐🚐🛆
Open 2 Apr-26 Sep Booking advisable Last arrival 20.00hrs Last departure noon
A pleasant open site in a lush meadow beside the River Wick, just five minutes' walk from the fishing town of Wick. A 6.5-acre site with 90 touring pitches.
Veg prep area.

Credit Cards

LOTHIAN

For the map of this county, see Borders

ABERLADY
Gosford Gardens Caravan Club Site (NT458793)
EH32 0PX ☎ 01875 870487 Signposted
▶ ▶ 🚐🚐
Open 26 Mar-25 Oct Booking advisable bank hols & Jul-Aug Last arrival 20.00hrs Last departure noon ➡

A charming, sheltered site in and around the walled garden of Gosford House, about half an hour's drive from Edinburgh. On A198, 1m E of Aberlady. An 8-acre site with 120 touring pitches.
Veg prep area.

🔌🏕☉📺🔥⛽🅿🛄🚽Ⓣ💧♿
➡️🔪⛰🎣🛒

Credit Cards 🔳 💳

DALKEITH

Fordel (NT359668)
Lauder Rd EH22 2PH ☎ 0131 663 3046 & 0131 660 3921 Signposted
▶▶★🚐£8-£10.75 🚐£8-£10.75 ⛺£6.50-£7.50
Open Mar-Oct Booking advisable Jul-Aug Last departure noon
A small, tree lined, grassy site on A68 1.5m S of Dalkeith. A 3-acre site with 35 touring pitches.

🔌🏕☉🅿❄☂⛽🛄⛽✖💧🏪🚿🎣🛒
➡️⛎🅿☉🎣
💷

Credit Cards 🔳 💳 💳 Ⓓ 🅲 🅂

DIRLETON

Yellowcraig Caravan Club Site (NT516853)
EH39 5DS ☎ 01620 850217 Signposted
Nearby town: Berwick
▶▶▶🚐🚐
Open 25 Mar-3 Oct Booking advisable bank hols & mid Jul-mid Aug Last arrival 20.00hrs Last departure noon
Sheltered from the shore by woodland the site is surrounded by dunes and ideal for families. 400 yds past Dirleton Castle, signed. A 7.5-acre site with 120 touring pitches.
Veg prep area.

🔌🏕☉📺🅿❄⛽🛄⛽🚽Ⓣ💧🐴♿
➡️⛎🅿🛒

Credit Cards 🔳 💳

DUNBAR

Thurston Manor Holiday Home Park (NT712745)
Innerwick EH42 1SA ☎ 01368 840643 Signposted
▶▶▶🚐£9-£11 🚐£9-£11 ⛺£9-£11
Open Mar-Oct Booking advisable Etr, bank hols & high season Last arrival 9.00hrs Last departure noon
A developing site with good facilities and level pitches. From A1, 6m N of Cockburnspath, take unclass rd signed Innerwick, in .5m turn R, and site in .5m on R. A 2.5-acre site with 100 touring pitches and 200 statics. Private lake, pony treking, fitness room, sauna.

🔌🏕☉📺🅿🔦🍺❄☂⛽🛄⛽🚽Ⓣ✖💧🏪
🚿🎣🐴🛒♿
➡️⛎🅿⛰🎣

💷

Credit Cards 🔳 💳

Camping & Caravanning Club Site (NT723773)
Barns Ness EH42 1QP ☎ 01368 863536 (in season) & 01203 694995 Signposted
▶▶♣★🚐£8.40-£9 🚐£8.40-£9 ⛺£8.40-£9
Open end Mar-early Nov Booking advisable bank hols & high season Last arrival 21.00hrs Last departure noon
A grassy, landscaped site close to the foreshore and lighthouse on a coastline noted for its natural and geological history. 4m E of Dunbar, approached off A1. Please see the advertisement on page 27 for details of Club Members' benefits. A 10-acre site with 80 touring pitches.

🔌🏕☉📺🅿⛽🛄🚽Ⓣ💧
➡️⛎🅿🎣🛒

Credit Cards 🔳 💳 💳

EDINBURGH

Mortonhall Caravan Park (NT265680)
38 Mortonhall Gate EH16 6TJ ☎ 0131 664 1533 Signposted
▶▶▶▶🚐🚐⛺
Open 28 Mar-Oct Booking advisable Jul-Aug Last arrival 22.00hrs Last departure noon
Located on the S side of Edinburgh within 20 minutes' car ride of the city centre, this site is part of a 200-acre estate surrounding the 18th-century Mortonhall mansion designed by Robert Adam. A large site with high standards. Take the new city bypass to junction

with A702 and follow signs to Mortonhall. A 22-acre site
with 250 touring pitches and 18 statics.

🔌📶☉▣🔋⚡◻❄♟⛰🛈⊘🚮⊤✕📞🐕
🛟♿
→∪▶🍴

MUSSELBURGH

Drum Mohr Caravan Park (NT373734)
Levenhall EH21 8JS ☎ 0131 665 6867 Signposted
▶▶▶▶ ♣ 🚐 £7.50-£8.50 🚐 £7.50-£8.50 🏕 £7.50-£8.50
Open Mar-Oct Booking advisable Jul-Aug Last arrival
22.00hrs Last departure noon
*This attractive park is set 2 miles east of Musselburgh
between the A198 and B1348. A 9-acre site with 120
touring pitches.*
See advertisement under EDINBURGH

🔌📶☉▣🔋❄⛰🛈⊘🚮⊤📞🛟♿
→▶🍴
£

NORTH BERWICK

Tantallon Caravan Park (NT570850)
Lime Grove E39 5NJ ☎ 01620 893348 Signposted
▶▶ 🚐🚐🏕
Open Mar-Oct Booking advisable Jul-Aug Last arrival
20.00hrs Last departure noon
*Level grass site in meadowland in urban area with direct
access to sea and beach. Located off A198 Dunbar road.
A 10-acre site with 250 touring pitches and 60 statics.*

🔌📶☉▣🔋⛰🛈⊘🚮⊤📞🛟
→∪▶◎⚓

STRATHCLYDE

ARDGARTAN

Ardgartan Loch Long Campsite (NN275030)
G83 7AL ☎ 01301 702293 & 840666 Signposted
Nearby town: Helensburgh
▶▶▶ ★ 🚐 £6.50-£9.50 🚐 £6.50-£9.50 🏕 £6.50-£9.50 ➡

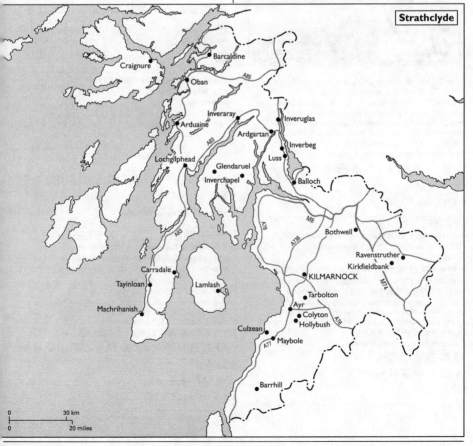

Strathclyde

Craignure
Barcaldine
Oban
A85
Inveraray
Arduaine
A83
Ardgartan
Inveruglas
Inverbeg
Lochgilphead
Glendaruel
Luss
Inverchapel
Balloch
A83
M8
A78
Bothwell
A736
Ravenstruther
Kirkfieldbank
Carradale
KILMARNOCK
M74
Tayinloan
Lamlash
Tarbolton
Machrihanish
Ayr
A76
Colyton
Hollybush
Culzean
Maybole
A77
Barrhill

0 ___ 30 km
0 ___ 20 miles

Open 31 Mar-30 Oct Booking advisable Jul-Aug Last
arrival 22.30hrs Last departure noon
*Situated on a small promontory alongside Loch Long
with access to shingle beach; a grassy site on two
levels. Direct access from A83 beside Loch ong at
Ardgartan before road turns to climb. A 17-acre site with
160 touring pitches and 40 statics.*
Slip-way for launching small boats.

🐾 📞 ☉ 🍴 🎠 🏧 🚰 ⊘ 🔌 ⬆ 🍴 🐕 🐴 🔔 ♿

➜ ∪ ⅄ ♪

Credit Cards 🏧 💳

ARDUAINE

Arduaine Caravan & Camping Park (NM800101)
PA34 4XA ☎ 01852 200331 Signposted
Nearby town: Kilmelford
▶ ▶ ♣ ★ 🚐 £7.50-£9.20 🚐 £6.50-£7.50 ▲ £3-£9.20
Open Mar-Oct Booking advisable Spring bank hol & Jul-
Aug Last arrival 22.00hrs Last departure noon
*Gently sloping grass site pleasantly situated by the
seashore beside a small jetty with views of Shuna,
Scarba, Jura and Luing. Access is from the A816. A 5-
acre site with 40 touring pitches.*
Free dinghy launching into sea.

🐾 📞 ☉ 🍴 🚰 ☀ 🔔 📞

➜ ∪ △ ⅄ ♪ 📷 🐾

🏧

AYR

Craigie Gardens Caravan Club Site (NS346217)
Craigie Rd KA7 2AY ☎ 01292 264909 Signposted
▶ ▶ ▶ 🚐 🚐
Open 26 Mar-1 Nov Booking advisable all times Last
arrival 20.00hrs Last departure noon
*A site well-screened by trees, within Craigie Park and
about ten minutes' walk from the centre of Ayr. A 7-acre
site with 95 touring pitches.*
Veg prep area.

🐾 📞 ☉ 🍴 🎠 ☀ 🏧 🚰 ⊘ ⬆ 🅣 📞 ♿

➜ ∪ ⅄ 📷 ♪ 🐾

Credit Cards 🏧 💳

Heads of Ayr Leisure Park (NS300184)
Dunure Rd KA7 4LD ☎ 01292 442269 Signposted
▶ ▶ ★ 🚐 £8.50-£11 🚐 £7.50-£10 ▲ £7.50-£10
Open Mar-Nov Booking advisable bank hols & Jul-Aug
Last arrival 23.30hrs Last departure 15.00hrs
*A flat grassy park .5m from beach overlooking Firth of
Clyde. On R of A719 Ayr to Dunure road, .5m S of Ayr. A
1.5-acre site with 36 touring pitches and 126 statics.*

🐾 📞 ☉ 🍴 🎠 🔍 ☀ ☀ 🍸 🏧 🚰 ⊘ ⬆ 🅣 ✕ 📞 🎪 🐴
🐾

➜ ∪ ⅄ 📷 ♪

🏧

Crofthead Caravan Park (NS365199)
KA6 6EN ☎ 01292 263516 Signposted
▶ ▶ 🚐 🚐
Open Etr & Apr-Sep (rs Mar & Oct shop & toilets
(weather dependant)) Booking advisable Etr, Whitsun &
Jul-Aug Last arrival dusk Last departure noon
*A mainly grassy site in a pleasant rural setting, 2m SE of
Ayr off A70. An 8.5-acre site with 50 touring pitches and
83 statics.*

🐾 📞 ☉ 🍴 🎠 🔍 🖵 ☀ 🏧 🚰 ⊘ ⬆ 🅣 📞 🎪 🍴
🐾

➜ ∪ ⅄ ◎ △ ⅄ 📷 ♪

BALLOCH

Tullichewan Caravan Park (NS383816)
Old Luss Rd G83 8QP ☎ 01389 759475 Signposted
▶ ▶ ★ 🚐 £6.90-£10.90 🚐 £6.90-£10.90 ▲ £5-£10.90
Open all year Booking advisable bank hols & Jul-Aug
Last arrival 22.00hrs Last departure noon
*A quiet and pleasant rural site near Loch Lomond,
surrounded by woodland and hills. Close to the A82. A
9-acre site with 120 touring pitches and 35 statics.*
Leisure suite with sauna, spa bath, sunbeds.

🐾 📞 ☉ 🍴 🎠 🔍 🖵 ☀ 🏧 🚰 ⊘ ⬆ 🅣 📞 ⅄ 🐴
🐾 ♿

➜ ∪ ▶ △ ⅄ ♪

Credit Cards 🏧 💳

BARCALDINE

Camping & Caravanning Club Site (NM966420)
PA37 1SG ☎ 01631 72348 (in season) & 01203 694995
Signposted
Nearby town: Oban
▶ ▶ ▶ ♣ ★ ⛽ £9.30-£10 ⛽ £9.30-£10 ▲ £9.30-£10
Open end Mar-early Nov Booking advisable bank hols &
Jul-Aug Last arrival 21.00hrs Last departure noon
*A sheltered site within the grounds of a former walled
garden, bordered by Barcaldine Forest, close to Loch
Creran, situated 10m N of Oban off A828. Winner of the
1995 Campsite of the Year Award for Scotland. Please
see the advertisement on page 27 for details of Club
Members' benefits. A 6-acre site with 75 touring pitches.*

Credit Cards

BARRHILL

Windsor Holiday Park (NX216835)
KA26 OPZ ☎ 01465 821355 Signposted
Nearby town: Girvan
▶ ▶ ▶ ★ ⛽ £6.50-£7 ⛽ £6.50-£7 ▲ £6-£6.50
Open all year (rs Nov-Feb open wknds only) Booking
advisable Jun-Aug Last arrival 22.00hrs Last departure
16.00hrs
*A small site in a rural location, well-screened from A714
by small, mature trees. 1m NW of village. A 6-acre site*

with 30 touring pitches and 50 statics.

Credit Cards

BOTHWELL

Strathclyde Country Park Caravan Site (NS717585)
Bothwellhaugh Rd G71 8NY ☎ 01698 266155
Signposted
▶ ▶ ▶
Open Apr-Oct Booking advisable Jun-Aug Last arrival
10.30hrs Last departure noon
*A pleasant level grass site situated in a country park
amidst woodland and meadowland with lots of
attractions. Direct access to park from junc 5 of M74. 250
touring pitches.*

See advertisement on page 234.

CARRADALE

Carradale Bay Caravan Site (NR815385)
PA28 6QG ☎ 01583 431665
Nearby town: Campbeltown
▶ ▶ ▶ ♣ ⛽ £6.50-£12 ⛽ £6.50-£12 ▲ £6.50-£12
Open Etr-Sep Booking advisable bank hols & Jul-Aug
Last arrival 22.00hrs Last departure noon
*A beautiful, natural site on the sea's edge with superb
views over Kilbrannan Sound to Isle of Arran. Approach
from north is via Tarbert, leaving by A83 Campbeltown
road; within 5m turn onto B8001, then B842 Carradale
road. This is a single-track road with passing places. In
Carradale take road to the pier, site is in .5m. An 8-acre
site with 75 touring pitches and 3 statics.*
Canoe & bicycle hire.

COYLTON

Sundrum Castle Holiday Park (NS405208)
KA6 6HX ☎ 01292 570057 & 570886 Signposted
Nearby town: Ayr
▶ ▶ ▶ ♣ ⛽ ⛽ ▲
Open 26 Mar-Oct (rs Etr-May bank hol entertainment
wknds only) Booking advisable bank hols & Jul-Aug
Last arrival 23.30hrs Last departure noon
*A large family holiday centre, with plenty of on-site
entertainment, just a 10 min drive from the centre of
Ayr. Set off the A70. A 23-acre site with 52 touring
pitches and 223 statics.*
Amusement arcade, cycle hire & entertainment.
See advertisement under AYR

Credit Cards

CULZEAN

Camping & Caravanning Club Site (NS247103)
Glenside KA19 8JX ☎ 01655 760627 (in season) & 01203
694995 Signposted
Nearby town: Maybole
►►► ♠ ★ ⊕ £9.30-£10 ⊕ £9.30-£10 ▲ £9.30-£10
Open end Mar-early Nov Booking advisable bank hols &
Jul-Aug Last arrival 21.00hrs Last departure noon
*A mainly level, grassy site situated at the entrance to the
castle and country park, surrounded by trees on three
sides and with lovely views over Culzean Bay. Signed at
entrance to Culzean Castle on A719. Please see the
advertisement on page 27 for details of Club Members'
benefits. A 6-acre site with 90 touring pitches.*

🔌 🛆 ⊙ 🗐 ⚲ ✳ 🛝 🛢 🖉 ⊕ 🆃 📞 🎋 🐕 🐎 ♿
→ ∪ ► 🎣 🛒

Credit Cards 🔳 ▦

DUNOON

See **Loch Eck**

GLENDARUEL

Glendaruel Caravan Park (NR005865)
PA22 3AB ☎ 01369 820267 Signposted
►►► ♠ ⊕ £8-£9 ⊕ £8-£9 ▲ £6-£9
Open Apr-Oct Booking advisable Spring bank hol & mid
Jul-Aug Last arrival 22.00hrs Last departure noon
*Attractive, grassy, level site in 23 acres of wooded
parkland in a valley surrounded by mountains. Situated
off A886, with many rare species of trees on site. A 3-*

acre site with 40 touring pitches and 30 statics.
Bicycles for hire, fishing sea trout & salmon.

🔌 🛆 ⊙ 🗐 ⚲ ✳ 🛝 🛢 🖉 ⊕ 🆃 📞 🎋 🐎
🛒
→ 🎣

Credit Cards 🔳 ▦

HOLLYBUSH

Skeldon Caravan Park (NS389144)
KA6 7EB ☎ 01292 560502 Signposted
Nearby town: Ayr
► ⊕ £7.50 ⊕ £8.50 ▲ £5-£6.50
Open Apr-Sep Booking advisable Jul-Aug Last arrival
20.30hrs Last departure 10.30hrs
*A sheltered grass site in a rural location on the banks of
the River Doon 2m from Dalrymple on B7034. A 2.5-acre
site with 20 touring pitches and 10 statics.*
First aid. Trout fishing on site.

🔌 🛆 ⊙ ⚲ ✳ 🛝 🛢 🖉 ⊕ 🆃 📞 🎋 🐎 🛒
→ ► 🎣
⊕

INVERARAY

Argyll Caravan Park (NN075055)
PA32 8XT ☎ 01499 302285 Signposted
►►► ★ ⊕ £8.50-£10.50 ⊕ £8.50-£10.50 ▲ £7-£9
Open Apr-Oct Last arrival anytime Last departure noon

A mainly grassy site with some hardstandings on the shores of Loch Fyne, with ample on-site facilities. 2.5m S of Inveraray on A83. A 6-acre site with 60 touring pitches and 241 statics.
Mini football pitch.

🏕️ 📷 ⊙ 🗗 🔧 🔦 ☀ 🍴 ♨ 🛢 🌿 ⊤ ✗ 📞 🧹 🐕 🦮
♿
→ ∪ ⬆ ♪
💷

INVERBEG

INVERBEG

Inverbeg Holiday Park (NS348983)
G83 8PD ☎ 01436 860267 & 0131 654 0142 Signposted
Nearby town: Luss
▶ ▶ ▶ ★ 🛢 £6-£7.50 🚐 £6-£7.50 �†ᵢ £6-£7.50
Open Mar-Oct Booking advisable Spring bank hol, Jul-Aug & hol wknds Last arrival 23.00hrs Last departure noon
A well-maintained site with some hardstanding for tourers, situated on a small promontory alongside Loch Lomond with direct access to shingle beach and a small marina. Signed with access off A82, 4m N of Luss. Very fast section of road and great care should be taken. A 4-acre site with 35 touring pitches and 120 statics.
Sailing & fishing.

🏕️ 📷 ⊙ 🗗 🔧 🔦 ⬜ ☀ 🚿 🛢 🌿 ⊤ 📞 🐕 🦮
→ ∪ ⬆ ✂ ♪
💷

INVERUGLAS

Loch Lomond Holiday Park (NN320092)
Loch Lomond Holiday Park G83 7DW ☎ 01301 704224 Signposted
Nearby town: Helensburgh
▶ ▶ ▶ ⚓ ★ 🛢 £6.50-£12 🚐 £6.50-£12
Open Mar-Oct (rs Dec-Jan main amenity building restricted hours) Booking advisable May-Aug Last arrival 22.00hrs Last departure 11.45hrs
A lovely setting on the shores of Loch Lomond with views of forests and mountains. Situated on A 82 between Tarbet and Ardlui. A 6-acre site with 18 touring pitches and 72 statics.
Satellite TV, pool tables.

🏕️ 📷 ⊙ 🗗 🔧 🔦 ⬜ ☀ 🛢 🌿 ⊤ 📞 🦮 🏠
🐕 🦮 ♿
→ ∪ ⬆ ✂ ♪
💷
Credit Cards 🔲 🔲 🔲

KILMARNOCK

Cunningham Head Estate Caravan Park (NS370418)
Cunningham Head, Irvine KA3 2PE ☎ 01294 850238 Signposted
▶ ▶ ★ 🛢 £6.50-£7.50 🚐 £6.50-£7.50 �†ᵢ £5-£7.50
Open Apr-Sep (rs Apr-Jun & Sep bar & games room open wknds only) Booking advisable Jul-Aug Last arrival 22.00hrs Last departure noon

A rural site in the grounds of a farmland estate, 3.5m NE of Irvine on B769. From Irvine take A736 Glasgow road, at Stanecastle roundabout turn E on to B769 Stewarton road. Park is 3m on left. A 7-acre site with 120 touring pitches and 70 statics.

🏕️ 📷 ⊙ 🗗 🔧 🔦 ☀ 🍴 ♨ 🛢 🌿 ⬆ ⊤ 📞
→ 🛁 ♫ 🦮
💷

KIRKFIELDBANK

Clyde Valley Caravan Park (NS868441)
ML11 9TS ☎ 01555 663951 Signposted
▶ ▶ 🛢 🚐 ⚓ �†ᵢ
Open Apr-Oct Booking advisable anytime Last arrival 23.00hrs Last departure noon
Level, grass site with trees and bushes set in mountains and hilly country with access to river. From Glasgow on A72, cross river bridge at Kirkfieldbank and site is on left. From Lanard on A72, turn right at bottom of very steep hill before going over bridge. A 5-acre site with 50 touring pitches and 115 statics.

🏕️ 📷 ⊙ 🗗 🦮 🛢 🌿 ⬆ ⊤ 📞 🦮
→ ∪ ⬆ ✂ 🛁 ♪

LOCH ECK (INVERCHAPEL)

Stratheck International Caravan Park (NS144865)
PA23 8SG ☎ 01369 840472 (at Inverchapel at S end of Loch) Signposted
Nearby town: Dunoon
▶ ▶ ▶ ★ 🛢 £6.50-£7 🚐 £6.50-£7 �†ᵢ £5-£7
Open Mar-Oct Booking advisable Jul-Aug Last arrival 22.00hrs Last departure noon
Attractive, grassy site at southern end of Loch Eck. Set in a valley bounded by trees and river but close to main road. 7m N of Dunoon on A815. A 13-acre site with 40 touring pitches and 52 statics.
Pets corner, football pitch & putting.

🏕️ 📷 ⊙ 🗗 🔧 🔦 ☀ 🍴 ♨ 🛢 🌿 ⬆ 📞 🐕 🦮
→ ∪ ⬆ ✂ ♪
💷

LOCHGILPHEAD

Lochgilphead Caravan Site (NR859881)
PA31 8NX ☎ 01546 602003 Signposted
▶ ▶ ▶ ★ 🛢 fr £6.50 🚐 fr £6.50 �†ᵢ fr £6.50
Open Apr-Oct Booking advisable Jul-Aug
Mainly level, grassy site close to the shore of Loch Gilp, an inlet of Loch Fyne. Situated beside the A83 and convenient to the town centre facilities. Fishing and sailing available on the Loch. A 7-acre site with 70 touring pitches and 30 statics.
Mountain bike hire.

🏕️ 📷 ⊙ 🗗 🔧 🔦 ☀ 🚿 🛢 🌿 ⬆ ⊤ 📞 🏠 🐕
🦮
→ ∪ ⬆ ♪
💷

LUSS

Camping & Caravanning Club Site (NS360936)
G83 8NT ☎ 01436 860658 (in season) & 01203 694995
Signposted
Nearby town: Dumbarton
► ► ★ ⊞ £9.30-£10 ⊞ £9.30-£10 ⅄ £9.30-£10
Open end Mar-early Nov Booking advisable bank hols &
Jul-Aug Last arrival 21.00hrs Last departure noon
*Lovely grassy site on W shore of Loch Lomond. .25m N
of Luss village on A82 Glasgow-Fort William road.
Please see the advertisement on page 27 for details of
Club Members' benefits. A 15-acre site with 90 touring
pitches.*

🏢 📞 ☉ ※ 🖽 🚿 🗬 🐴 🖫
→ ⅄ 🐋

Credit Cards ▨ ▨ ▨

MACHRIHANISH

Camping & Caravanning Club Site (NR647207)
East Trodigal PA28 6PT ☎ 01586 810366 (in season) &
01203 694995
Nearby town: Campbeltown
► ► ★ ⊞ £8.20-£8.80 ⊞ £8.20-£8.80 ⅄ £8.20-£8.80
Open end Mar-early Nov Booking advisable bank hols &
high season Last arrival 21.00hrs Last departure noon
*A very open site with superb sea views, situated
adjacent to the golf course. On B843 .75m before village.
Please see the advertisement on page 27 for details of
Club Members' benefits. A 6-acre site with 90 touring
pitches.*

🏢 📞 ☉ 🗬 🔍 ※ 🚿 🗬 🐴 🖫 ⅃ ㄥ
→ ▶ 🐋

Credit Cards ▨ ▨ ▨

MAYBOLE

The Ranch (NS286102)
Culzean Rd KA19 8DU ☎ 01655 882446
► ► ► ► ⊞ ⊞
Open Mar-Oct & wknds in winter
*A small well run touring site with good views and many
on site amenities. Situated on the L of B7023, 1m S of
Maybole towards Culzean. A 9-acre site with 28 touring
pitches and 68 statics.*
Mini gym, sauna & sunbed.

🏢 📞 🗒 🗬 🖽 🛢 ⅃ 🖾

OBAN

Oban Divers Caravan Park (NM841277)
Glenshellach Rd PA34 4QJ ☎ 01631 562755
► ► ► ♣ ★ ⊞ £6-£7 ⊞ £6-£7 ⅄ fr £6
Open 15 Mar-15 Nov Booking advisable Etr, Whit & Jul-
Aug ⊗
*A well-maintained site amidst mountain scenery with a
stream running through. The site specialises in facilities
for divers. A 4-acre site with 42 touring pitches.*

🏢 📞 ☉ 🗬 ※ 🖽 🛢 🚿 🗐 ⅃ 🏛 🗬 🖫 ㄥ
→ ∪ ▶ 🛆 ⅄ 🎦 🐋 🗗 🖾

RAVENSTRUTHER

Newhouse Caravan & Camping Park (NS926456)
ML11 8NP ☎ 01555 870228 Signposted
Nearby town: Lanark
► ► ► ★ ⊞ fr £6.50 ⊞ fr £6.50 ⅄ fr £4
Open Mar-Oct Booking advisable Jul-Aug Last arrival
22.00hrs Last departure noon
*Pleasant level grass and gravel site, with young trees
and bushes, situated on A70 Ayr-Edinburgh road, 3m E
of Lanark. A 5-acre site with 45 touring pitches and 3
statics.*
Caravan storage compound.

🏢 📞 ☉ 🗒 🗬 ※ 🖽 🛢 🚿 🗐 🗵 🗖 ⅃ 🏛 🗬 🐴 🖫
ㄥ
→ ∪ ▶ ⅄ 🐋
⊞

TARBERT

See **Tayinloan**

TARBOLTON

Middlemuir Park (NS439263)
KA5 5NR ☎ 01292 541647 Signposted
Nearby town: Ayr
► ► ► ♣ ⊞ ⊞ ⅄
Open all year Booking advisable bank hols & Jul-Aug
Last arrival 18.00hrs Last departure noon
*A rural site in the partly-walled garden where
Montgomerie House used to stand. Set in rolling
farmland off the B743 Ayr-Mauchline road. A 17-acre
site with 25 touring pitches and 45 statics.*

🏢 📞 ☉ 🗒 🗬 🔍 ※ 🖽 🛢 🚿 🗵 🗖 ⅃ 🐴 🖫 ㄥ
→ ∪ ▶ 🐋

TAYINLOAN

Point Sands Holiday Park (NR698484)
Point Sands PA29 6XG ☎ 01583 441263 & 441215
Signposted
► ► ► ♣ ★ ⊞ £7.50-£8 ⊞ £6.50-£8 ⅄ £4-£7
Open Apr-Oct Booking advisable Jul-Aug Last arrival
23.00hrs Last departure 21.00hrs
*Attractive level site by lovely safe sandy beach on
western shore of Kintyre peninsula, with superb views
of Gigha, Islay and Jura.*
*Direct access from A83 at Tayinloan. A 15-acre site with
60 touring pitches and 70 statics.*

🏢 📞 ☉ 🗒 🗬 ※ 🖽 🛢 🚿 🗖 ⅃ 🏛 🖫 ㄥ
→ 🐋

TAYSIDE

For the map of this county, see Central

ABERFELDY

Aberfeldy Caravan Park (NN858495)
Dunkeld Rd PH15 2AQ ☎ 01887 820662
► ► ► ★ ₱ £7.15-£8.20 ₱ £7.15-£8.20 ▲ £5.50-£8.20
Open late Mar-late Oct Booking advisable Jul-mid Sep
Last arrival 20.00hrs Last departure noon
A very well-run and well-maintained site, with good facilities and some landscaping. Set at the eastern end of the town and lying between main road and banks of the River Tay. Good views from site of surrounding hills. A 4-acre site with 98 touring pitches and 36 statics.

Credit Cards ▨ ▨ ▨

AUCHTERARDER

Auchterarder Caravan Park (NN964138)
Nether Coul PH3 1ET ☎ 01764 663119 (1m E off B8062)
Signposted
► ► ► ♦ ₱ £7-£8.50 ₱ £7-£8 ▲ £5-£7
Open all year Booking advisable Jul-Aug Last arrival 22.00hrs Last departure noon
A small, level touring site, well-run and well-maintained. From N turn right off A9 on A823 to Auchterarder, after 2 miles turn left onto B8062 signed Dunning. Turn left after 100m into site. A 2-acre site with 23 touring pitches.
Private fishing.

⚏◍⊙▯※🇮🚩🔧⛲⛅🇫⏁🛒🚻⚘
→∪▶🎵
💷

BIRNAM

Erigmore House Holiday Park (NO036416)
PH8 9XX ☎ 01350 727236 Signposted
► ► ► ₱ ₱ ▲
Open Mar-Oct Booking advisable 22 Mar-Oct Last arrival 22.00hrs Last departure 14.00hrs
A predominantly touring site in the grounds of 18th-century Erigmore House which has a wide variety of unusual trees including Japanese maple and cherry. Site well-secluded from the main road and a considerable degree of privacy can be found. Situated on B898. A 10-acre site with 31 touring pitches and 189 statics.
Entertainment.

⚏🚽🇮◍⊙▯🚩🎏⚘※🍴🇫⛲⛅
🇫
→▶🎵
Credit Cards ▨ ▨

BLAIR ATHOLL

AWARD Q

Blair Castle Caravan Park (NN874656)
PH18 5SR ☎ 01796 481263
Signposted
Nearby town: Pitlochry
► ► ► ► ♦ ♦♦ ₱ £7.50-£9.50 ₱ £7.50-£9.50 ▲ £5-£9.50
Open Apr-late Oct (rs Apr-Jun & Sep-mid Oct restaurant & shop restricted) Booking advisable bank hols & Jul-Aug Last arrival 21.30hrs Last departure noon
Attractive site set in impressive seclusion within the Atholl estate, surrounded by mature woodland and the R Tilt. A 20-acre site with 268 touring pitches and 105 statics.
See advertisement under PITLOCHRY

⚏🇮◍⊙▯🚩🔧⛅※🗂️🇮🛒🖇⊞⏁✖🇫🚗🚿
🚩⚘🇫
→∪▶🎵
💷
Credit Cards ▨ ▨ ▨ 🅢

◯◯◯◯◯◯◯◯◯

River Tilt Caravan Park (NN875653)
PH18 5TE ☎ 01796 481467 Signposted
► ► ► ♦ ₱ £12-£14 ₱ £11-£13 ▲ £4-£14
Open mid Mar-Nov Booking advisable Jul-Aug Last arrival 22.00hrs Last departure 11.00hrs
Level, grass site with trees and bushes set in hilly woodland country on the banks of the River Tilt, next to golf course. 7m N of Pitlochry on A9, take B8079 to Blair ➡

Atholl, and site at rear of Tilt Hotel.. A 2-acre site with 37
touring pitches and 92 statics.
Multi-gym, sauna & solarium.
See advertisement under PITLOCHRY

🔌 📻 ☉ 🗗 🗜 ⚡ ☀ 🏔 🛈 🔗 ⊞ ✕ 🔌 🏛 🐴
➜ ∪ ▶
⏏

BRIDGE OF CALLY

**Corriefodly Holiday Park
(NO134513)**
PH10 7JG ☎ 01250 886236
Signposted
Nearby town: Blairgowrie
▶ ▶ ▶ ⚫ 🏕 🖈 ⊡ £7-£10 🚐 £7-£10 ▲ £4-£10
Open early Dec-early Nov Booking advisable bank hols
& Jul-Aug Last arrival 22.00hrs Last departure noon
A secluded riverbank site in a wooded area 150 yards N
of Bridge of Cally on A924. A 5-acre site with 38 touring
pitches and 127 statics.
Bowling green & fishing on site.

🔌 📻 ☉ 🗗 🗜 ⚡ ☀ 🍽 🏔 🛈 🔗 🔌 ♿
➜ ∪ ▶ 🎣 🛠
⏏

CARNOUSTIE

Woodlands Caravan Park (NO560350)
Newton Rd DD7 6HR ☎ 01241 854430 & 853246
Signposted
▶ ▶ ▶ ⚫ 🚐 🚐 ▲
Open late Mar-early Oct Booking advisable Jul-mid Aug
Last arrival 21.00hrs Last departure noon
An excellent, well-maintained site with good facilities.
Set in a quiet area of town, well-signed from A930. A
5.5-acre site with 108 touring pitches and 4 statics.

🔌 📻 ☉ 🗗 🏔 🛈 🔌 ♿
➜ ∪ ▶ 🎣 🛠

CRIEFF

Crieff Holiday Village (NN857225)
Turret Bank PH7 4JN ☎ 01764 653513 Signposted
▶ ▶ ▶ ★ 🚐 £7.45-£8.15 🚐 £7.45-£8.15 ▲ fr £6
Open all year Booking advisable Jul-Aug Last arrival
mdnt
A level grassy site by the riverside, near to Crieff and
adjacent to the A85. A 3-acre site with 40 touring pitches
and 40 statics.

🔌 📻 ☉ 🗗 🗜 ⚡ 🖵 ☀ 🏔 🛈 🔗 ⊞ 🇹 🔌 🏛 🐴
🛠
➜ ∪ ▶ 🔱 🎣

Credit Cards 🟦 💳 💳

DUNKELD

See **Birnham**

EDZELL

Glenesk Caravan Park (NO602717)
DD9 7YP ☎ 01356 648565 & 648523 (2m NW off B966)
Signposted
Nearby town: Brechin
▶ ▶ ▶ 🚐 £6.50-£7.50 🚐 £6.50-£7.50 ▲ £5-£6
Open Apr-Oct Booking advisable public hols & mid Jun-
Aug Last arrival 22.00hrs Last departure 16.00hrs
A carefully improved and maintained woodland site
surrounding a small fishing lake. Situated on unclass
road to Glen Esk, 1m N of the B966. An 8-acre site with
45 touring pitches and 10 statics.

🔌 📻 ☉ 🗗 🗜 ⚡ 🖵 🏔 🛈 🔗 ⊞ 🇹 🔌 🏛 🎋 🐴
🛠
➜ ∪ ▶ 🔱 🎣

FORFAR

Lochside Caravan Park (NO450505)
Forfar Loch Country Park DD8 1BT ☎ 01307 464201 &
468917 Signposted
▶ ▶ ▶ 🚐 🚐 ▲
Open late Mar-early Oct Booking advisable mid Jun-Aug
Last arrival 21.00hrs Last departure noon
A pleasant, well laid out site close to the loch and
leisure centre. Well-signed off ring road (A94). A 4.75-
acre site with 74 touring pitches.

📻 ☉ 🏔 🔌 🛠
➜ 🎣

INCHTURE

Inchmartine Caravan Park & Nurseries (NO263277)
Dundee Rd PH14 9QQ ☎ 01821 670212 & 686251
Signposted
Nearby town: Perth
▶ 🏕 ★ 🚐 £8-£9 🚐 £8-£9
Open Mar-Oct Last arrival 20.00hrs Last departure noon
🐾
A quiet site with excellent toilet facilities, adjacent to
A85 Perth-Dundee road. An 8-acre site with 45 touring
pitches.

🔌 📻 ☉ 🗜
➜ ∪ 🛠

KENMORE

Kenmore Caravan & Camping Park (NN772458)
PH15 2HN ☎ 01887 830226 Signposted
Nearby town: Aberfeldy
▶ ▶ ▶ ▶ ★ 🚐 £8-£12 🚐 £7-£11 ▲ £6-£10
Open 25 Mar-Oct Booking advisable mid Jul-mid Aug
Last arrival 22.00hrs Last departure 14.00hrs

KENMORE CARAVAN & CAMPING PARK
▶▶▶▶

**Taymouth Holiday Centre
Kenmore, Aberfeldy, Perthshire PH15 2HN
Telephone: 01887 830226**

Pleasant site by the River Tay. Ideal touring centre. Beautiful forest and hill walks or mountain treks. Excellent golf course on site (par 70) with others nearby. Fishing on the river or Loch Tay. Most water activities available and a swimming pool 6 miles away in Aberfeldy. Pony trekking also nearby. Facilities include a recreation field, two children's play areas, a dog walking area, hook up points and ample hot water in dish washing, laundry and toilet blocks. The Byre Bistro offers excellent bar and restaurant facilities with families welcome, there are also a variety of places to eat well locally. The site is quiet at night and owner supervised.

A pleasant riverside site with an air of spaciousness and a very good licensed bar/restaurant. On A827 opposite Loch Tay 8.5 miles W of Aberfeldy. A 12-acre site with 160 touring pitches and 60 statics.
Cycle hire, 9 hole golf, games & TV room.

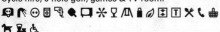

→ ∪ ▶ ⚠ ✦ ♪
⊞

Credit Cards

KINLOCH RANNOCH

Kilvrecht Campsite (NN623567)
PH17 ☎ 01350 727284
▶ ★ 🚐 fr £5 🚐 fr £5 ▲ fr £3
Open 26 Mar-25 Oct
A basic site in a large clearing in the forest, about .75 mile from Loch Rannoch shore. Approach along unclass road along loch shore with Forestry Commission signs. A 17-acre site with 60 touring pitches.

⚠ ☰ ☂ ☲
→ ▶ ✦ ♪

KIRRIEMUIR

Drumshademuir Caravan Park (NO381509)
Roundyhill DD8 1QT
☎ 01575 573284 Signposted
▶▶▶▶ ♠ ⁑⁂ ★ 🚐 £8-£8.50 🚐 £8-£8.50 ▲ £5.50-£6
Open mid Mar-end Oct Booking advisable public hols &

Jun-Aug Last arrival 23.00hrs Last departure 18.00hrs
Part-sloping grass site in valley 2.5m S of Kirriemuir on A928. A 7.5-acre site with 80 touring pitches and 34 statics.
Bar food & putting.

→ ∪ ▶ ⚠ ♪
⊞

MONIFIETH

Tayview Caravan Park (NO502322)
Milton Mill DD5 4NZ ☎ 01382 534341 & 532837
Signposted
Nearby town: Dundee
▶▶ 🚐🚐 ▲
Open Apr-Oct Booking advisable Jul-Aug Last arrival 22.00hrs Last departure 12.30hrs
A seafront site close to town centre and amenities. Signs from A930 when approaching from north. No signs on south approach but follow signs for Barry Links. An 8-acre site with 165 touring pitches and 2 statics.

→ ∪ ▶ ⁑ ♪ ▣ ☲
⊞

MONTROSE

South Links Caravan Park (NO725575)
Traill Dr DD10 8EJ ☎ 01674 72026 & 72105
Signposted
▶▶▶▶ 🚐🚐 ▲
Open late Mar-early Oct Booking advisable mid Jun-Aug Last arrival 21.00hrs Last departure noon
A well-maintained site with good facilities, partly overlooked by a processing plant. A 10.75-acre site with 172 touring pitches.

→ ▶ ♪ ☲

PERTH

Camping & Caravanning Club Site (NO108274)
Scone Racecourse, Scone PH2 6BB ☎ 01738 552323
(in season) & 01203 694995 Signposted
▶▶▶ ★ 🚐 £9.40-£10.20 🚐 £9.40-£10.20
▲ £9.40-£10.20
Open end Mar-early Nov Booking advisable bank hols & peak periods Last arrival 21.00hrs Last departure noon
A sheltered site in wooded area adjacent to the racecourse off A93. Please see the advertisement on page 27 for details of Club Members' benefits. A 14-acre site with 150 touring pitches and 20 statics.

→ ∪ ▶ ⁑ ♪

Credit Cards ▨ ▨ ▨

Cleeve Caravan Park (NO097227)
Glasgow Rd PH2 0PH
☎ 01738 639521 & 474864
▶▶▶♦♦♦ ★ ♞ £7.20-£8.20 ▲ £5-£8.20
Open late Mar-late Oct Booking advisable Jul-mid Sep Last arrival 21.00hrs Last departure noon
A recently re-developed site with excellent facilities adjacent to the A93 Perth to Glasgow road, 2m W of Perth. A 5.5-acre site with 100 touring pitches.
Free use of microwave.

Credit Cards

PITLOCHRY

Faskally Caravan Park (NN916603)
PH16 5LA ☎ 01796 472007 Signposted
▶▶▶▶ ★ ♞ £8.65-£9.60 ♞ £8.25-£9.30 ▲ £7.75-£8.55
Open 15 Mar-Oct Booking advisable Jul-Aug Last arrival 23.00hrs
A secluded riverbank site in sloping meadowland surrounded by trees. 1.5 miles N of Pitlochry on B8019. A 23-acre site with 255 touring pitches and 65 statics.
Steam room, spa, sauna & mini golf.

Credit Cards

Milton of Fonab Caravan Site (NN945573)
PH16 5NA ☎ 01796 472882 Signposted
▶ ▶ ▶ ★ 🚐 £8.50-£9 🚐 £8.50-£9 ▲ £8.50-£9
Open Apr-Oct Booking advisable Jul-Aug Last arrival 21.00hrs Last departure 13.00hrs
Level, grass site with mature trees on banks of River Tummel, .5m S of town off A924. A 12-acre site with 154 touring pitches and 36 statics.

🔲🔧🌾📶⊙🔟🦞✳🛈⊘🔑🐕🎿🛥
➜∪🅿◎🛥🦶🎿

TUMMEL BRIDGE

Tummel Valley Holiday Park (NN764592)
PH16 5SA ☎ 01882 634221 Signposted
▶ ▶ ▶ ▶ 🚐🚐▲
Open end Mar-end Oct Booking advisable bank & school hols Last arrival 20.00hrs Last departure 14.00hrs
Well-developed site amongst mature forest in this attractive valley. From A9 N of Pitlochry turn W on B8019. A 4-acre site with 110 touring pitches and 105 statics.
Bicycle hire, crazy golf, fishing rod hire.

🔲🌾📶⊙🔟🦞🔦 ●✳☥🛎🏔🛈⊘⊞🔲✂🔑♿
🎋♿⚲
➜🦶

SCOTTISH ISLANDS

For the map of these islands, see
Strathclyde

ARRAN, ISLE OF

LAMLASH

Middleton Caravan & Camping Park (NS027301)
KA27 8NN ☎ 01770 600251 & 600255 Signposted
▶ ▶ ▶ 🚐🚐▲
Open late Apr-mid Oct Booking advisable Jul-Aug (for static caravans only) Last arrival 21.30hrs Last departure noon no cars by caravans
A grassy site sheltered by hills and mature trees, with lovely views. Close to sea and village amenities in a very pleasant location. A 3.5-acre site with 70 touring pitches and 60 statics.

🔲🌾📶⊙🔟🦞✳🛈⊘🔑
➜🦶◎🎿🦶🎿

MULL, ISLE OF

CRAIGNURE
Shieling Holidays (NM724369)
PA65 6AY ☎ 01680 812496 Signposted
▶▶▶♠★⚑ £8.50-£9.50 ⚑ £8.50-£9.50 ⚑ £8.50-£9.50
Open Apr-Oct Booking advisable Spring bank hol & Jul-Aug Last arrival 22.00hrs Last departure noon
A lovely site on the water's edge with spectacular views. A 3-acre site with 30 touring pitches and 12 statics. Adventure playground, boat hire.

SKYE, ISLE OF

DUNVEGAN
Dunvegan Caravan Park (NG260477)
IV55 8WA ☎ 01470 521206 Signposted
▶▶⚑⚑⚑
Open Apr-Sep Booking advisable high season Last arrival 22.00hrs Last departure noon
A well-equipped site with clean facilities. On A850 .25m E of A863. A 2-acre site with 33 touring pitches.

EDINBANE
Loch Greshornish Caravan Site (NG343524)
Borve, Arnisort IV51 9PS ☎ 01470 582230 Signposted
Nearby town: Portree
▶▶★⚑ fr £6 ⚑ fr £6 ⚑ fr £6
Open Apr-Oct Booking advisable Jul-Aug Last arrival 22.00hrs Last departure noon
A pleasant, open site, mostly level and with a high standard of maintenance. Situated by the loch-shore at Edinbane, approx 12m from Portree on the A850 Dunvegan road. A 5-acre site with 130 touring pitches.

WALES

CLWYD

ABERGELE
See **Betws-Yn-Rhos**

BANGOR-ON-DEE
Camping & Caravanning Club Site (SJ385448)
The Racecourse LL13 0DA ☎ 01978 781009 (in season) & 01203 694995 Signposted
▶▶▶★⚑ £8.40-£9 ⚑ £8.40-£9 ⚑ £8.40-£9
Open end Mar-end Oct Booking advisable bank hols & peak periods Last arrival 21.00hrs Last departure noon
A mainly level, grassy site within the racecourse which lies in a bend of the River Dee. Please see the advertisement on page 27 for details of Club Members' benefits. A 2-acre site with 100 touring pitches.

Credit Cards 🃏

BETWS-YN-RHOS
Hunters Hamlet Caravan Park (SJ928736)
Sirior Goch Farm LL22 8PL ☎ 01745 832237
Nearby town: Abergele
▶▶▶👬★⚑ £8-£11 ⚑ £7-£11
Open 22 Mar-Oct Booking advisable bank hols & Jul-Aug Last arrival 23.00hrs Last departure noon
A delightful little site next to the owners' Georgian farmhouse. An excellent purpose-built toilet block with good quality fittings and furniture. From A55 into Abergele take A548, turn right in 3m onto B5381, and site in .5m on left. A 1.5-acre site with 23 touring pitches. Stabling for horses.

Credit Cards 🃏

CAERWYS
Encil-y-Creyr Heron's Retreat (SJ131716)
Caerwys Hill CM7 5AD ☎ 01352 720585 & 720100 Signposted
▶▶▶★⚑ fr £6.50 ⚑ fr £6.50 ⚑ fr £5
Open Mar-Nov Booking advisable bank hols Last arrival noon
Former quarries, long abandoned and returned to nature, now being developed along sympathetic lines. Set beneath range of hills, with superb views. On B5122 between Caerwys and Afon Wen. A 4.5-acre site with 40 touring pitches.

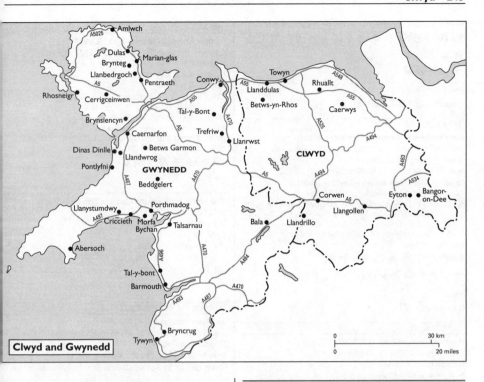

Clwyd and Gwynedd

CORWEN

Llawr-Betws Farm Caravan Park (SJ016424)
LL21 0HD ☎ 01490 81224 Signposted
▶▶ ⊞ ⊞ Å
Open Mar-Oct Booking advisable bank hols & Jul-Aug
Last arrival 23.00hrs Last departure noon
Mainly level site with grass and mature trees, 3m W of
Corwen off A494 Bala road. A 5-acre site with 65 touring
pitches and 72 statics.
Fishing.

→ ∪ ► ⅃ ⚌ ♪

EYTON

Plassey Touring Caravan & Leisure Park (SJ353452)
The Plassey LL13 0SP ☎ 01978 780277 Signposted
Nearby town: Wrexham
▶▶▶ ★ ⊞ £6.50-£8.50 ⊞ £6.50-£8.50 Å £6.50-£8.50
Open Mar-Oct (rs Mar, Apr & Oct swimming pool
closed) Booking advisable bank hols & school hols Last
arrival 20.00hrs
A mainly level grassy site with trees and meadowland,
off the B5426. A 10-acre site with 120 touring pitches
and 40 statics.

Sauna, sunbed, badminton, table tennis,9 hole golf.

🔌📻☉📷🍴🍽 🔍☀🏕🎢 🛅🖊✉🚽🆃✖📞🏪
🐴🐕♿
➜⛽🅿◎🎵
💷

Credit Cards 🏧 🎫 ▨ 🔄

Bron Y Wendon Caravan Park (SH904786)
Wern Rd LL22 8HG ☎ 01492 512903 Signposted
Nearby town: Colwyn Bay
▶ ▶ ▶ ♣♠ 🚐 £6.50-£8.50 🚑 £6.50-£8.50
Open 21 Mar-Oct Booking advisable bank hols Last
arrival anytime Last departure 11.00hrs
*Sea views from every pitch and excellent purpose-built
ablution block. Developing into a first class site. Tightly
sandwiched between main railway line and new N
Wales coast highway (A55). An 8-acre site with 110
touring pitches.*

🔌📻☉📷🍴🔍⛲🛁📞🐴🐕♿
➜⛽🅿◎🔺🍴🎵🛅
💷

Credit Cards 🎫

Hendwr Caravan Park (SJ035386)
LL21 0SN ☎ 01490 440210 Signposted
Nearby town: Corwen
▶ ▶ ▶ ♣ ★ 🚐 fr £6 🚑 fr £6 ▲ fr £6
Open Apr-Oct (rs Nov-Mar no toilet facilities during this
period) Booking advisable bank & school hols Last
arrival 22.00hrs Last departure 16.00hrs
*Level grass site with mature trees near river, hills,
woods and moorland. SW of Corwen on A5, left onto
B4401 for 4m. A 4-acre site with 40 touring pitches and
80 statics.*
Wet weather camping facilities.

🔌📻☉📷🍴☀🛁📏🆃🎢📞🛅
➜⛽🎵
💷

Ty-Ucha Caravan Park (SJ232415)
Maesmawr Rd LL20 7PP ☎ 01978 860677 Signposted
▶ ▶ ▶ ♣ 🚐 fr £6.50 🚑 fr £6
Open Etr-Oct (rs Mar toilet block closed) Booking
advisable public hols Last arrival 22.00hrs Last
departure 14.00hrs
*A very well-run site in beautiful surroundings
conveniently placed close to A5, 1m E of Llangollen.
Ideal for country and mountain walking, with small
stream on its southern boundary. A 4-acre site with 40
touring pitches.*

🔌📻☉🔍☀🛁📏🆃🆃📞🛅
➜⛽🅿🍴🎵📷
💷

Penisar Mynydd Caravan Park (SJ093770)
Caerwys Rd LL17 0TY ☎ 01745 582227 (2m NE)
Signposted
Nearby town: Dyserth
▶ ★ 🚐 fr £5.50
Open Etr or Apr-Oct Booking advisable bank hols
*A beautifully situated site, close to seaside resort of
Rhyl. 2m NE of Penisar. From Chester take A55 westerly
beyond Prestatyn exit, and take second right turn in 2
miles. From Llandudno take first left at top of Rhuallt
Hill. A 2-acre site with 30 touring pitches.*

🔌📻☉☀🏕🛁📏📞
➜🍴🎵

The White House Hotel Caravan Site (SJ070750)
☎01745 582155
▶ ▶ 🚐🚑▲
Open all year
*A small campsite with good transit facilities.Situated off
A55 in village. A 2-acre site with 35 touring pitches.*
🔌📻

Ty Mawr Holiday Park (SH965792)
Towyn Rd LL22 9HG ☎ 01745 832079
Nearby town: Rhyl
▶ ▶ ▶ 🌐 ★ 🚐 £8-£14 🚑 £8-£14 ▲ £8-£14
Open Etr-Oct (rs Apr (excluding Etr)) Booking advisable

A delightful select level park with easy access from the
B4401. Situated on a family farm in the Dee Valley beside a
trout stream. Winner of the AA's coveted Environment
Award. The Park offers modern clean facilities including
electric hook-up, dish washing room, launderette, together
with a shop and four Scandinavian self catering bungalows
for hire. Wonderful walking in the Berwyn Mountains,
fishing, water sports, and golf all nearby. Central location
for touring North and Mid Wales.
Hendwr Caravan & Camping Park
Llandrillo, Corwen, Clwyd LL21 0SN
Tel: 01490 440210

at all times Last departure 10.00hrs

A well laid out coastal site with very good leisure facilities, on the A548 .25m west of Towyn village. An 18-acre site with 348 touring pitches and 352 statics.

Free evening entertainment, sauna, solarium.

🔌 📷 ⊙ 🗄 🖳 🔧 🔦 ☀ 🍷 🏔 🛢 🔌 ✕ 🍴 🏇 🧺
♿

→ ∪ ⛵

Credit Cards ◪ ▦

DYFED

ABERAERON

Aeron Coast Caravan Park (SN462633)
North Rd SA46 0JF ☎ 01545 570349
▶ ▶ ▶ 🚐 £6-£8.50 🚐 £5.50-£7.50 ▲ £5.50-£7.50

Open Etr or Apr-Oct Booking advisable bank & school hols Last arrival 20.00hrs Last departure noon

A large site sloping gently towards the sea, run by enthusiastic owners. On A487 at entrance to Aberaeron from the N, turn right immed ay petrol stn. An 8-acre site with 50 touring pitches and 150 statics.

Disco & indoor leisure rooms.

🔌 📷 ⊙ 🗄 🔧 🔦 🔦 📺 ☀ 🍷 🏔 🛢 🔌 ⊞ T 🔌 🧺
🏓

→ ∪ ◎ ⛵ ⊹ 🥍 🔱

💷

Shawsmead Caravan Club Site (SN448578)

Shawsmead Caravan Club Site (SN448578)
Oakford, LLanarth SA47 0RN ☎ 01545 580423 (3m SSW)
▷ 🚐 🚐

Open 26 Mar-26 Sep Booking advisable bank hols & Jul-Aug

A peaceful meadowland site with views towards the coast and Cardigan Bay. From the north on A487, descend into Llanarth, and turn right signed Mydroilyn. ➡

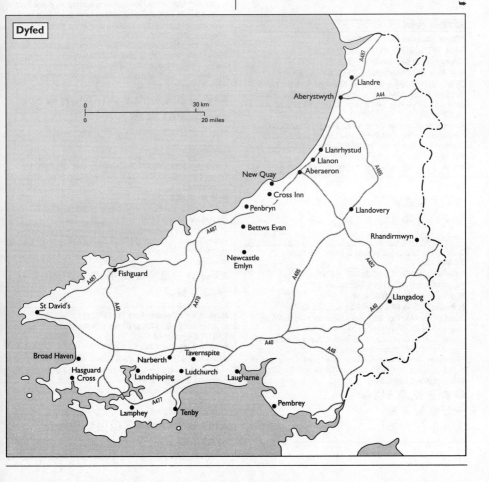

Dyfed

In .5m continue over crossroads signed Oakford. Site on right on 1.25m. A 4-acre site with 50 touring pitches.

🔌 ⓘ 🏋

→ ∪ ▶ ⤴ ♪

Credit Cards 💳 💳

ABERYSTWYTH

Ocean View Caravan Park (SN592842)

North Beach, Clarach Bay SY23 3DT ☎ 01970 828425 & 623361 (off A487, N)

▶ ▶ ★ 🚐 fr £6.50 🚐 fr £6.50

Open Apr-Oct Booking advisable bank hols Last arrival 22.00hrs Last departure noon

A neat and tidy site on gently sloping ground in a sheltered valley with views to the sea. Follow unclass rd signed Clarach from S end of Bow St on A487. A 2-acre site with 24 touring pitches and 50 statics.

🔌 📻 ⊙ ⓘ ⊘ ⊞ 📞 🐴

→ ▶ 📻 ♪ 🔲 🏋

💷

BETTWS EVAN

Pilbach Caravan Park (SN306476)

SA44 5RT ☎ 01239 851434 Signposted

Nearby town: Aberporth

▶ ▶ ▶ ★ 🚐 £7.50-£9 🚐 £7.50-£9 ▲ £7.50-£9

Open Spring bank hol-Sep (rs Mar-Spring bank hol & Oct swimming pool closed) Booking advisable Spring bank hol & Jul-Aug Last arrival 22.00hrs Last departure 10.30hrs

An exceptionally well-run small site set in secluded countryside. 3m N of Newcastle Emlyn and 7m E of Cardigan. A 3-acre site with 65 touring pitches and 70 statics.

🔌 📻 ⊙ 🔲 ⛏ ⤳ 🔍 ☀ 🍷 🅰 ⓘ ⊘ ⊞ 🔲 ✖ 📞 🐴
🏋

→ ∪ ▶ ⛺ 📻 ♪

Credit Cards 💳

BROAD HAVEN

Creampots Touring Caravan & Camping Park (SM882130)

Havenway SA62 3TU ☎ 01437 781776 (5m W of Haverfordwest off B4341) Signposted

Nearby town: Haverfordwest

▶ ▶ 🚐 £5-£6.75 🚐 £4.50-£6.25 ▲ £2.75-£6.75

Open Etr or Mar-Oct Booking advisable mid Jul-Aug Last arrival 23.00hrs Last departure noon

Large, well-maintained fields with a good toilet block. Turn L off B4341 Haverfordwest-Broad Haven road at Broadway, and Creampots is second park 500 yards on R. A 5-acre site with 65 touring pitches and 1 static.

Milk, eggs & papers daily.

🔌 📻 ⊙ ☀ 🅰 ⓘ ⊞ 🔲 ♿

→ ∪ ⛏ ⤴ ♪ 🏋

💷

South Cockett Caravan & Camping Park (SM879135)

SA62 3TU ☎ 01437 781296 & 781760 (1.5m E off B4341) Signposted

Nearby town: Broadhaven

▶ ▶ ★ 🚐 £4.75-£6.50 🚐 £4.25-£6 ▲ £4.25-£6.50

Open Etr-Oct Booking advisable Jul-Aug

Small farm-style campsite rurally located and offering high standards of modern toilet facilities. Conveniently positioned close to the coastline and is a good touring base. A 6-acre site with 60 touring pitches and 1 static.

🔌 📻 ⊙ 🔲 ☀ 🅰 ⓘ ⊘ ⊞ 🏋

→ ∪ ⤴ ♪

CROSS INN

(AWARD)

Camping & Caravanning Club Site (SN383566)

Llwynhelyg SA44 6LW

☎ 01545 560029 (in season) & 01203 694995 Signposted

Nearby town: Cardigan

▶ ▶ ▶ ◆ 👫 ★ 🚐 £9.30-£10 🚐 £9.30-£10 ▲ £9.30-£10

Open end Mar-early Nov Booking advisable bank hols & peak periods Last arrival 21.00hrs Last departure noon

An excellent, attractive touring site in an elevated rural position. Winner of the 1995 Campsite of the Year Award for Wales. From A487 at Synod take A486, signed New Quay, then left in centre of Cross Inn village with site in 1mile. Please see the advertisement on page 27 for details of Club Members' benefits. A 13-acre site with 90 touring pitches.

🔌 📻 ⊙ 🔲 ⛏ ☀ 🏔 🅰 ⓘ ⊘ ⊞ 🔲 📞 🐴 🏋 ♿

Credit Cards 💳 💳 💳

FISHGUARD

Fishguard Bay Caravan & Camping Site (SM984383)

Dinas Cross SA42 0YD ☎ 01348 811415 (2m E off A487) Signposted

▶ ▶ ▶ 🚐 🚐 ▲

Open Mar-9 Jan Booking advisable Jul-Aug Last departure noon

Well-run part level and sloping grass site with bushes near the sea. 1m N of A487. A 3-acre site with 50 touring pitches and 50 statics.

View point.

🔌 🚗 📻 ⊙ 🔲 ⛏ 🔍 🔲 ☀ 🏔 🅰 ⓘ ⊘ ⊞ 🔲 📞 🏋

→ ∪ ⤴ ⛺ ♪

Gwaun Vale Touring Park (SM977356)

Llanychaer SA65 9TA ☎ 01348 874698 (1.5m SE on B4313) Signposted

▶ ▶ ▶ 🚐 £5-£7 🚐 £5-£7 ▲ £5-£7

Open Mar-9 Jan Booking advisable Jul-Aug

A beautiful and immaculate site run by an enthusiastic owner. 1.5m from Fishguard on the B4313 Llanychaer/Gwaun Valley road. A 1.75-acre site with 30 touring pitches.

Free loan of Boules, video films, guide books.

🔌 📻 ⊙ 🔲 ⛏ ☀ 🏔 🅰 ⓘ ⊘ ⊞ 🔲 📞 🏭 🐴 🏋

→ ∪ ⤴ ⛺ ♪

HASGUARD CROSS

Hasguard Cross Caravan Park (SM850108)
SA62 3SL ☎ 01437 781443 Signposted
Nearby town: Haverfordwest
▶ ▶ ▶ ★ ⊞ £4.85-£6.95 ⊞ £4.85-£6.95
Open all year Booking advisable Spring bank hol & Jun-Aug Last arrival 23.00hrs Last departure noon
A very clean, efficient and well-run site in Pembrokeshire National Park with views of surrounding hills. 1.5m from sea and beach at Little Haven. Approach to B4327 from Haverfordwest to Dale, after 7m turn right at crossroads and site is first entrance on right. A 3-acre site with 25 touring pitches and 35 statics.

🛇 ⋒ ⊙ ✳ ♀ 🅸 ➕ T ◖ 🐾 ⅀
→ ∪ ▶ ⌂ ↘ ✔
⊞

Redlands Touring Caravan Site (SM851109)
Little Haven SA62 3UU ☎ 01437 781301
Nearby town: Haverfordwest
▶ ▶ ▶ ♠ ★ ⊞ £6-£8.50 ⊞ £6-£8.50
Open Etr-mid Sep Booking advisable peak periods Last departure noon
A superb level grass site, in Pembrokeshire National Park, 1.5m from sea and beach at Little Haven. 7m W of Haverfordwest on B4327 Dale Road. A 5-acre site with 60 touring pitches.

🛇 ⋒ ⋒ ⊙ ✳ ➕ ◖ 🐕 ⅄
→ ∪ ▶ ⌂ ↘ ✔ ⅀

LAMPHEY

Freshwater East Caravan Club Site (SS015979)
Freshwater East SA71 5NL ☎ 01646 672341 (2m S) Signposted
Nearby town: Pembroke
▶ ▶ ▶ ⊞ ⊞ Å
Open 26 Mar-1 Nov Booking advisable Spring bank hols & Aug-Sep Last arrival anytime Last departure noon
Site at the bottom of a hill, with mainly level, grassy pitches bounded by trees. Only two mins from the sands. Caravans should not be towed to the beach area. From Pembroke take Tenby road to Lamphey (A4139), turn onto B4584 signed Freshwater East and turn R in 1.75m signed Stackpole & Trewent. Site signed in .25m. A 3.5-acre site with 130 touring pitches.

🛇 ⋒ ⊙ 🖫 🏳 ✳ /Ⅱ 🅸 ∅ ➕ T ◖ 🏠 ↻
→ ∪ ⌂ ✔ ⅀
Credit Cards 💳 💳 💳 💳

LANDSHIPPING

New Park Farm (SN026111)
SA67 8BG ☎ 01834 891284
Nearby town: Narberth
▶ ▶ ⊞ £5.50 ⊞ £5.50 Å £5.50
Open May Day wknd-Oct Booking advisable peak periods Last arrival 20.00hrs Last departure noon
A nice, quiet site on a smallholding with basic but adequate facilities. 7m W of Narberth, along unclass rd

off A4075. A 2-acre site with 5 touring pitches and 30 statics.

🛇 ⋒ ⊙ 🖫 ✳ 🅸 ∅ ➕ T ◖ 🏠
→ ∪ ↘ ✔ ⅀

LAUGHARNE

Ants Hill Caravan Park (SN299118)
SA33 4QN ☎ 01994 427293 Signposted
▶ ▶ ▶ ★ ⊞ £6.50-£9.50 ⊞ £6.50-£8 Å £6.50-£8
Open Etr-Oct Booking advisable Jul-Aug & public hols Last arrival 23.00hrs Last departure 10.30hrs
A small, well-run touring site on sloping grass, located near the village, on the Taff estuary. Care should be taken on descent into Laugharne on A4066 as site entrance is on minor road to left. A 4-acre site with 60 touring pitches and 60 statics.

🛇 ⋒ ⊙ ⌇ ◀ ⊡ ✳ ♀ /Ⅱ 🅸 ∅ ➕ T ◖ 🐾 ⅀
→ ∪ ▶ ✔ 🖫
⊞

LITTLE HAVEN

See **Hasguards Cross**

LLANDOVERY

Erwlon Caravan & Camping Park (SN776343)
Brecon Rd SA20 0RD ☎ 01550 20332 Signposted
▶ ▶ ▶ ⊞ £5-£8 ⊞ £5-£8 Å £5-£6
Open all year Booking advisable bank hols Last arrival anytime Last departure noon
Long established family-run site set beside a brook in the Brecon Beacons foothills. On the A40 outside ➡

Llandovery. An 8-acre site with 40 touring pitches.

🔷🔶☉🔲🔳✳️🏔🔋🔹🔽🔌🔆🛏🐴🔻
➔💧🎵

LLANDRE

Riverside Park (SN634878)
Lon Glanfred SY24 5BY ☎ 01970 820070 Signposted
Nearby town: Borth
▶▶▶🔹🔷🔶🏕
Open Mar-Oct Booking advisable bank & school hols
Last arrival 23.30hrs Last departure noon
A quiet site with good quality facilities and easy access
to the seaside. Set amongst well-wooded hills and
bounded by a stream. On A487, 4m north of
Aberystwyth, take B4353 and turn right at second
turning. A 4-acre site with 24 touring pitches and 76
statics.
River fishing on site.

🔷🔶☉🔲🔳✳️🏔🔋🔹🔽🔲🆃🔆🔽🚿🏚🏕🐴
🔻♿
➔💧🏷🔺🌿🎵

See advertisement on page 247.

LLANGADOG

Abermarlais Caravan Park (SN695298)
SA19 9NG ☎ 01550 777868 & 777797 Signposted
Nearby town: Llandovery
▶▶▶★🔶 fr £6.50 🔶 fr £6.50 🏕 fr £6.50
Open Apr-Oct (rs Nov, Dec & Mar 1 wc, water point no
hot water if frosty) Booking advisable bank hols & 15
Jul-Aug Last arrival 23.00hrs Last departure noon
An attractive, well-run site with a welcoming
atmosphere. Part-level, part-sloping grass in a wooded
valley on edge of Brecon Beacons National Park. It is by
the River Marlais and off A40 Llandeilo-Llandovery road.
A 7-acre site with 88 touring pitches.
Volleyball, badminton court & softball tennis net.

🔷🔶☉✳️🏔🔋🔹🔽🔲🆃🔆🛏🐴🔻
➔💧🎵
💷

LLANON

Woodlands Caravan Park (SN511668)
SY23 5LX ☎ 01974 202342 Signposted
Nearby town: Aberaeron
▶▶▶★🔶£6.50-£9.50 🔶£5.50-£8 🏕£5.50-£8
Open Apr-Oct (rs Mar toilet block closed) Booking
advisable school hols Last arrival 21.30hrs Last
departure noon
A level grass site surrounded by mature trees and
shrubs near woods and meadowland, adjacent to a
stoney beach. 11m from Aberstwyth on A487. A 4-acre
site with 80 touring pitches and 60 statics.

🔷🔶☉🔲🔳✳️🔋🔹🔽🔲🆃🔆🐴🔻
➔💧🏷🔺🎵
💷

LLANRHYSTUD

Pengarreg Caravan Park (SN539697)
SY23 5DJ ☎ 01974 202247 Signposted
▶▶🔶🔶🏕
Open Mar-Oct Booking advisable Last arrival mdnt Last
departure 10.00hrs
A gently sloping site fronted by a pebble beach, with
cliff walks and boat launching facilities. On A487 W of
Llanrhystud at S end of village. A 7-acre site with 50
touring pitches and 155 statics.
Slipway to beach for sailing.

🔷🔶☉🔲🔳🔍✳️🍴🏔🔹🔽🆃🔆🔻
➔🏷🎵

LUDCHURCH

Woodland Vale Caravan Park (SN140113)
SA67 8JE ☎ 01834 83319
▶▶▶🔶🔶
Open Mar-Oct Booking advisable bank hols & Jul-Aug
Last arrival 21.00hrs Last departure 14.00hrs 🐕
Site with informally sited pitches set between areas of
water created in an old quarry. A 1.5-acre site with 25
touring pitches and 80 statics.

🔷🔶☉🔲🔳🔽🔍✳️🍴🏔🔋🔆🔻
➔💧🎵

NARBERTH

Allensbank Holiday Park (SN113134)
Providence Hill SA67 8RF ☎ 01834 860243
▶▶▶🔶🔶
Open Whitsun-15 Sep (rs Etr-Whitsun & 16 Sep-Oct
swimming pool closed bar Sat only) Booking advisable
Jul-Aug Last arrival 22.30hrs Last departure noon
A well-run attractive site, constantly improving. Just S
of Narberth on A478. A 2-acre site with 11 touring
pitches and 18 statics.
Table tennis, shooting/boules/darts comps.

🔷🔶☉🔲🔳 🔍🔋🔳✳️🍴🏔🆃🔆🔻
➔💧🏷◎🎵

Noble Court Caravan Site (SN111158)
Redstone Rd SA67 7ES ☎ 01834 861191 Signposted
Nearby town: Tenby
▶▶▶★🔶£8-£13.50 🔶£8-£13.50 🏕£8-£13.50
Open Mar-Oct (rs early & late season swimming pool
closed) Booking advisable Jul-Aug Last arrival 22.00hrs
Last departure noon
Mostly sloping site with good views and a high standard
of service. On B4313 between Narberth & A40. A 6-acre
site with 92 touring pitches and 60 statics.
30 Acres of adjoining land for walks & picnics.

🔷🔶☉🔲🔳🔽🔍✳️🍴🏔🔋🔳❌🔆🔽🏚🏕🏚
🐴♿
➔💧🏷🎵🔻
💷

Credit Cards 💳 💳 💳

NEWCASTLE EMLYN

Afon Teifi Caravan & Camping Park (SN338405)
Pentrecagal SA38 9HT ☎ 01559 370532 (2m E A484)
▶ ▶ ▶ ✿ 🐾 £6-£7 🚐 £6-£7 ▲ £5-£7
Open Apr-Oct (rs Nov-Mar when facilities are limited)
Booking advisable peak periods Last arrival 23.00hrs
Very attractive and well-managed site in secluded valley. A 6-acre site with 110 touring pitches and 3 statics.

🏢 🚲 📶 ⊙ 🗓 🌂 🔍 ✳ 🅰 🛢 🌿 🔁 🎁 🆃 ♨ 🔨 🐕 ⅙

→ ∪ ▶ 💧 ⚇ 🍴 ⌨ 🛒

💷

Cenarth Falls Holiday Park (SN265421)
Cenarth SA38 9JS ☎ 01239 710345 Signposted
▶ ▶ ▶ 🧍🧍 🚐 £7.75-£11.75 🚐 £7.75-£11.75 ▲ £7.75-£11.75
Open Mar-9 Jan Booking advisable bank hols & Jul-Aug
Last arrival 20.00hrs Last departure noon
A rapidly developing, former static site, very well run with excellent facilities. A 2-acre site with 20 touring pitches and 89 statics.
Clubhouse, pool table & video machines.

🏢 📶 ⊙ 🗓 🌂 ⚡ 🔍 ✳ 🅰 🛢 🔁 ✂ 🛒 🛍 ⅙

→ ∪ ⚇ 🍴 🛒 ⌨

Credit Cards 🃏 💳 💳

NEW QUAY

Cei Bach Country Club (SN409597)
Parc-y-Brwcs, Cei Bach SA45 9SL ☎ 01545 580237 (off A487 onto B4342 signed to Cei Bach) Signposted
▶ ▶ ▶ ✿ ★ 🚐 £6-£10 🚐 £6-£10 ▲ £6-£10
Open Good Fri-last Sun in Sep Booking advisable Etr, Spring bank hol & school hols Last arrival 22.00hrs Last departure 11.00hrs
A very good site in a beautiful situation overlooking Cardigan Bay with views of the distant cliffs. The attractive setting, thoughtful landscaping of the park, and the welcoming attitude of owners the Wynne family have singled this park out as the 1996 Winner for Wales of the AA's Campsite of the Year Awards. For details of all the award winners, see the colour section at the front of the book. Turn off A487 onto B4342 road to New Quay, then follow signs for Cei Bach. A 3-acre site with 60 touring pitches.

🏢 📶 ⊙ 🗓 🔍 ✳ 🅰 🛢 🔁 ✂ 🛒 🛍 🐕 🖥

→ ∪ 💧 ⚇ 🍴 🛒

💷

PEMBREY

Pembrey Country Park Caravan Club Site (SN415005)
SA16 0EJ ☎ 01554 834369 (1m SW) Signposted
Nearby town: Llanelli
▶ ▶ 🚐 🚐 ▲
Open 26 Mar-3 Jan Booking advisable bank hols & Jul-Aug Last departure noon
A well-sheltered site within a 250-acre country park with a vast range of outdoor sporting activities, and a 7-mile stretch of safe, sandy beach 1m away. Take A484 to Pembrey then L at signs for country park and Cefn Sidan Beach. An 8-acre site with 120 touring pitches.

🏢 📶 ⊙ 🌂 ✳ 🅰 🛢 🌿 🔁 🆃 🛒 🖥 ⅙

→ ∪ ▶ 💧 ⚇ 🍴 🛒

Credit Cards 🃏 💳 💳

PENBRYN

Talywerydd Touring Caravan & Camping Park (SN297507)
SA44 6QY ☎ 01239 810322 Signposted
Nearby town: Cardigan
▶ ▶ ▶ 🚐 £8.50 🚐 £8.50 ▲ £8.50
Open Mar-Oct Booking advisable Jul-Aug Last arrival 22.00hrs Last departure 11.00hrs
Small family site with seaviews from every pitch, off A487. Take 2nd turn off A487 signed Penbryn, and site 500yds on left. A 4-acre site with 20 touring pitches.
Crazy golf.

🏢 📶 ⊙ 🗓 🌂 🍴 🔍 ✳ 🅰 🛢 🔁 ✂ 🛒 👘 🐕 🔨

→ ∪ ▶ ⊙ 💧 ⚇ 🍴 🛒

RHANDIRMWYN

Camping & Caravanning Club Site (SN779435)
SA20 0NT ☎ 01550 760257 (in season) & 01203 694995 Signposted
Nearby town: Llandovery
▶ ▶ ▶ ✿ 🧍🧍 ★ 🚐 £9.30-£10 🚐 £9.30-£10 ▲ £9.30-£10
Open end Mar-end Oct Booking advisable bank hols & peak periods Last arrival 21.00hrs Last departure noon ➤

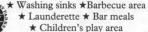

Set on the banks of the Afon Tywi near the Towy Forest and the Llyn Brianne reservoir, this first class site has superb views on all sides. Take A40 through Llandovery, turn right immediately after crossing river at sharp left-hand bend, signed Rhandirmwyn. At T junction turn right recrossing river, and then left. In approx 6m at Royal Oak Inn site signed on left. Please see the advertisement on page 27 for details of Club Members' benefits. An 11-acre site with 90 touring pitches.

🎮 📻 ☉ 🍴 ✻ 🔌 ⌀ 🏕 🛋 💂 🐕 🕏 🛒 🛠

→ 🍴

Credit Cards

ⵔⵔⵔⵔⵔⵔⵔⵔⵔ

ST DAVID'S

Caerfai Bay Caravan & Tent Park (SM759244)
SA62 6QT ☎ 01437 720274 Signposted
▶▶▶ 🚐🚐🔺

Open Etr-Oct Booking advisable school hols Last arrival 21.00hrs Last departure 11.00hrs
Grassy site with bushes set in meadowland, with magnificent coastal scenery overlooking St Brides Bay - bathing beach 300yds from park entrance. Off A487, end of unclass road to Caerfai Bay. A 7-acre site with 80 touring pitches and 35 statics.

🎮 📻 ☉ 📷 🍴 ✻ 🔌 ⌀ 🛋 💂

→ 🔌 🌂 △ ┿ 🍴 🛒

Lleithyr Meadow Caravan Club Site (SM746271)
Whitesands SA62 6PR ☎ 01437 720401 (1.5m NW)
▶▶▶ 👫 🚐🚐

Open 26 Mar-26 Sep Booking advisable Spring bank hols & Jun-Aug
An ideal holiday site, close to many outdoor activities. Sheltered by three headlands. An 8-acre site with 120 touring pitches.

🏔 🔌 🛒

→ 🔌 🌂 ┿ 🍴

Camping & Caravanning Club Site (SM805305)
Dwr Cwmdig, Berea SA62 6DW ☎ 01348 831376 (in season) & 01203 694995 Signposted
▶▶ ★ 🚐 £9.30-£10 🚐 £9.30-£10 🔺 £9.30-£10
Open end Mar-end Sep Booking advisable bank hols & peak periods Last arrival 21.00hrs Last departure noon
Immaculately kept small grassy site in open country near the Pembrokeshire Coastal Path. Situated at the junction of two unclass roads 1.5m W of Croesgoch on the A487 St David's-Fishguard road. Please see the advertisement on page 27 for details of Club Members' benefits. A 4-acre site with 40 touring pitches.

🎮 📻 ☉ 📷 🍴 ⌀ 🛋 💂 🕏 🔌 🏮

→ 🔌 🍴

Credit Cards

Hendre Eynon Camping & Caravan Site (SM773280)
SA62 6DB ☎ 01437 720474 Signposted
▶▶ 🚐🚐🔺

Open May-Sep (rs 27 Mar-Apr one toilet block & showers only) Booking advisable school hols Last

Visit one of the highest graded parks of the area and enjoy a relaxing holiday at very competitive prices. The park is landscaped, family run and ideally situated just one mile from Tenby and Saundersfoot. Colourful grounds slope gently towards the sea a few hundred yards away. Rowston prides itself on its friendly atmosphere and its range of facilities including electric hook ups. Also caravan/log cabins to hire. The perfect base from which to explore the beaches, cliffs and coves of the renowned Pembrokeshire Coast National Park.
Where families make friends . . .
Rowston Holiday Park, New Hedges, Nr.
Tenby, Pembrokeshire SA70 8TL
Telephone: 01834 842178

arrival 21.00hrs Last departure noon
A robust site on a working farm with new toilet block. 2m NE of St Davids on unclassified road. A 7-acre site with 48 touring pitches and 2 statics.

🎮 📻 ☉ 📷 ✻ 🔌 🛋 💂 🕏 🐕 🛒 🛠

→ 🔌 🌂 △ ┿ 🍴 🛒

💷

Tretio Caravan & Camping Park (SM787292)
SA62 6DE ☎ 01437 720270 & 781359 Signposted
▶▶ 🚐 £5-£7 🚐 £4.50-£6.50 🔺 £3-£6.50
Open 14 Mar-14 Oct Booking advisable bank hols & mid Jul-Aug Last arrival 23.00hrs Last departure 17.00hrs
A gently sloping touring site with well-converted facilities. A 4.5-acre site with 40 touring pitches and 5 statics.

🎮 📻 ☉ 🍴 ✻ 🏔 🔌 ⌀ 🛋 💂 🕐 🕏 🐕 🏮 🐕 🛒 🛠

→ 🔌 🌂 ◎ △ ┿ 🍴

💷

TAVERNSPITE

Pantglas Farm Caravan Park (SN175122)
SA34 0NS ☎ 01834 831618 Signposted
Nearby town: Whitland
▶▶ ★ 🚐 £4.50-£6 🚐 £4.50-£6 🔺 £3.50-£5
Open Etr-15 Oct Booking advisable Spring bank hol & Jul-Aug Last arrival 23.00hrs Last departure 11.00hrs
Small touring site on B4328 between Ludchurch and Tavernspite. A 3.5-acre site with 45 touring pitches.

Pets corner. Year round caravan weekly storage. £2

🔌 📶 ☉ 🗑 ✳ 🅰 🛈 🖉 🧺 🦽 ♨ 🎏

→ ∪ ⏷ 🐕

🔣

TENBY

Rowston Holiday Park (SN133024)
New Hedges SA70 8TL ☎ 01834 842178 & 814090
Signposted
▶ ▶ ▶ ▶ ♠ 🚐 £7-£14 🚐 £7-£14 Å £5-£14
Open Mar-mid Oct (rs Oct-Jan 10 no site shop &
laundry) Booking advisable May & Jul-Aug Last arrival
21.00hrs Last departure 10.00hrs
*A really top class site in all ways, commanding views
over woodland and Carmarthon Bay. A 10-acre site with
100 touring pitches and 136 statics.*
Dishwashing sinks under canopy.

🔌 🦽 📶 ☉ 🗑 � ✳ 🅰 🛈 🖉 🧺 🆃 🦽 🐕 🦴 🛒
🦽
→ ∪ ⏷ 🍴 📹 🎵

Well Park Caravan & Camping Site (SN128028)
SA70 8TL ☎ 01834 842179 Signposted
▶ ▶ ▶ ▶ ★ 🚐 £5-£10 🚐 £5-£10 Å £4.50-£8
Open Apr-Oct (rs Apr-mid May & mid Sep-Oct shop
closed) Booking advisable Spring bank hol & Jul-Aug
Last arrival 22.00hrs Last departure 11.00hrs
*An excellent, well-run site with trees and bushes. 1.5m
N of Tenby off A478 New Hedges by-pass. A 7-acre site
with 100 touring pitches and 42 statics.*

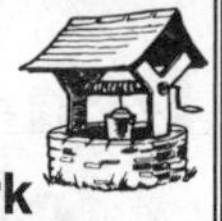

Off-licence in shop.

🔌 📶 ☉ 🗑 � 🌂 🗄 ✳ 🅰 🛈 🖉 🧺 🆃 🦽 🐕
🛒
→ ∪ ⏷ 🍴 📹 🎵

🔣

Kiln Park Holiday Centre (SN119002)
SA70 7RB ☎ 01834 844121
▶ ▶ ▶ ♦ 🚐 Å
Open Mar-Oct (rs Mar-mid May & Oct) Booking
advisable all times Etr-Sep Last arrival 21.00hrs Last
departure 10.00hrs no cars by caravans
*A large, commercial, touring, camping and static
holiday site, situated on level ground on the town's
outskirts. A short walk through dunes leads to the sandy
south-facing beach. On A4139. A 103-acre site with 220
touring pitches and 620 statics.*
Entertainment complex.

🔌 🦽 📶 ☉ 🗑 � 🏹 🎾 🥂 ✳ 🅰 🛈 🖉 🆃 🍴 🔌
🍺 🐕 🛒
→ ∪ ⏷ 🌀 ⛵ 🍴 📹 🎵

Credit Cards

Trefalun (SN093027)
Devonshire Dr, St Florence SA70 8RH ☎ 01646 651514
Signposted
▶ ▶ ▶ ♦ 🚐 🚐 Å
Open Etr-Sep Booking advisable bank hols & Jul-Aug
Last arrival 20.00hrs Last departure noon ➤

*A well-maintained level grass site with bushes and trees
W of St Florence 3m off B4318. A 7-acre site with 35
touring pitches and 5 statics.*

🔌 📵 ☉ 🅿 🔻 ⚒ 🏔 🛈 🚿 ⊞ 💧 🐕 🔥
→ ∪ ▶ ◎ ⌖ ✗ 🍽 🔧 🏋

Credit Cards 🔲 🔲

Wood Park Caravans (SN128025)
New Hedges SA70 8TL ☎ 01834 843414 Signposted
▶ ▶ ▶ ★ 🚐 £5-£9.50 🚐 £5-£9.50 ▲ £4.50-£7.50
Open Spring bank hol-Sep (rs Etr-Spring bank hol &
Sep-Oct bar shop & launderette may not open) Booking
advisable Spring bank hol & Jul-Aug Last arrival
22.00hrs Last departure 10.00hrs
*A well-run, slightly sloping, part-level grass site with
trees and bushes. 1.5m N of Tenby off A478 New
Hedges by-pass. A 3-acre site with 60 touring pitches
and 90 statics.*
Outside dish/clothes washing area.

🔌 📵 ☉ 🅿 🔻 🗜 ⚒ 🍷 🏔 🛈 🚿 ⊞ 🏋
→ ∪ ▶ 🔻 ⌖ ✗ 🍽 🔧

Carew Airfield Caravan Club Site (SN053032)
Sageston SA70 8SH ☎ 01646 651662 Signposted
▶ ▶ 🚐 🚐 ▲
Open 26 Mar-4 Oct Booking advisable bank hols & Jul-
Aug
*A pleasant, level site divided into five pitching areas by
trees and shrubs. On A477 at Sageston; site entrance*

*through service stn forecourt. A 5.5-acre site with 45
touring pitches.*

🔌 ☉ 🅿 ⚒ 🛈 🚿 ⊞ 💧 🐕 🏋 ♿
→ ∪ ▶ ◎ 🔻 ⌖ 🍽 🔧

Credit Cards 🔲 🔲

GWENT

For the map of this county, see
Glamorgan

DINGESTOW

Bridge Caravan Park & Camping Site (SO459104)
Bridge Farm NP5 4DY ☎ 01600 740241 Signposted
Nearby town: Monmouth
▶ ▶ ▶ ★ 🚐 fr £6 🚐 fr £6 ▲ fr £6
Open Etr-Oct Booking advisable bank hols Last arrival
22.00hrs Last departure 16.00hrs
*An excellent site in a quiet village setting, signposted
from Raglan and located off the A449, South Wales-
Midlands road. A 4-acre site with 94 touring pitches.*
Fishing.

🔌 📵 ☉ 🅿 🔻 ⚒ 🛈 🚿 ⊞ 🇹 💧 🐕 🔥 🏋
→ ∪ ▶ ⌖ 🍽 🔧
💷

Tredegar House & Park
Newport, South Wales NP1 9YW
Telephone (01633) 816650

"A unique setting"

A quiet corner of the beautiful parkland surrounding a magnificent 17th century mansion

Modern amenities include electric hook-ups, hot showers and washing machine

Tours of House • Adventure Playground
Carriage Rides • Boating • Craft Workshops

Newport

NEWPORT

Tredegar House & Park (ST285855)
NP1 9YW ☎ 01633 816650 & 815880 (2.5m west A48 close to M4 junc 28) Signposted
▶ ▶ ▶ ★ 🚐 fr £6 🚐 fr £6 ⚠ £4-£6
Open Etr-Oct Booking advisable public hols & Jul-Aug Last arrival 21.00hrs Last departure noon
Set in peaceful corner of a country park, sheltered by mature trees and shrubs, the touring park offers a full range of excellent facilities. A 4-acre site with 55 touring pitches.
House tours, craft workshop, carriage rides, boating.

🔌 📶 ⊙ ♀ ⚙ ✕ ℃ 🎋 🐕 ♿
➔ ∪ ▶ ⅄ 😋 🎵 📅 🔋
Credit Cards 🔷 ▬ ▤ 💳

OAKDALE

Penyfan Caravan & Leisure Park (SO189012)
Manmoel Rd NP2 0HY ☎ 01495 226636 (off B4251) Signposted
Nearby town: Blackwood
▶ ▶ ▶ 🚐 🚐 ⚠
Open all year Booking advisable bank hols
A brand new site with purpose built facilities, and plans for many improvements. Landscaping work still going on, but site shows tremendous potential. A 4-acre site with 75 touring pitches.

See advertisement under NEWPORT

🔌 📶 ⊙ ◀ ⬜ ✳ ♀ ⚙ ✕ ℃ 🏛 🎋 🐕 🔋
➔ ▶ 😋 🎵 📅
🔋
Credit Cards 🔷 ▬

GWYNEDD

For the map of this county, see Clwyd

ABERSOCH

AWARD

Bryn Cethin Bach Caravan Park (SH304290)
Lon Garmon LL53 7UL
☎ 01758 712719
Nearby town: Pwllheli
▶ ▶ ▶ 🌳 👪 ★ 🚐 £8-£10 🚐 £8-£10
Open Apr-Oct (rs Mar-May shop closed) Booking advisable Spring bank hol & Jul-Aug Last arrival 18.00hrs Last departure noon
A well-run family site within .5m of sandy beaches, the harbour and all the facilities of Abersoch. Offering lovely views and a first class toilet block. A 2-acre site with 15 touring pitches and 53 statics.
Lake & fishing.

🔌 📶 ⊙ 📅 🏴 ✳ 🔒 🎬 ℃ 🐕 🖼 🔋
➔ ∪ ▶ ⚠ ⅄ 😋 🎵
🔋

⚪⚪⚪⚪⚪⚪⚪

Pant-Gwyn Cottage (SH305262)
Sarn Bach LL53 7ET ☎ 01758 712268 & 740439 Signposted
▶ 🚐 £7.50-£10 🚐 £6.50-£7.50 ⚠ £6-£7
Open Mar-Oct Booking advisable from March Last arrival 23.00hrs Last departure noon
Gently sloping family site in quiet elevated position near to Abersoch, on the Lleyn Peninsula. Very sharp turn opposite the telephone kiosk in Sarn Bach for site 200yds on right. A 6-acre site with 97 touring pitches and 4 statics.

🔌 📶 ⊙ ✳ 📅 🐕 🖼
➔ ∪ ▶ ⚠ ⅄ 😋 🎵 🔋

ANGLESEY, ISLE OF

For the map, see Clwyd

AMLWCH

Point Lynas Caravan Park (SH474930)
Llaneilan LL68 9LT ☎ 01407 831130 & 01248 852423
▶ ★ 🚐 £5-£11 🚐 £5-£8 ⚠ £3-£10   ➡

Open Mar-Oct Booking advisable bank hols Last arrival
22.00hrs Last departure noon
*This first-class site is near a sheltered rocky cove, safe
for swimming. A 2-acre site with 6 touring pitches and
44 statics.*
Childrens sandpit & climbing bars.

🛱 🕅 ⊙ 🎗 ⊘ ⊞ ℄ 🛱 ⍫
→ ▶ 🥄 🗊 🏊
⊞

BRYNSIENCYN

Fron Caravan & Camping Site (SH472669)
LL61 6TX ☎ 01248 430310 Signposted
▶ ▶ ▶ 🚐 £7.50 🚚 £7-£7.50 ⚑ £4.50-£7.50
Open Etr-Sep Booking advisable Spring bank hol & Jul-
Aug Last arrival 23.00hrs Last departure noon
*Quiet family site in pleasant rural area, ideally situated
for touring Anglesey and North Wales. Off A4080
Llanfair PG-Newborough road. A 5.5-acre site with 60
touring pitches.*

🛱 🕅 ⊙ 🍴 ⋛ ⚓ ✳ 🏔 🎗 ⊘ ⊞ 🆃 ℄ ⍫ 🏊
→ ▶ 🥄
⊞

BRYNTEG

Nant Newydd Caravan Park (SH485814)
LL78 8JH ☎ 01248 852842 & 852266 Signposted
Nearby town: Bangor
▶ ▶ ▶ ▶ 👫 ★ 🚐 £6.50-£10 🚚 £6.50-£10 ⚑ £6.50-£10
Open Mar-Oct (rs May & Sep pool restricted) Booking
advisable Jul-Aug Last arrival mdnt Last departure
17.00hrs
*Gently sloping grass site with mature trees and bushes
set in meadowland adjacent to main road, 1m from
Brynteg on B5110 towards Llangefni. A 4-acre site with
30 touring pitches and 83 statics.*
Satalite TV & licensed shop.
See advertisement under BENLLECH BAY

🛱 🕅 ⊙ 🗊 🍴 ⋛ ⚓ 🗖 ✳ 🏔 🎗 ⊘ ⊞ 🆃 ℄ 🎪
🛱 🐕 🏊 ♿
→ ∪ ▶ 🔺 ♨ 🥄

Ysgubor Fadog Caravan & Camping Site (SH497820)
Ysgubor Fadog LL78 8QA ☎ 01248 852681 Signposted
▶ ▶ ★ 🚐 £5 🚚 £5 ⚑ £3-£5
Open Etr-Sep Booking advisable Whitsun & school hols
Last arrival 20.00hrs Last departure 18.00hrs
*A peaceful and remote site reached along a narrow lane
where care is needed. From Benllech take B5108, and
after sports field take 3rd on left. A 2-acre site with 15
touring pitches and 1 static.*

🛱 🕅 ⊙ ✳ ⊞ 🛱 🐕 ⍫
→ ∪ 🥄 🗊 🏊
⊞

CERRIGCEINWEN

Tregof Caravan Park (SH413745)
LL62 5EH ☎ 01407 720315 Signposted
Nearby town: Llangefni
▶ ▶ 🚐 🚚 ⚓
Open Apr-Oct Booking advisable 3 wks prior if possible
Last departure 13.00hrs
*A well-run site set amidst trees and bushes within easy
reach of the sea and golf course. From A5 junction
B4422 Cerrigceinwen road take A5 westwards for 1.5m
and turn left (unclass), or from Holyhead direction take
A5 through Gwalchmai and in 2m turn right (unclass). A
6-acre site with 68 touring pitches.*

🛱 🕅 ⊙ ✳ ⚓ ⊘ ⊞ 🆃
→ ▶ 🥄 🏊

DULAS

Tyddyn Isaf Caravan Park (SH486873)
Lligwy Bay LL70 9PQ ☎ 01248 410203 (.5m off A5025
between Benllech & Amlwch) Signposted
Nearby town: Benllech
▶ ▶ ▶ ▶ 🍴 🚐 £9.50-£11 🚚 £8-£10 ⚑ £8-£8.50
Open Mar-Oct (rs Mar-Etr & Oct clubhouse limited, shut
from mid Sept) Booking advisable May bank hol & Jun-
Aug Last arrival 22.00hrs Last departure 11.00hrs
*Site located on gently rising ground adjacent to sandy
beach affording magnificent views. A 6-acre site with 60
touring pitches and 50 statics.*

🛱 🕅 ⊙ 🗊 🍴 🗖 ✳ 🍺 🏔 ⚓ ⊘ ⊞ 🆃 ✖ ℄ 🛒 🛱
🐕 🏊
→ ∪ ▶ 🔺 ♨ 🥄

LLANBEDRGOCH

Ty Newydd Caravan Park & Country Club (SH508813)
LL76 8TZ ☎ 01248 450677 Signposted
Nearby town: Benlech
▶ ▶ ▶ 🚐 £5-£13 🚚 £5-£13 ⚑ £5-£13
Open Whit-mid Sep (rs Mar-Whit & mid Sep-Oct
club/shop wknds only outdoor pool closed) Booking
advisable Etr, Whit & Jul-Aug Last arrival 23.30hrs Last
departure 10.00hrs
*A low density site with a new health centre. There are
plans to improve all facilities. Site N of village on
unclass rd between A5025 and B5108. A 4-acre site with
40 touring pitches and 60 statics.*
Health centre.
See advertisement under BENLLECH BAY

🛱 🕅 ⊙ 🗊 🍴 ⋛ ⚓ ✳ 🍺 🏔 ⚓ ⊘ ⊞ 🆃 ✖ ℄
🏊 ♿
→ ∪ ▶ 🔺 ♨ 🥄
⊞

MARIANGLAS

Home Farm Caravan Park (SH498850)
LL73 8PH ☎ 01248 410614
▶ ▶ ▶ ★ 🚐 £6-£8 🚚 £6-£8 ⚑ £5-£8
Open Apr-Oct Booking advisable bank hols Last arrival
21.00hrs Last departure noon
A first class site with friendly, helpful owners. On A5025,

2m N of Benllech, with park entrance 300 metres beyond church. A 6-acre site with 61 touring pitches and 72 statics. Indoor adventure playground.

🔌📷🌂☉🔍🍴🚫🏕⚠🚰🚲⚡🔋📞🚿🐴⚓

➜🚶⛵💧🎣🏪

🏧

PENTRAETH

Rhos Caravan Park (SH517794)
LL75 8DZ ☎ 01248 450214 Signposted
Nearby town: Benllech
▶ ▶ ▶ £6-£8.50 🚐 £5-£8.50 ▲ £5-£7.50
Open Etr-Oct (rs Mar shop & showers) Booking advisable Spring bank hol & Jul-Aug Last arrival 22.00hrs Last departure noon
Site on level, grassy ground off main road to Amlwch. A 15-acre site with 98 touring pitches and 60 statics.

🔌📷🌂☉🚿⚠🚰🚲⚡🔋📞🐴🏪

➜🚶⛵🎣🏪♿

🏧

RHOSNEIGR

Bodfan Farm (SH324737)
LL64 5XA ☎ 01407 810563
Nearby town: Holyhead
▶ 🚐🚐▲
Open Etr-Oct Booking advisable Apr-Sep Last arrival 23.00hrs Last departure 23.00hrs
A farm site on gentle sloping ground with sea and country views. Within walking distance of sea. A 15-acre site with 60 touring pitches.

📷☉🌂☉🚿⚠🚰

➜🚶⛵🎣🏪

BALA

Camping & Caravanning Club Site (SH961391)
Crynierth Caravan Park, Cefn-Ddwysarn LL23 7IN
☎ 01678 530324 (in season) & 01203 694995 (3.25m NE off A494)
▶ ▶ ▶ 👫👫 🚐 £9.30-£10 🚐 £9.30-£10 ▲ £9.30-£10
Open end Mar-early Nov Booking advisable bank hols & peak periods Last arrival 21.00hrs Last departure noon
A quiet pleasant site with interesting views and high class facilities. Situated just off A494 4m E of Bala. Please see the advertisement on page 27 for details of Club Members' benefits. A 4-acre site with 50 touring pitches.

🔌📷🌂☉🚿⚠🚰🚲📞🐴🏪♿

➜🚶⛵🎣🏪

Credit Cards 🔲 🔳 🔳

Pen-y-Garth Camping & Caravan Park (SH938348)
Rhos-y-Gwalia LL23 7ES ☎ 01678 520485 Signposted
▶ ▶ ▶ ★ 🚐 £6-£8 🚐 £6-£8 ▲ £4-£8
Open Mar-Oct (rs Mar-Jun restaurant closed ex bank hols) Booking advisable bank hols & Jul-Aug Last arrival 22.00hrs Last departure noon
A level site with well-laid out pitches for tourers, amidst attractive scenery. From Bala take B4391 and in 1m follow unclass rd signed YH/Lake Vyrnwy. Site on right at top of

hill. A 20-acre site with 63 touring pitches and 54 statics. Dish washing rooms, table tennis & croquet.

🔌📷🌂☉🔍🍴🚫🏕⚠🚰🚲⚡🔋📞🚿💈🏪

🐴🏪♿

➜🚶⛵🎣👓🏪

Pen Y Bont Touring & Camping Park (SH932350)
Llangynog Rd LL23 7PH ☎ 01678 520549
▶ ▶ 🚐🚐▲
Open Apr-Oct Booking advisable all year Last arrival 21.30hrs Last departure 13.00hrs
Part-level, part-sloping, grass and gravel site with trees and bushes set in mountainous woodland country, adjacent to river Dee and Bala Lake. .5m from Bala on side of B4391. A 7-acre site with 85 touring pitches.
Dish washing & vegetable preparation area.

🔌📷🌂☉🚫⚠🚰🔋📞🏪

➜🚶⛵💧🎣👓🏪☉

Tytandderwen Caravan Site (SH953363)
LL23 7EP ☎ 01678 520273
▶ 🚐🚐▲
Open Etr-Oct Booking advisable peak periods
An open site quite close to the River Dee, with somewhat spartan facilities. 3m SE of Bala on the Bala-Llangynog (B4391) road. A 3-acre site with 45 touring pitches and 60 statics.

🔌📷🌂☉🚫⚠🚰🚲⚡📞

➜🚶⛵💧🎣🏪🎣☉🏪

BARMOUTH

Hendre Mynach Caravan Park (SH605170)
Llanaber Rd LL42 1YR ☎ 01341 280262 Signposted
▶ ▶ ▶ ★ ⊞ £6.50-£10 ⊞ £6-£9 ▲ £5-£9
Open Mar-Oct (rs Mar-Etr) Booking advisable bank hols
& Jul-Aug Last arrival 23.00hrs Last departure noon
*A lovely site with immaculate facilities, situated off the
A496 on the northern outskirts of Barmouth and near to
railway, with almost direct access to promenade and
beach. A 10-acre site with 205 touring pitches.*
TV & satellite hook ups.

🎮 📷 ⊙ 🗑 🗨 ☀ ⚠ 🅿 ⌀ T ✕ 📞 🐎 🐾
→ ⊍ 🍴 🛒
💷

BEDDGELERT

Beddgelert Forest Campsite (SH578491)
LL55 4UU ☎ 01766 890288 & 01492 640578 Signposted
▶ ▶ ▶ ♣ ★ ⊞ fr £7 ⊞ fr £7 ▲ fr £7
Open all year Booking advisable 31 Mar-Sep Last arrival
22.00hrs Last departure 14.00hrs
*Well-run and very popular site amidst trees and bushes.
Set in mountainous woodland country near to river and
main road. Site in 1m N of Beddgelert on A4085. A 25-
acre site with 280 touring pitches.*

🎮 📷 ⊙ 🗑 ☀ ⚠ 🅿 ⌀ 🗑 T 📞 🛒 ♿
→ 🍴

Credit Cards 🟦 💳

BENLLECH BAY

See **Brynteg & Llanbedrgoch**

BETWS GARMON

Bryn Gloch Caravan & Camping Park (SH534574)
LL54 7YY ☎ 01286 650216 Signposted
Nearby town: Caernarfon
▶▶▶▶ ♣ ★ ➡ fr £7.80 ➡ fr £7.80 ▲ fr £7.80
Open all year Booking advisable school & bank hols Last arrival 23.00hrs Last departure 17.00hrs
An excellent family-run site with new and improved toilets, and some level pitches. Site on A4085 between Beddgelert and Caernarfon. A 12-acre site with 92 touring pitches and 14 statics.
Family bathroom & mother & baby room.
See advertisement under CAERNARFON

🔫 🛒 📞 ⊙ 🗑 🖇 🐃 🐾 ❑ ☀ ☗ 🛦 🛢 🖉 ⊞ Ⓣ ✕ ☎
🚿 ♨ 🎇 🐴 👜 🛒 🐕
→ ∪ ▶ ◎ ♣ ⚓ ♪
£

BRYNCRUG

Woodlands Holiday Park (SH618035)
LL36 9UH ☎ 01654 710471 (2m NE) Signposted
Nearby town: Tywyn
▶▶▶ ➡ £6 ➡ £6
Open Etr & Apr-Oct Booking advisable Jul-Aug Last arrival 22.00hrs Last departure 11.00hrs
A tarmac site at the end of a large holiday complex, partly surrounded by trees. 2m from Tywyn on B4405 road to Tal-y-Llyn. A 2-acre site with 20 touring pitches and 122 statics.
Entertainment in high season.

🔫 📞 ⊙ 🗑 🐃 🐾 ❑ ☀ ☗ 🛦 🛢 ✕ ☎ 🎇 🐴 🐕
→ ∪ ▶ ⚓ 🎱 ♪

CAERNARFON

Bryn Teg Holiday Park (SH524636)
Llanrug LL55 4RF ☎ 01286 871374 & 01492 532197 (3m E A4086)
▶▶▶▶ ★ ➡ £5-£9.50 ➡ £5-£9.50 ▲ £5-£9.50
Open Etr-14 Jan (rs mid Oct-Etr pool, bar & shop closed) Booking advisable bank hols & peak season Last arrival 20.00hrs Last departure noon
A large site set in undulating countryside, with mostly level pitches. A 10-acre site with 168 touring pitches and 287 statics.
12 acre lake with coarse & trouting fishing.

🔫 📞 ⊙ 🗑 🖇 🐃 🐾 ❑ ☀ ☗ 🛦 🛢 🖉 Ⓣ ✕ ☎ 🛒
🚿 🐴 👜 🛒 🐕
→ ∪ ▶ ⚓ 🎱 🎇 ♪
£

Credit Cards 🃏 💳

Cadnant Valley Caravan Park (SH487628)
Cadnant Valley Park, Llanberis Rd LL55 2DF ☎ 01286 673196 Signposted
▶▶▶ ➡ £6.40-£8.40 ➡ £6.20-£8 ▲ £6-£7.50

Open 15 Mar-Oct Booking advisable bank hols & Jul-Aug Last arrival 22.00hrs Last departure noon
Situated close to the main Caernarfon-Llanberis road and conveniently near the town. Level, terraced pitches in a secluded, landscaped, wooded valley with some near a stream. A 4.5-acre site with 60 touring pitches.
Outdoor table tennis.

Glan Gwna Holiday Park (SH502622)
Caethro LL55 2SG ☎ 01286 673456
▶ ▶ ▶ ★ ⊞ £6-£11 ⊞ £6-£11 ▲ £6-£11
Open Etr-Oct (rs mid Apr-May & mid Sep-Oct some facilities are closed) Booking advisable bank hols Last arrival 23.00hrs Last departure noon
Take A4085 signed Beddgelert, 1m from Caernarfon. A 7-acre site with 100 touring pitches and 130 statics.
Horse riding, solarium & fishing.

Ty'n yr Onnen Mountain Farm Caravan & Camping (SH534588)
Waunfawr LL55 4AX ☎ 01286 650281 Signposted
▶ ▶ ★ ⊞ £7-£8 ⊞ £6-£7 ▲ £5-£7
Open Spring bank hol-Oct (rs Etr open if weather premitting) Booking advisable Spring bank hol & Jul-Aug Last arrival 21.00hrs Last departure 10.00hrs
A very good site in the magnificent surroundings of a

200-acre sheep farm, with some level pitches. Site along narrow unclass rd from post office at S end of Waunfawr. A 4-acre site with 20 touring pitches and 4 statics.
Fishing.

Riverside Camping (SH505630)
Caer Glyddyn, Pont Rug LL55 2BB ☎ 01286 672524 & 678781 eves (2m E on A4086) Signposted
▶ ⊞ £6-£8.50 ⊞ £5.50-£7 ▲ £2-£6
Open Etr-end Oct Booking advisable Jul-Aug Last arrival anytime Last departure 20.00hrs
Level, grassy site bordered by a salmon river, 2m E of Caernarfon on A4086. A 4.5-acre site with 55 touring pitches.
River swimming, camp fires allowed on river bank.

Conwy Touring Park (SH779757)
LL32 8UX ☎ 01492 592856 (1.5m S on B5106) Signposted
▶ ▶ ▶ ♠ ★ ⊞ £4.85-£10.25 ⊞ £4.85-£10.25 ▲ £4.10-£10.25

CONWY TOURING PARK

▶▶▶

Conwy, Gwynedd LL32 8UX
Tel: Aberconwy (01492) 592856

Set amidst spectacular scenery Conwy Touring Park is perfect for your touring or camping holiday, only ½ mile south of Conwy on the B5106 road. Ideal for touring Snowdonia, Anglesey and the resorts of Llandudno and Betws-y-Coed.

Our facilities include FREE Hot showers; Clubhouse, Bar-food, Outdoor Adventure Playground with Indoor Adventure playground and Games room, Launderette, Shop, Electric hook-ups. Evening entertainment.

Pitches from £4.85 per night (low season).

Special offers available at other times.

Open Etr-Oct Booking advisable public hols & Jul-Aug Last arrival 21.00hrs Last departure noon
An excellent site, well laid out with a good range of facilities. A 70-acre site with 300 touring pitches. Indoor playground monitored by staff.

🏕 🐾 ⊙ 🔍 ※ 🛒 ⚠ 🚿 🖍 🗂 🅃 ✕ 🔌 🐕 🛍 ᚨ ♿
→ ∪ ▶ ♪

Credit Cards 🔲 🔲 🔲 🔲

CRICCIETH

Llwyn-Bugeilydd Farm (SH498398)
LL52 0PN ☎ 01766 522235 Signposted
▶ ▶ ★ 🚐 £5-£7.50 🚐 £5-£7 ▲ £5-£6.50
Open Etr or Apr-Oct Booking advisable Etr, Whit & Jul-Aug Last departure 11.00hrs
A beautiful little site, level and with sea and mountain views. Situated 1m N of Criccieth on B4411. First site on right. A 6-acre site with 45 touring pitches.

🏕 🐾 ⊙ 🔍 ※ 🛒 ⚠ 🚿 🖍 🗂 🔌 ᚨ 🐕 🛍
→ ∪ ▶ ◎ ⚠ ⚓ 🏓 ♪ 🐾
💷

Tyddyn Cethin Farm (SH492404)
LL52 0NF ☎ 01766 522149
▶ ▶ ★ 🚐 £6.50-£8 🚐 £6.50-£8 ▲ £4.50-£6.50
Open Mar-Oct Booking advisable Feb-Mar Last arrival 22.00hrs Last departure noon
A very good quiet family holiday site with enthusiastic proprietors, on banks of River Dwyfor. Travel N from Criccieth on B4411 and Tyddyn Cethin is 4th site on

right. An 8-acre site with 60 touring pitches and 40 statics.
Fishing on site.

🏕 🐾 🐾 ⊙ 🛒 ※ ⚠ 🚿 🖍 🗂 🏓 🐕
→ ∪ ▶ ◎ ⚠ ⚓ ♫ ♪ 🐾
💷

Cae-Canol Caravan & Camping Site (SH488402)
LL52 0NB ☎ 01766 522351
▶ 🚐 🚐 ▲
Open Apr-Oct Booking advisable
A level, grassy, well-sheltered site with trees set in meadowland 2m from town on the B4411. A 3-acre site with 30 touring pitches and 20 statics.
Free trout fishing private stretch river Dwyfach.

🏕 🐾 ⊙ ※ ⚠ 🚿 🖍 🗂
→ ∪ ▶ ⚓ ♪ ◎ 🐾

Tyddyn Morthwyl (SH488402)
LL52 0NF ☎ 01766 522115 Signposted
▶ ★ 🚐 fr £4.50 🚐 fr £4 ▲ fr £4.50
Open Etr-Oct (rs Mar & Oct) Booking advisable Spring bank hol & Jul-Aug Last departure 14.00hrs
A quiet, sheltered site with good level grassy pitches, ideal for families. Conveniently situated N of B4411, 1.5m from centre of Criccieth. A 10-acre site with 60 touring pitches and 22 statics.

🏕 🐾 ⊙ ⚓ ※ 🗂 📞
→ ∪ ▶ ⚓ ♪ 🐾
💷

DINAS DINLLE

Dinlle Caravan Park (SH443568)
LL54 5TW ☎ 01286 830324 (2m W of Dinas Dinlle coast) Signposted
▶ ▶ ▶ 🚐 £4.50-£9.50 ▲ £4.50-£9.50
Open May-Aug (rs Mar-Apr & Sep-Oct club shop & take-away restricted hours) Booking advisable Spring bank hol & Jul-Aug Last arrival 23.00hrs Last departure noon
Well-kept grassy level site, adjacent to sandy beach; good views to Snowdonia. An 11-acre site with 200 touring pitches and 138 statics.
See advertisement under CAERNARFON

🏕 🐾 ⊙ 🛒 🔍 ⚡ 🔍 🗂 ※ 🛒 ⚠ 🚿 🖍 🗂 🅃 📞 🛍 ♿
→ ♪
💷

Credit Cards 🔲 🔲

LLANDWROG

White Tower Caravan Park (SH454566)
LL54 5UH ☎ 01286 830649 Signposted
Nearby town: Caernarfon
▶ ▶ ▶ 🚐 🚐 ▲
Open Mar-Oct (rs Mar-mid May & Sep-Oct swimming pool & bar wknds only) Booking advisable bank hols & Jul-Aug Last arrival 23.00hrs Last departure noon
A level, well-maintained site with lovely Snowdonia views, 1.5m from village along Tai'r Eglwys Road. (Turn ➡

opposite Harp Inn). A 3-acre site with 52 touring pitches and 52 statics.

🔲 📻 ☉ 🗟 🦃 ⇃ ⛏ ⟷ ☀ ♈ /𝕄 🔦 ⊘ 🔳 🅣 ⚓ ➰
🐞 ♿
→ ∪ ⏵ ⌂ ⅏ ✦ ➷
🔁

LLANRUG

See **Caernarfon**

LLANRWST

Bodnant Caravan Site (SH805609)
Nebo Rd LL26 0SD ☎ 01492 640248 Signposted
▶ ▶ ♠ 🚐 £5.25-£6.25 🚐 £5.25-£6.25 ▲ £5.25-£6.25
Open Mar-end Oct Booking advisable Etr, May Day,
Spring bank hol & Jul-Aug Last arrival 22.00hrs Last
departure 11.00hrs
*Small, well-maintained, level touring site, S of village off
A470. Twelve times winner of 'Wales in Bloom'
competition for best kept touring caravan site in Wales.
A 4-acre site with 40 touring pitches.*

🔲 📻 ☉ 🦃 /𝕄 🔦 ⊘ 🔳 ⚓ 🐕 🔁
→ ⅏ ➷ 🖥 🐞
🔁

Maenan Abbey Caravan Park (SH790656)
LL26 0UL ☎ 01492 660630 Signposted
▶ ▶ 🚐 £4-£8.50 🚐 £4-£8.50
Open Mar-Oct Booking advisable peak periods Last
arrival 22.30hrs Last departure noon
*An excellent site, level, grassy and well-screened, in the
beautiful Conwy Valley. Site on A470 2m N of Llanrwst.
A 3-acre site with 26 touring pitches and 72 statics.*

🔲 📻 ☉ 🔦 ⚓
→ ∪ ⏵ ➷
🔁

LLANYSTUMDWY

Camping & Caravanning Club Site (SH469384)
Tyddyn Sianel LL52 0LS ☎ 01766 522855 (in season) &
01203 994995 Signposted
Nearby town: Criccieth
▶ ▶ ▶ ♦♦ ★ 🚐 £9.30-£10 🚐 £9.30-£10 ▲ £9.30-£10
Open end Mar-early Nov Booking advisable bank hols &
peak periods Last arrival 21.00hrs Last departure noon
*Well-maintained, attractive grassy site alongside the
A497 with a good range of facilities. Please see the
advertisement on page 27 for details of Club Members'
benefits. A 4-acre site with 70 touring pitches.*
Playfield

🔲 📻 ☉ 🗟 🦃 🔆 🔦 ⊘ 🔳 ⚓ 🐕 🐞 ♿
→ ∪ ⏵ ⅏ ➷
Credit Cards 💳 💳 💳

MORFA BYCHAN

Gwyndy Caravan Park (SH543371)
Black Rock Sands LL49 9YB ☎ 01766 512047 Signposted
Nearby town: Porthmadog
▶ ▶ ▶ ★ 🚐 £6-£8 🚐 £6-£8 ▲ £6-£8
Open Mar-Oct Booking advisable bank hols & Jul-Aug
Last departure 11.00hrs
*A quiet family site a minute's walk to the beach at Black
Rock Sands. A 5-acre site with 15 touring pitches and 44
statics.*

🔲 📻 ☉ 🗟 🦃 🔆 🔦 ⊘ 🔳 🐞
→ ∪ ⏵ ⌂ ⅏ 📹 ➷

PONTLYFNI

Llyn-y-Gele Farm & Caravan Park (SH432523)
LL54 5EL ☎ 01286 660283 & 660289 Signposted
Nearby town: Caernarfon
▶ ▶ 🚐 £7-£8 🚐 £5-£7 ▲ £5-£7
Open Etr-Sep Booking advisable Jul-Aug Last arrival
22.00hrs Last departure 13.00hrs
*Quiet farm site within 5-7 minutes' walking distance of
the beach. Centrally situated for touring the Lleyn
Peninsula, Anglesey and Snowdonia, off A499. A 4-acre
site with 26 touring pitches and 24 statics.*

🔲 📻 ☉ 🔆 /𝕄 🔦 🐕
→ ∪ ➷ 🐞
🔁

PONT-RUG

See **Caernarfon**

PORTHMADOG

Tyddyn Llwyn Caravan Park & Camping Site (SH561384)
Black Rock Rd LL49 9UR ☎ 01766 512205
▶ ▶ ♠ ★ 🚐 £10-£12 🚐 £8-£10 ▲ £6-£8
Open Mar-Oct Last arrival 23.00hrs Last departure noon
*This site consists of both level and slightly sloping
pitches in beautiful countryside overlooked by hills. A
14-acre site with 230 touring pitches and 52 statics.*

📻 ☉ 🗟 🔆 ☀ 🔦 ⊘ 🔳 ✖ ⚓ 🐞
→ ∪ ⏵ ⌂ 📹 ➷

TALSARNAU

Barcdy Touring Caravan & Camping Park (SH623368)
LL47 6YG ☎ 01766 770736 Signposted
Nearby town: Harlech
▶ ▶ ▶ ♠ ★ 🚐 £6.50-£7.50 🚐 £6.50-£7.50 ▲ £6.50-£7.50
Open Spring bank hol-mid Sep (rs Etr-Spring bank hol &
mid Sep-Oct only two fields open, food shop closed)
Booking advisable from Feb ⊘
*A quiet picturesque site on the southern edge of the
Vale of Ffestiniog near Dwryd estuary. Very well-run and
maintained. On A496 N of Talsarnau. A 12-acre site with
68 touring pitches and 30 statics.*
Dishwashing sinks hot water charged.

🔲 📻 ☉ 🗟 🦃 🔆 🔦 ⊘ 🔳 🅣 ⚓ 🎋 🐞
→ ➷
🔁

Llechollwyn Farm (SH596358)
Ynys LL47 6TH ☎ 01766 780414
▷
Open all year Booking advisable Last arrival anytime Last departure anytime
Level grass field almost on the sea's edge of Traeth Bach, with views across estuary to Portmeirion. From Ynys travel S on A496, take sharp right turn an continue for 1m. A 4-acre site with 15 touring pitches.

TAL-Y-BONT

Benar Beach Camping & Touring Park (SH573226)
LL43 2AR ☎ 01341 247571
▶▶
Open Mar-3 Oct Booking advisable peak periods
Friendly family site 1 mile from A496 halfway between Harlech and Barmouth. Adjacent to sandy beach with view of mountains. A 5-acre site with 40 touring pitches.
Satellite & TV hook-ups.

TAL-Y-BONT (NEAR CONWY)

Tynterfyn Touring Caravan Park (SH768692)
LL32 8YX ☎ 01492 660525
Nearby town: Conwy
▶ ★ fr £4 fr £4 £3-£5
Open Mar-Oct Booking advisable bank hols & Jul-Aug Last arrival 22.00hrs Last departure noon
Small, family site on level ground situated in the lovely Conwy Valley. On the B5106, .25m N of village. A 2-acre site with 15 touring pitches.

TREFRIW

Plas Meirion Caravan Park (SH783630)
Gower Rd LL27 ORZ ☎ 01492 640247
Nearby town: Betws-y-Coed
▶▶ £7-£9.50 £6-£8.50
Open Etr-Oct Booking advisable school hols Last arrival 22.00hrs Last departure 10.30hrs
A level site with mature trees set in the Conwy Valley. Off B5106. A 2-acre site with 11 touring pitches and 16 statics.
Table tennis, mountain bikes.

TYWYN

See **Bryncrug**

Ynysymaengwyn Caravan Park (SH601021)
LL36 9RY ☎ 01654 710684
▶▶ ★ £4-£6.50 £3-£4
Open Etr or Apr-Oct Booking advisable Jul-Aug Last arrival 23.00hrs Last departure noon
This site is ideally situated with the full amenities of the seaside on one hand and beautiful countryside and hills on the other. On right of A493 almost halfway between Bryncrug and Tywyn. A 4-acre site with 80 touring pitches and 115 statics.

POWYS

ABERCRAF

Dan-yr-Ogof Show Caves Caravan & Tenting Park (SN841160)
SA9 1GJ ☎ 01639 730284 Signposted
Nearby town: Swansea
▶▶ ★ fr £6 fr £6 fr £4
Open wk before Etr-Oct Last arrival 20.00hrs Last departure noon
A part-level, grassy site with mature trees. Hardstanding for caravans. Set in Beacons National Park, with a river on one side. 3m N of village on A4067 Sennybridge road. Follow signs for 'Dan-yr-Ogof Caves'. A 5-acre site with 60 touring pitches.
Dry ski slope, fishing & trekking centre.

Bishop's Meadow Caravan Park,
Hay Road, Brecon, Powys LD3 9SW
Telephone: 01874 622051 & 622392
AA ▶▶▶ ETB ✓✓✓✓
Conveniently situated on the outskirts of Brecon on the B4602, approximately one mile from the town centre. The park has 50 level pitches with electrical hook-ups and all have excellent views of the Brecon Beacons.
The high standards of the park are reflected in the good facilities offered. The Restaurant is open all day, every day and offers a comprehensive menu for snacks and main meals. The Lounge Bar, open every evening and recently refurbished offers a friendly and relaxed atmosphere for all the family. A small shop provides many essential items. Heated outdoor swimming pool with patio. Children's play area. Dogs welcome on leads.

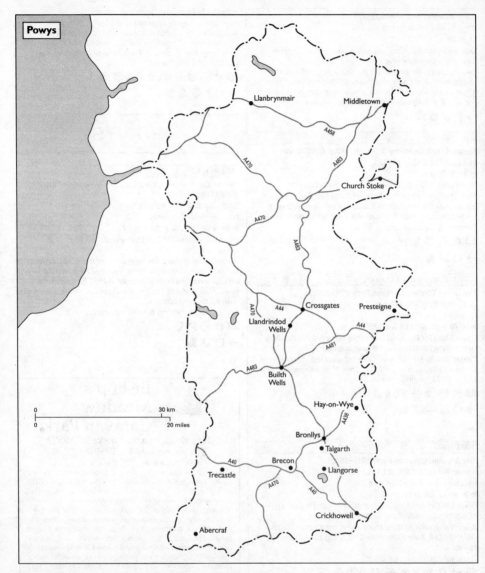

Powys

- Llanbrynmair
- Middletown
- Church Stoke
- Crossgates
- Presteigne
- Llandrindod Wells
- Builth Wells
- Hay-on-Wye
- Bronllys
- Talgarth
- Brecon
- Llangorse
- Trecastle
- Crickhowell
- Abercraf

0 30 km
0 20 miles

Open Etr-Oct Booking advisable bank & school hols
Very attractive and well-appointed small site offering commanding views of the Brecon Beacons. Ideal as a touring base or for longer stays. Adjacent to the A470, 1m E of Brecon. A 15-acre site with 130 touring pitches. Adventure playground, off-licence, dish washing.

🔌🍴🌳⊙📺🏕️✳️⚠️🅰️🅿️🚻📞🔚🔀🎪🐕🐾 &

➔🛒🅿️🍴🎪🎣

Aberbran Caravan Club Site (SN983294)
Aberbran LD3 9NH ☎ 01874 622424 (3.5m W)
▷ ★ 🚐 £7-£8 🚗 £7-£8
Open 29 Mar-16 Sep Booking advisable bank hols & Aug Last arrival 20.00hrs Last departure noon
A small, peaceful site on the edge of the Brecon Beacons National Park, ideal for a walking or birdwatching holiday. From Brecon bypass (A40) follow Llandovery signs for 3.25m then turn R at Aberbran sign. Site on L in .5m past certified site. A 2-acre site with 29 touring pitches.

🔌⚠️🅰️🅿️🚻📞🐾

➔🛒🅿️🎪🍴🎣📺🎣

Credit Cards 🏧 💳

BRONLLYS

Anchorage Caravan Park (SO142351)
LD3 0LD ☎ 01874 711246 & 711230 Signposted
Nearby town: Brecon
▶▶▶ 🚐 fr £6 🚗 fr £6 🅰️ fr £6
Open all year (rs Nov-Mar TV room closed) Booking advisable bank hols Last arrival 23.00hrs Last departure 18.00hrs
A well-maintained site. Touring pitches are on grassy slopes and level ground with good mountain views of the Brecon Beacons National Park. 8m NE of Brecon. An 8-acre site with 110 touring pitches and 101 statics. Baby bath room.

🔌🔀🍴⊙📺🏕️💬🖥️✳️⚠️💧🅿️🚻📞🏕️🐕 &

➔🛒🍴🎣

💷

BUILTH WELLS

Llewelyn Leisure Park (SO003514)
Cilmery LD2 3NU ☎ 01982 552838 & 01831 101052 (2m W on A483) Signposted
▶▶▶ 🚐 🅰️
Open Etr-Oct (rs Nov-Etr toilet/shower facilities in house) Booking advisable Jul-Aug Last arrival 22.00hrs Last departure 11.00hrs
A small site with great potential situated 2m W of Builth Wells, on S of A483 in Cilmery Village. A 0.75-acre site with 25 touring pitches and 26 statics. Free library service.

🔌🍴⊙📺🏕️🖥️🍴🖥️✳️⚠️🅰️💧🖥️📺📞🏕️
🎣

➔🛒🅿️🎪🍴

Credit Cards 🏧 💳

Fforest Fields Caravan & Camping Park (SO100535)
Hundred House LD1 5RT ☎ 01982 570220
▶▶ 🚐 £6.50-£7 🚗 £5.50-£6 🅰️ £4
Open Etr & Apr-Oct Booking advisable bank hols & Jul-Aug
A sheltered site in a hidden valley. On A481, one mile before Hundred House village. A 7-acre site with 40 touring pitches.

🔌🍴⊙📺✳️⚠️🅰️🖥️📞🐕

➔🛒⊙⛵🎪🍴🎣

💷

CHURCH STOKE

Bacheldre Watermill Touring & Camping Park (SO243928)
Bacheldre Watermill SY15 6TE ☎ 01588 620489 (2.5m W off A489 Churchstoke / Newtown) Signposted
Nearby town: Montgomery
▶▶ 🚐 fr £6 🚗 fr £6 🅰️ fr £6
Open Etr-Oct Booking advisable bank hols
Lovely little site with working water mill. A 2-acre site with 16 touring pitches.

🔌🍴⊙✳️

Daisy Bank Caravan Park (SO303929)
SY15 6EB ☎ 01588 620471 Signposted
Nearby town: Bishops Castle
▶▶ 🚐 £5-£6.75 🚗 £5-£6.75
Open Feb-Nov Booking advisable bank hols Last arrival 22.00hrs Last departure 19.00hrs
A brand new site, well-landscaped with quality facilities. Marvellous views and welcoming owners. From A49 at Craven Arms take A489 to Churchstoke. Turn off 1.5m after Bishops Castle. A 6-acre site with 40 touring pitches.

🔌🍴⊙✳️⚠️🅰️💧🖥️🔳🏕️🐕🐾 &

➔🛒🎣

CRICKHOWELL

Riverside Caravan & Camping Park (SO215184)
New Rd NP8 1AY ☎ 01873 810397 Signposted
▶▶▶ 🚐 £5.50-£10.50 🚗 £4.50-£6.50 🅰️ fr £3
Open Mar-Oct Booking advisable for stays over 1 wk Last arrival 23.00hrs
A clean and well-maintained site, adjacent to the River Usk, in lovely tranquil surroundings. A 3.5-acre site with 35 touring pitches and 20 statics.

🔌🍴⊙✳️🅰️💧🖥️📞🎣 &

➔🛒🅿️🎪🍴

CROSSGATES

The Park Motel (SO081651)
Rhayader Rd LD1 6RF ☎ 01597 851201
Nearby town: Llandrindod Wells
▶▶ ★ 🚐 fr £4 🚗 fr £4 🅰️ fr £4
Open Mar-Oct Booking advisable bank hols Last arrival 22.30hrs Last departure noon
This quiet rural site, set in beautiful countryside, has flat pitches and is well-sheltered by trees. It is an ideal ➥

touring centre, situated off A44. A 1-acre site with 10 touring pitches and 15 statics.

🔌📶🚻⊙🔗🔲❄️🍸🚐🗑️🧴📶🗂️✕🔌⬇️🔋
➔⛵🏴‍☠️🍴☎️🎵🗑️

💷

HAY-ON-WYE

Hollybush Inn (SO205406)
HR3 5PS ☎ 01497 847371 (Off B4350) Signposted
▶ ★ 🚐 fr £6 🚐 fr £5 ⚑ fr £5
Open Good Fri-Oct Booking advisable bank hols Last arrival 23.00hrs Last departure 13.00hrs
A neat little site adjacent to a small inn and close to the R Wye. 2m from Hay-on-Wye off B4350. A 3-acre site with 22 touring pitches and 5 statics.
Canoe launch.

🔌📶⊙❄️🍸✕🔌🏠🍴🐕‍🦺
➔⛵🏴‍☠️

LLANBRYNMAIR

Gwern-y-Bwlch Caravan Club Site (SH877036)
SY19 7EB ☎ 01650 521351 (1.5m W)
Nearby town: Machynlleth
▷ 🚐🚐
Open 26 Mar-4 Oct Booking advisable Spring bank hol Last arrival 20.00hrs Last departure 20.00hrs
A lovely, quiet site with pitched terraces and splendid views across the valley to the mountains. On final approach to site proceed with caution to avoid overshooting minor road. A 5-acre site with 43 touring pitches.

🔌❄️🔋🗂️🔌
➔⛵🏴‍☠️🎵🔋
Credit Cards 💳 💳

LLANDRINDOD WELLS

Disserth Caravan & Camping Park (SO034584)
Disserth, Howey LD1 6NL ☎ 01597 860277 Signposted
▶ ▶ ▶ 🚐 £5.95-£7.25 🚐 £5.95-£7.25 ⚑ £5.95-£7.25
Open Mar-Oct Booking advisable early as possible Last arrival 22.00hrs Last departure noon
A peaceful site nestling in a beautiful valley on the banks of R Ithon, a tributary of the R Wye. Take A470 from Aberystwyth towards Builth Wells, turn left at Newbridge on Wye, and right towards Disserth. A 2.5-acre site with 25 touring pitches and 21 statics.
Private trout fishing.

🔌📶⊙🗂️🔔❄️🍸🚐🗑️🗂️✕🔌🏠🔋
➔⛵🏴‍☠️🔺🎵🍴🎵

💷

Dalmore Camping & Caravanning Park (SO045568)
Howey LD1 5RG ☎ 01597 822483 (Howey 3m S A483)
Nearby town: Builth Wells
▶ ▶ ★ 🚐 £5-£6 🚐 £5-£6 ⚑ £5-£6
Open Mar-Oct Booking advisable Jun-Aug Last arrival 22.00hrs Last departure noon
A clean, tidy site on A483 but screened from road and traffic noise by hedgerow. Wonderful views. 1.5m S of

village. A 2-acre site with 22 touring pitches and 19 statics.

🔌📶⊙❄️🚐🗑️🧴🗂️🔌🏠🐕‍🦺🔋
➔⛵🏴‍☠️⊙🍴☎️🎵🗑️

💷

LLANGORSE

Lakeside Caravan Park (SO128272)
LD3 7TR ☎ 01874 84226
Nearby town: Brecon
▶▶▶🚐🚐⚑
Open Jun-Sep (rs Apr, May & Oct swimming pool clubhouse & restaurant) Booking advisable peak periods Last arrival 21.30hrs Last departure noon
A much improved site with an enthusiastic warden. A 2-acre site with 40 touring pitches and 72 statics.
Boat hire & launching, windsurfing, fishing.

🔌📶⊙🏐🔗❄️🍸🚐🗑️🧴🗂️✕🔌⬇️🏠🐕‍🦺🔋
➔⛵🔺🏴‍☠️🎵
Credit Cards 💳 💳

MIDDLETOWN

Bank Farm Caravan Park (SJ293123)
SY21 8EJ ☎ 01938 570526 & 570260 Signposted
Nearby town: Welshpool
▶ ▶ ★ 🚐 £6-£7 🚐 £6-£7 ⚑ fr £5
Open May-Oct Booking advisable bank hols Last arrival 20.00hrs Last departure noon
Part-level, part-sloping grass site near hills, mountains and woodland. A 2-acre site with 20 touring pitches and 33 statics.
Trout pool.

🔌📶⊙🏐🔗❄️🚐🔋🗂️🏠🐕‍🦺♿
➔🏴‍☠️🎵

💷

PRESTEIGNE

Rock Bridge Park (SO294654)
LD8 2NF ☎ 01547 560300 Signposted
▶ ▶ ▶ ★ 🚐 £7-£8.50 🚐 ⚑ £3-£7
Open Apr-Sep Booking advisable public & school hols Last arrival 21.30hrs Last departure noon ✗
Part-level, part-sloping grass site with trees and bushes, set in meadowland with access to River Luga. 1m W of Presteigne off B4356. A 3-acre site with 35 touring pitches and 30 statics.

🔌📶⊙🗂️❄️🔔🔋🗂️🏠🔋♿
➔🏴‍☠️🎵

TALGARTH

Riverside International (SO148346)
Bronllys LD3 0HL ☎ 01874 711320 & 712064 Signposted
Nearby town: Brecon
▶ ▶ ▶ ★ 🚐 £8-£9 🚐 £8-£9 ⚑ £8-£9
Open Etr-Oct Booking advisable bank hols & Jul-Aug Last arrival 22.00hrs Last departure 16.00hrs ✗
Well-appointed touring site with pitches available on riverside. Elevated position with magnificent views of the Black

Riverside International
Caravan & Camping Park
Talgarth, Brecon, Powys LD3 0HL
Telephone: (01874) 711320

A well maintained. clean and friendly family
run site situated on the edge of the Brecon
Beacons National Park with panoramic
views of the Black Mountains. An ideal
location for touring Mid and South Wales.
Full facilities on site including a games
room and bathroom with baby changing
facilities. Leisure centre with heated pool,
sauna, solarium, jacuzzi and fitness room.
There is a well stocked bar with full bar
snack menu. Vegetarians well catered for. A
takeaway service is also available.
On site there is 800 yards FREE trout
fishing.
Sorry no dogs allowed.

**For further details write or ring for
brochure.**

AA ▶▶▶

*Mountains. Off A479. A 9-acre site with 80 touring pitches.
Leisure facilities, sauna, jacuzzi, sunbed & gym.*

🔌🚐🏠☉🗑🍴🔌 🔦🚪☀️🍴🛢💊🗑⊞✕
🔦⚕️🛏♿
➔🔱⛺💧🌿🍴🐾

TRECASTLE

Cross Inn & Black Mountain Caravan Park (SN773259)
Llanddeusant SA19 9YG ☎ 01550 740621
Nearby town: Llandeilo
▶▶ ★ 🚐 fr £6 🚐 fr £5 ⛺ £4-£5
Open all year Booking advisable bank hols Last
departure 10.30hrs
*A small site with adequate facilities. Take unclassified
road south out of Trecastle, pass Castle Hotel and
continue for approx seven miles. A 5-acre site with 40
touring pitches and 20 statics.*

🔌🏠☉🗑☀️🍴🛢💊🗑✕🔦⚕️
➔🔱▶🌿
💷

SOUTH GLAMORGAN

CARDIFF

Pontcanna Caravan Site (ST171773)
Pontcanna Fields, off Sophia Close, Riverside CF1 9JJ
☎ 01222 398362 & 471612
▶▶▶ 🚐 fr £11.25 🚐 fr £11.25

Open Mar-Oct Booking advisable Last arrival telephone
Last departure noon
*An excellent site with good amenities, and very close to
centre of Cardiff. A 2-acre site with 43 touring pitches.*

🔌🏠🗑🔌💊🍴♿
➔🔱▶☉💧🌿🎦🍴🐾

LLANTWIT MAJOR

Llandow Touring Caravan Park (SS956713)
CF7 7PB ☎ 01446 794527 & 792462 (2m NW)
Signposted
Nearby town: Cowbridge
▶▶▶ ★ 🚐 £6-£7 🚐 £6-£7
Open Mar-Oct Booking advisable bank hols & end Jun
Last arrival 10.00hrs Last departure noon
*Newly established rural site with purpose-built facilities.
Within easy reach of Glamorgan's Heritage Coast, and a
short distance from Cardiff and Porthcawl. A 6-acre site
with 100 touring pitches.*
Caravan Storage

🔌🏠☉🗑☀️🛢💊🌿⊞🔦🛏🐾🐾
➔🔱🎦🧦🍴
💷

Acorn Camping & Caravan Site (SS973678)
Ham Ln South CF61 1RP ☎ 01446 794024 & 0589 421112
Signposted
▶▶ 🚐 £6-£7 🚐 £6-£7 ⛺ £6-£7
Open Etr or Mar-Oct Booking advisable bank hols & Aug
Last arrival 23.00hrs Last departure noon
*A quiet country site on meadowland. From Llantwit
Major follow B4265 south. A 4.5-acre site with 90
touring pitches and 15 statics.*

🔌🏠☉🔦☀️🛢💊🌿⊞🅣🔦🛏♿
➔🔱🧦

WEST GLAMORGAN

FAIRWOOD

Blackhills Caravan Park (SS582915)
Blackhills Rd Fairwood Common SA2 7JN ☎ 01792
207065 Signposted
▶▶▶ 🚐🚐⛺
Open Apr-Oct Booking advisable May & Jul-Aug Last
departure noon
*Mainly level grass site in meadowland. 6m SW of
Swansea along A4118 then unclass road for 1m. A 13-
acre site with 90 touring pitches and 120 statics.*

🔌🏠☉🗑🔦☀️🛢💊🌿⊞🔦🛏🐾🐾
➔🔱▶💧🍴

RHOSSILI

Pitton Cross Caravan & Camping Park (SS434877)
SA3 1PH ☎ 01792 390593 (2m W of Scurlage on B4247)
Nearby town: Swansea
▶▶▶ ★ 🚐 £7.50-£9.50 🚐 £7.50-£9 ⛺ £7-£9 ➡

South and West Glamorgan, Gwent

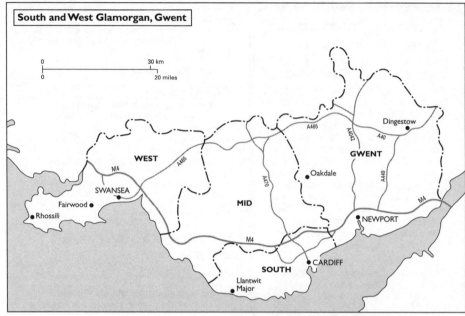

Open Etr-Oct (rs Mar some facilities may be closed)
Booking advisable Spring bank hol & Jul-Aug Last
arrival 21.00hrs Last departure noon
*Constantly improving site run by enthusiastic
proprietors. A 6-acre site with 100 touring pitches.*
Motor caravan service bay, pets corner.

🔧 📞 ☎ 💿 🔆 🗻 🛅 💧 🚽 ⊞ T 🔌 🛒 🐕 🛁 ♿
→ ∪ ▶ ⚓ 🎿 ⚓

£

Credit Cards ▧ ▨ ▨

Pitton Cross ▶▶▶
Caravan Park
RHOSSILI, GOWER,
WEST GLAMORGAN, SA3 1PH
Telephone: Gower (01792) 390593

Pitton Cross is set amid scenic National Trust
coastline with rugged cliffs, sandy beaches
and secluded coves. This family run park
offers good countryside recreation with
unspoilt seaside, water sport, walking,
cycling and bird watching. A flat site with
ample space between pitches and extensive
views to Lundy Island and the Brecon
Beacons. Colour brochure a pleasure.

SWANSEA

Riverside Caravan Park (SS679991)
Ynys Forgan Farm, Morriston SA6 6QL ☎ 01792 775587
(1m NE of A48/A4067 unclass 1m M4 junc 45)
Signposted
▶ ▶ ▶ ★ 🚐 £8-£9 🚐 £7-£8 🅰 £5-£7
Open all year Booking advisable bank hols Last arrival
mdnt Last departure noon
*An ideal base for touring Mumbles, Gower beaches and
Brecon National Park. A 70-acre site with 120 touring
pitches.*
Fishing on site by arrangement.

🔧 📞 ☎ 💿 🍴 🔦 ⚓ ☐ 🔆 🍺 🗻 💧 🚽 ⊞ T
🐕 🛁 ♿
→ ∪ ▶ 🎿 ⛺ ⚓
£

Northern Ireland & The Republic of Ireland

Please note that caravan and camping parks are listed county by county and under alphabetical order of place name within each county. Northern Irealnd counties are listed first, followed by those in the Republic. Place names are highlighted on the location map, but no map references are given in directory entries.

Prices for parks in the Republic of Ireland are given in Irish Punts (IR£)

NORTHERN IRELAND

CO ANTRIM

BALLYCASTLE

Silver Cliffs Holiday Village
21 Clare Rd BT54 6DB ☎ 012657 62550 (0.25m W off A2) Signposted
▶ ▶ ▶ ★ 🏠 £6-£8 🚐 £6-£8 ▲ £6-£8
Open 17 Mar-Oct Booking advisable 11-25 Jul & 22-25 Aug Last arrival 20.00hrs Last departure 17.00hrs
A typical large seaside site with a swimming pool and bar. Close to the beach and River Glenshesk, .25m W of Ballycastle off B15. A 2-acre site with 50 touring pitches and 250 statics.
Sun beds, sauna, & snooker.

🏠📶☉🔲🍴🐟 🔦❄🎱🏔🚻🚿🍴🎯🅿🚽✗🛁🍴🌳
🍴🛒♿
→ ∪ ▶ ⅄ ♪
Credit Cards 🪙

CUSHENDALL

Cushendall Caravan Camp
62 Coast Rd BT44 0QW ☎ 012667 71699 Signposted
▶ ▶ 🏠🚐▲
Open mid Mar-mid Oct Booking advisable peak periods Last arrival 23.00hrs Last departure 14.00hrs
A pleasant site next to the beach and sailing club on the A2, 1m S of town. A 1-acre site with 14 touring pitches and 55 statics.

🏠☉🔲🍴🐟♿🍴🛒🌳🍴
→ ∪ ▶ ☉ 💧 ⅄ ♪

CUSHENDUN

Cushendun Caravan Park
14 Glendun Rd BT44 0PX ☎ 01266 74254 Signposted
▶ ▶ 🏠🚐▲
Open Mar-Oct Booking advisable Jul-Aug Last arrival 22.30hrs Last departure 12.30hrs
A small toruing site with mostly level pitches next to larger static site. From A2 take B52 for 1m, clearly signed. A 0.5-acre site with 15 touring pitches and 50 statics.

🏠🐟🔦♿🔦🖥🏔🅿🗂✗🛒🍴🛒
→ ∪ ▶ ⅄ ♪

LARNE

Curran Caravan Park
131 Curran Rd ☎ 01574 272313 Signposted
▶ ▶ ▶ ★ 🏠 £6.50-£8 🚐 £6.50-£8 ▲ fr £4
Open Apr-Sep Booking advisable main season

A tidy and very clean council site ideal for the ferry. Site on A2 .25m from ferry, and clearly signed. A 3-acre site with 40 touring pitches.
Bowling & putting greens.

🏠🐟🏔🍴🏔🌳🐕
→ ∪ ▶ ☉ ⅄ 🎱 ♪ 🔲 🛒

PORTBALLINTRAE

PortBallintrae Caravan Park
Ballaghmore Av BT57 8RX ☎ 012657 31478 Signposted
Nearby town: Bushmills
▶ ▶ ★ 🏠 £9-£11 🚐 £9-£11 ▲ £2.50-£9
Open Apr-Sep Booking advisable Etr & Jul-Aug Last arrival 20.30hrs Last departure 14.00hrs
Very tidy site, popular for Giants Causeway. In Portballintrae village clearly signed from A2, .25m from Bushmills Distillery. A 5-acre site with 53 touring pitches and 150 statics.

🏠🐟☉🔲❄🏔🍴♿🐕♿
→ ▶ ⅄ ♪
💷

CO DOWN

CASTLEWELLAN

Castlewellan Forest Park
Dept of Agriculture, Forest Service BT31 9BH ☎ 01396 778664 Signposted
▶ ▶ ▶ 🔦🏠🚐▲
Open all year Booking advisable wknds & Jul-Aug Last arrival 22.00hrs Last departure 16.00hrs
Attractive forest park site, situated down a long drive with views of the castle. Site broken up into smaller areas by mature trees and shrubs. Off A25 in Castlewellan; turn right at Upper Square and turn into Forest Park, clearly signed. A 5-acre site with 90 touring pitches.
Lake, arboretum, fishing on site. First aid.

🏠🐟☉✗🍴🛒🏔🌳🐕🛒♿
→ ∪ ♪

NEWCASTLE

Tollymore Forest Park
☎ 01396 722428 Signposted
▶ ▶ ▶ 🏠🚐▲
Open 15 Mar-15 Nov (rs 16 Nov-14 Mar) Booking advisable Jul & Aug & wknds Apr-Sep Last arrival 21.00hrs Last departure 17.00hrs
Popular site with family field and large tent area. From A2 at Newcastle take B180, and site clearly signed on right. A 7.5-acre site with 100 touring pitches.

🏠🐟☉🔲🍴🌀✗🍴🏔🌳🛒♿
→ ∪ ▶ ☉ 💧 ⅄ 🎱 ♪

CO FERMANAGH

LISNASKEA

Lisnaskea Caravan Park
BT92 0NZ ☎ 01365 721040 Signposted
► ► ★ ♛ £7-£8 ♞ £7-£8 ⚲ £4.50-£5.50
Open Apr-Sep Booking advisable Jul-Aug Last arrival
21.00hrs Last departure noon
*From A34 turn onto B514 for Lisnaskea, and site signed
.5m before town. A 4-acre site with 43 touring pitches.*

🎮 📻 ☺ ☀ 𝔸 ⚓ 🐕 ♿
→ ∪ ▶ ⅄ 📻 ♩ 🔲 ⚑

CO LONDONDERRY

CASTLEROCK

Castlerock Holiday Park
24 Sea Rd ☎ 01265 848381 Signposted
► ► ► ★ ♛ £5-£8.50 ♞ £5-£8.50 ⚲ £5-£8.50
Open Etr-Oct Booking advisable Jul-Aug Last arrival
21.00hrs Last departure noon
*A mainly static site at the seaside with a tidy touring
area, 2 minutes from the beach. From A2 to Castlerock,
turn right before the rlwy stn into site; signed. A 2-acre
site with 40 touring pitches and 210 statics.*

🎮 📻 ☺ ⚓ 𝔸 ⚓ ♩ ⊡ 🆃 ⚲ ⛪
→ ∪ ▶ ⅄ ♩ ⚑

REPUBLIC OF IRELAND

CO CLARE

KILLALOE

**Lough Derg Caravan and
Camping Park**
☎ 061 376329 Signposted
► ► ► ► ► ♧ ♣♣ ✿ Holiday Centre ★ ♛ IR£6-IR£10
♞ IR£6-IR£10 ⚲ IR£6-IR£10
Open 29 Apr-Sep Last arrival 21.00hrs Last departure
noon ⚸
*A 4.5-acre site with 57 touring pitches and 15 statics.
Boats for hire, boat slipway, fishing.*

🎮 📻 ☺ 🔲 ⏻ ⚓ ⚓ ☀ 𝔸 ♩ ⊡ 🆃 ✗ ⚲ ⛪ ⚑
→ ∪ ▶ ⚓ ⅄ ♩

KILRUSH

Aylevarroo Caravan and Camping Park
☎ 065 51102 (2m E on R473) Signposted
► ► ► ♧ ♛ IR£6.50-IR£7.50 ♞ IR£6.50-IR£7.50 ⚲
IR£6.50-IR£7.50
Open 11 May-14 Sep Booking advisable Last arrival
22.00hrs Last departure noon ⚸
*A 7.5-acre site with 36 touring pitches and 10 statics.
Basketball court.*

🎮 📻 ☺ ⚲ ⚓ 🔲 ☀ 𝔸 ⚓ ♩ ⚲
→ ∪ ▶ ⚓ ⅄ ♩ ⚑

LAHINCH

Lahinch Camping and Caravan Park
☎ (065) 81424 Signposted
► ► ► ► ♣♣ ♛ IR£6.50-IR£7 ♞ IR£6-IR£6.50 ⚲ IR£6-
IR£6.50
Open May-Sep Booking advisable mid Jul-mid Aug Last
arrival 23.00hrs Last departure noon
*A 5-acre site with 115 touring pitches and 12 statics.
Bicycle hire.*

🎮 📻 ☺ 🔲 ⏻ ⚓ ⚓ 🔲 ☀ 𝔸 ⊡ ⚲
→ ∪ ▶ ⅄ ♩ ⚑

O'BRIENS BRIDGE

Shannon Cottage Caravan and Camping Park
☎ 061 377118
► ► ► ♧ ★ ♛ IR£8-IR£11 ♞ IR£7-IR£10 ⚲ IR£6-IR£11
Open Mar-Oct (rs Nov-Feb access through caretaker)
Booking advisable day before arrival Last arrival
22.00hrs Last departure noon
*A 1-acre site with 21 touring pitches.
Sauna, boating, fishing, cycling, nature reserve.*

🎮 📻 ☺ 🔲 ⏻ ⚓ ⚓ ☀ 𝔸 ♩ ⊡ ✗ ⚲ 🐕 ▦ ⚑
→ ∪ ▶ ◎ ⚓ ⅄ ♩

Credit Cards 🔲 ▦

CO CORK

BALLINSPITTLE

Garrettstown House Holiday Park
☎ 021 778156 Signposted
► ► ► ► ♞ ♛ ⚲
Open 19 May-16 Sep (rs Etr-18 May) Last arrival
22.00hrs Last departure noon
*A 7-acre site with 60 touring pitches and 80 statics.
Disco, ceilidh, campers' kitchen*

🎮 ☺ 🔲 ⚓ ⚓ ☀ 𝔸 ⚓ ♩ ⊡ 🆃 ✗ ⚲ ⚑
→ ♩ 🔲

GARRETTSTOWN HOUSE HOLIDAY PARK ►►►►

Garrettstown, Kinsale, Co Cork
Tel: 00 353 21 778156/775286

Top class spacious park in old world setting of Garrettstown estate near beach and forest. Ideally located for touring, scenic, historic and amenity areas of the south. Kinsale, gourmet centre of Ireland is 6 miles. Cork/Ringaskiddy ferryport 25 miles. Numerous facilities and activities on site or within 16 km.

Recommended by all main camping clubs including BFE 4 star

BALLYLICKEY

Eagle Point Caravan and Camping Park
☎027 50630 Signposted
Nearby town: Bantry
►►►►► ♣ ♦♦ ⊕ **Holiday Centre ★ ⊕** IR£8.50-IR£11 ⊕ IR£8.50-IR£10.50 ▲ IR£8.50-IR£11
Open May-Sep Last arrival 23.00hrs Last departure noon ⊗
A 20-acre site with 125 touring pitches.

🔌 🔦 ⊙ 🗑 ◔ ⚒ ❄ ⚙ 🛉 🔌 🔒 ⚷ ♿
➔ ∪ ▶ ♪

BLARNEY

Blarney Caravan & Camping Park
Stone View ☎ 021 385167 Signposted
►►► ⊕ IR£5-IR£6 ⊕ IR£5-IR£6 ▲ IR£5-IR£6
Open all year Booking advisable anytime Last arrival mdnt Last departure noon
A 3-acre site with 40 touring pitches.
Mini golf.

🔌 🔦 ⊙ 🍴 ⬜ ❄ ⚙ ⚷ ⛏ 🐴 🔒
➔ ∪ ▶ ◎ ♪ 🗑

CROOKHAVEN

Barley Cove Caravan Park
☎028 35302 Signposted
►►►►► ♣ ♦♦ **Holiday Centre** ⊕ ⊕ ▲

Open Etr & Jun-1 Sep (rs May & Sep) Booking advisable 7 Jul-17 Aug Last arrival 21.00hrs Last departure noon ⊗
A 5-acre site with 100 touring pitches and 50 statics.
Pitch & putt, children's playhouse

🔌 🛒 🔦 ⊙ 🗑 🍴 ◔ ⚒ ❄ ⚙ 🛉 🔦 ⚷ ⊕ Ⓣ ✕ ⚷ ♨
🈺 🔒 ♿
➔ ∪ ▶ ♪

GLANDORE

Meadow Camping Park
Kilfinnin
☎ 028 33280 Signposted
Nearby town: Skibbereen
► ♣ ♦♦ ⊕ ⊕ IR£7 ▲ IR£7
Open 15 Mar-Sep Booking advisable Jul-Aug Last arrival 22.30hrs Last departure noon ⊗ no cars by tents
A 1-acre site with 19 touring pitches.
Dining room.

🔌 🔦 ⊙ 🗑 ❄ ⚷
➔ ∪ ◎ ⬟ ⚘ ♪ 🔒

CO DONEGAL

PORTSALON

Knockalla Caravan Park
☎074 59108 & 53213 Signposted
►►►► ♣ ⊕ ▲
Open Apr-mid Sep Last arrival 18.00hrs Last departure noon
A 2.5-acre site with 70 touring pitches and 75 statics.
Campers kitchen.

🔌 🔦 ⊙ 🗑 🍴 ⚒ ❄ ⚙ 🛉 🔦 ⚷ ⊕ ⚷ ♨ 🔒
➔ ∪ ▶ ◎ ⚘ ♪

CO DUBLIN

SHANKILL

Shankill Caravan Park
Sherrington Park ☎ 01 2820011
►►► ⊕ ⊕ ▲
Open all year Last departure noon
A 7-acre site with 82 touring pitches and 9 statics.

🔌 🔦 ⊙ ❄ 🛉 ⚙ ⊕ ⚷ 🔒
➔ ∪ ▶ ⚘ ⚑ ♪ 🗑

CO KERRY

CAHERDANIEL

Wave Crest Caravan and Camping Park
☎066 75188 Signposted
▶▶▶▶ 🚐🚐 🛆
Open Apr-Sep Last arrival 22.00hrs Last departure noon
A 4.5-acre site with 45 touring pitches and 2 statics.
Boat anchorage, fishing & pool room.

🎪🅿☉◎🔋🔍✳🕭🛄🗑🖉🔲✕🕯🏧🌲🐕
🐾♿
→🗘🅿🛆❄🎵

CASTLEGREGORY

Anchor Caravan Park
☎066 39157 Signposted
Nearby town: Tralee
▶▶▶▶ 👥🚐 IR£8-IR£9 🚐 IR£8-IR£9 🛆 IR£6-IR£9
Open Etr-Sep Last arrival 22.00hrs Last departure noon
A 5-acre site with 24 touring pitches and 6 statics.

🎪🅿☉◎🔋🔍🔲✳🕭🔲🕯🌲🐕🐾♿
→🗘🅿◎🛆❄🎵

KILLARNEY

Fossa Caravan Park
Fossa ☎ 064 31497 & 31496 (2.5m SW on R562)
▶▶▶▶▶ Holiday Centre ★ 🚐 IR£9.50-IR£10 🚐
IR£9.50-IR£10 🛆 IR£9.50-IR£10
Open Etr-Sep (rs Oct & Mar/Apr restaurant & takeaway closed) Booking advisable Jul-Aug Last arrival 23.00hrs Last departure noon
A 6-acre site with 100 touring pitches and 20 statics.
Campers kitchens & bikes for hire.

🎪🅿☉◎🔋🔍🔍🔲✳🕭🖉🔲✕🕯🛒🏧
🐾♿
→🗘🅿◎❄🎵🎵

Credit Cards 🔲 🔲 🔲 🔲 🔲

Flesk Caravan & Camping Park
Muckross Rd ☎ 064 31704 (1m S) Signposted
▶▶▶▶ 👥★🚐 IR£7-IR£7.50 🚐 IR£7-IR£7.50 🛆 IR£7-IR£7.50
Open mid Mar-mid Oct Booking advisable Last arrival 21.00hrs Last departure noon
A 7-acre site with 72 touring pitches.
Bike hire.Bar/club, tennis, pool all within 50 mtrs.

🎪🅿☉◎🔋🔍🔲✳🕭🖉🔲🕯🛒🏧🌲🐕
🐾♿
→🗘🅿◎🛆❄🎵🎵

Credit Cards 🔲

Fleming's White Bridge Caravan Park
Ballycasheen ☎ 064 31590
(1m E off N22) Signposted
▶▶▶▶ 🚐👥★ 🚐 IR£8-IR£8.50 🚐 IR£7.50-IR£8 🛆 IR£7-IR£8.50
Open Mar-Oct (rs 17 Mar-15 May no shop) Booking advisable Jul-Aug Last arrival 21.30hrs Last departure 23.30hrs
A 7-acre site with 52 touring pitches.

🎪🅿☉◎🔋🔍🔲✳🔲🕯🏧🌲🐾
→🗘🅿◎🛆❄🎵🎵

LAURAGH

Creveen Park
Healy Pass Rd ☎ 064 83131 (1m SE on R574) Signposted
▶▶★🚐 fr IR£5 🚐 fr IR£5 🛆 fr IR£5
Open Etr-Oct Booking advisable Aug bank hol Last arrival mdnt Last departure noon
A 2-acre site with 20 touring pitches.

🎪🅿☉◎🔋🔲✳🕭🖉🔲✕🌲🐕🐾
→❄🎵🎵

WATERVILLE

Waterville Caravan and Camping
Spunkane ☎ 066 74191 Signposted
▶▶▶▶★🚐 IR£6-IR£6.50 🚐 IR£6-IR£6.50 🛆 IR£6-IR£6.50
Open Etr-Sep Booking advisable Jul-Aug Last departure noon
A 4.5-acre site with 59 touring pitches and 22 statics.
Playroom, cycle hire, babysitting arranged.

🎪🅿☉◎🔋🔍🔲✳🕭🖉🔲🔲🕯🛒🏧🐾
♿
→🗘🅿❄🎵

CO KILKENNY

BENNETTSBRIDGE

Nore Valley Park
☎056 27229
Nearby town: Kilkenny
▶▶▶★🚐 fr IR£7 🚐 fr IR£6 🛆 IR£5-IR£7
Open Mar-Oct Booking advisable bank hols & Jul Last arrival 22.00hrs Last departure 16.00hrs
A 4-acre site with 70 touring pitches.
Bread & farm produce, river walks, crazy golf.

🎪🅿☉🔍🔲✳🕭🖉🕯🏧🌲🐕🐾♿
→🅿🎵

CO MAYO

ACHILL ISLAND

Keel Sandybanks Caravan & Camping Park
Keel ☎ 094 32054 Signposted
▶ ▶ ▶ ▶ 🚐 🚐 👤
Open 28 May-10 Sep Last arrival 22.00hrs Last departure noon
A 14-acre site with 88 touring pitches and 12 statics.
On Keel beach.

🔌 🏕 ⊙ 🗄 🏷 ❑ ☀ 🏔 🛈 📞 🛒 🎏 🎋 🐴 🛥 ♿
→ ▶ ⛵ ❧ 🎣

KNOCK

Knock Caravan and Camping Park
☎094 88100 & 88223 Signposted
Nearby town: Ballyhaunis
▶ ▶ ▶ 🚐 IR£5-IR£5.50 🚐 IR£5-IR£5.50 👤 IR£5-IR£5.50
Open Apr-Sep Booking advisable Aug Last arrival 20.00hrs Last departure noon
An 8-acre site with 58 touring pitches and 8 statics.

🔌 🏕 ⊙ 🗄 🏷 🍴 ❑ ☀ 🏔 🛈 🧺 🎱 🕎 📞 🎏 ♿
→ ∪ ▶ 🎣 🐚

CO ROSCOMMON

ATHLONE

Hodson Bay Caravan & Camping Park
Hodson Bay, Kiltoom ☎ 01902 92448 Signposted
▶ ▶ ★ 🚐 fr IR£7.50 🚐 fr IR£7.50 👤 fr IR£7.50
Open 9 May-15 Sep Booking advisable bank hols & last wk Jul-1st wk Aug Last arrival 22.30hrs Last departure noon 🚫
A 2-acre site with 32 touring pitches and 2 statics.

🔌 🏕 ⊙ 🗄 🏷 🍴 ❑ ☀ 🏔 🛈 🧺 🎱 🕎 📞 🎏 🍴
🐚 ♿
→ ∪ ▶ ⛵ ❧ 🍴 🎣
£

BOYLE

Lough Key Forest Park
☎079 62363 & 62212
Signposted
▶ ▶ ▶ ▶ 🌂 🏔 🚐 🚐 IR£6.50-IR£7.50 🚐 IR£6.50-IR£7.50 👤 IR£6.20-IR£7.25
Open 3-14 Apr & early May-early Sep Booking advisable 3 wks before arrival Last arrival 22.00hrs Last departure noon no cars by tents
A 15-acre site with 72 touring pitches.

🔌 🏕 ⊙ 🗄 ❑ 🏔 🍴 📞 🎏 🐚 ♿
→ ∪ ▶ ❧ 🍴 🎣

CO SLIGO

ROSSES POINT

Greenlands Caravan & Camping Park
☎071 77113 & 45618 Signposted
▶ ▶ ▶ ▶ 🚐 🚐 👤
Open 21 May-1 Sep Last arrival 20.00hrs Last departure noon
A 4-acre site with 42 touring pitches.

🔌 🏕 ⊙ 🗄 🍴 ❑ ☀ 📞 ♿
→ ▶ ◎ ⛵ 🎣 🐚

STRANDHILL

Strandhill Caravan Park
☎071 68120 Signposted
▶ ▶ 🚐 🚐 👤
Open May-14 Sep Booking advisable Jul-26 Aug Last arrival 23.00hrs Last departure 14.00hrs
A 10-acre site with 28 touring pitches and 12 statics.

🔌 🏕 ⊙ 🗄 🏷 🍴 ❑ ☀ 🏔 🛈 🧺 📞 🐚
→ ∪ 🎣

CO TIPPERARY

AHERLOW

Ballinacourty House Camping and Caravan Park
☎062 56230 Signposted
Nearby town: Tipperary
▶ ▶ ▶ ▶ 🍴 🚐 🚐 👤
Open Etr-end Sep Booking advisable high season & bank hols Last arrival 22.00hrs Last departure noon
A 5-acre site with 58 touring pitches.
Mini-golf.

🔌 🏕 ⊙ 🏷 🍷 🍴 ❑ ☀ ⛳ 🏔 🧺 🎱 ✂ 📞 🏛 🎏
🎏 🐚
→ ∪ ▶ 🍴 🎣

CO WATERFORD

CLONEA

Casey's Caravan Park
☎058 41919 Signposted
Nearby town: Dungarvan
▶ ▶ ▶ 🍴 ★ 🚐 IR£9-IR£9.50 🚐 IR£9-IR£9.50 👤 IR£9-IR£9.50
Open 15 May-10 Sep Booking advisable May-Jun Last arrival 22.00hrs Last departure noon

A 4.5-acre site with 40 touring pitches and 90 statics.
Crazy golf & games room.

🎯 📞 ⊙ 🍴 🔌 🖵 ☀ 🗻 🛢 ⌀ 🔧 📞 🛒
➔ ⛵ 🛴 ♨ 🎵

CO WESTMEATH

BALLYKEERAN

Lough Ree Caravan and Camping Park
☎0902 78561 & 74414 Signposted
► ► 🚐 🚍 ⚠
Open Apr-2 Oct Booking advisable bank hols
A 5-acre site with 40 touring pitches and 2 statics.

🎯 📞 ⊙ 📞 🛒

MULLINGAR

Lough Ennell Holiday Village

☎044 48101 Signposted
► ► ► ⚓ 👫 ✚ 🚐 🚍 ⚠
Open 15 Jan-20 Dec (rs Oct-15 Mar prior bookings only)
Booking advisable 15 Jul-Aug Last arrival 22.30hrs Last departure noon
A 4-acre site with 65 statics.

🎯 📞 ⊙ ☍ 🔌 🖵 ☀ 🗻 🛢 ⌀ ✕ 📞 🛒
➔ ⛵ 🛴 △ 🛴 ♨ 🎵 🔲

Credit Cards 🟦 💳

🜼🜼🜼🜼🜼🜼🜼🜼🜼🜼🜼

CO WEXFORD

COURTOWN HARBOUR

Poulshone Carvan Park
Poulshone ☎ 01 908993 Signposted
► ► ► 🚐 🚍
Open Etr-Sep Last arrival 20.00hrs Last departure 15.00hrs
A 4-acre site with 6 touring pitches and 40 statics.

🎯 📞 🔲 🛢
➔ ⛵ 🛴 ♨ 🎵 🛒

FETHARD

Ocean Island Caravan Park
Booley Hill ☎ 051 97148 Signposted
► ► ► 🚐 🚍 ⚠
Open Etr-Sep Last arrival 22.00hrs Last departure noon
A 3-acre site with 40 touring pitches and 18 statics.

🎯 📞 ⊙ 🔲 🍴 🔌 ☀ 🗻 🛢 ⌀ 🔲 🕨 📞 🛒
➔ ⛵ 🛴 ♨ 🎵

KILMUCKRIDGE

Morriscastle Strand Family Caravan & Camping
Morriscastle ☎ 053 30124 & 01 4535355 (off-season)
Signposted
► ► ► 🚐 🚍 ⚠
Open Jul-27 Aug (rs May-Jun & 28 Aug-Sep shop,
reception, games room, take-away food) Booking
advisable Whitsun wknd & mid Jul-mid Aug Last arrival
22.00hrs Last departure 16.00hrs ⊘
A 16-acre site with 100 touring pitches and 150 statics.
Dish washing room, indoor cooking facilities.

🎯 📞 ⊙ 🔲 ☍ 🔌 ☀ 🗻 🛢 ⌀ 📞 🕨 🛒 ♿
➔ ⛵ 🛴 🔲 ♨ 🎵

ROSSLARE

Rosslare Holiday Park
☎053 45720 & 32427 Signposted
Nearby town: Wexford
► ► ► ► ★ 🚐 IR£6.50-IR£7.50 🚍 IR£6.50-IR£7.50 ⚠
IR£6.50-IR£7.50
Open Apr-1 Oct Booking advisable Jul-Aug Last arrival
mdnt Last departure 15.00hrs
A 6.5-acre site with 20 touring pitches and 20 statics.

🎯 📞 ⊙ 🔲 🍴 ☍ 🔌 ☀ 🗻 ⌀ 🔲 T 📞 🛒 ♿
➔ ⛵ 🛴 🔲 △ 🛴 ♨ 🎵

WEXFORD

WEXFORD

Ferrybank Caravan Park
Ferrybank
☎ 053 44378 & 43274 Signposted
► ► ► ♣ ♦♠ ★ ⊞ IR£8-IR£10.50 ⊞ IR£8-IR£10.50
⅄ IR£3.50-IR£8
Open Whit wknd-Aug (rs Etr & Sep) Booking advisable
Whit wknd & Aug bank hol Last departure 16.00hrs
A 10-acre site with 130 touring pitches.

🔦 🛏 ⊙ 🗃 ⏰ 🔌 ⊡ ☀ ⚠ ✕ ☎ 🚿 🎋 🐾 ⅄
➔ ∪ ► ⤴ 🎥 ♫

CO WICKLOW

DONARD

Moat Farm Caravan & Camping Park
☎045 404727 Signposted
► ► ► ♣ ♦♠ ⊞ £8 ⊞ £8 ⅄ £6
Open all year Booking advisable bank hols & Jun-Aug
Last arrival 22.30hrs Last departure noon
A 2.75-acre site with 40 touring pitches.

🔦 🛏 ⊙ 🗃 ⏰ ⊡ ☀ ⚠ 🎋 ⌀ ⊞ ☎ 🚐 🎋 🐾 ⅄
➔ ► ♫ 🐾

RED CROSS

River Valley Caravan Park
☎0404 41647 Signposted
► ► ► ► ► ♣ ♦♠ ☯ Holiday Centre ⊞ ⊞ ⅄
Open 17 Mar-23 Sep Booking advisable bank hols & Jul-
Aug Last arrival 23.00hrs Last departure noon
A 16-acre site with 60 touring pitches and 20 statics.
Crazy golf, bowling green & wine & cocktail bar.

🔦 🛏 ⊙ 🗃 ⏰ ⚲ 🔌 ⊡ ☀ ⚠ 🎋 ⌀ Ⓣ ✕ ☎ 🎋 🐾
♿
➔ ∪ ► ♫

ROUNDWOOD

Roundwood Caravan Park
☎01 2818163 Signposted
Nearby town: Bray
► ► ► ► ♣ ♦♠ ★ ⊞ IR£7-IR£9 ⊞ IR£7-IR£9 ⅄ IR£7-IR£9
Open Apr-Sep Booking advisable Jun-Aug Last arrival
11.00hrs Last departure noon
A 5-acre site with 45 touring pitches and 33 statics.
Campers kitchen & dining room.

🔦 🛏 ⊙ 🗃 ⏰ 🔌 ⊡ ☀ ⚠ 🎋 ⌀ ⊞ ☎ 🎋 🐾
➔ ∪ ► ♫

This is the checklist compiled by one of our campsite inspectors to ensure that he leaves nothing behind when he sets off either from home or from park visits with a towed caravan. We thought you might like to share his handy hints, and save yourself from embarassment ... or worse.

- Check that all interior caravan items are safely stored, cupboards are closed, loos not full of moveable objects, all interior electrics set correctly. Remember that vase of flowers!

- Check roof lights are closed and windows secure.

- Corner steadies should be up tightly, blocks cleared away, steps stowed.

- Disconnect electric hook-ups to site and check that gas bottles are turned off.

- Make sure electrics to car are secure.

- Check that the tow-hook safety wire is clipped on, and, if used, that the anti-snake device is fitted correctly.

- Visually check that caravan number plate is secure – and that it reads the same as the one on the car.

- Using a second person to stand behind the caravan, check that all lights and indicators are working correctly.

- Move forward about 15 metres, then stop, get out and inspect your pitch for any items which have been left under the caravan.

- Check that the caravan door is locked and secure.

- Another useful and potentially life-saving tip is to travel always with a small fire extinguisher, fire blanket or both. Fires in caravans and tents are all too commonplace, and once started can take hold very quickly. By the time help has come, or you have gone to find the site's fire-fighting equipment, a tent in particular can already have burned down completely. Never treat fire lightly.

- If you use Calor Gas, they issue a free directory of stockists and dealers. Simply call free on 0800 626 626.

Before You Go

Useful Addresses

CAMPING AND CARAVANNING CLUB
Greenfields House
Westwood Way
Coventry CV4 8JH
Tel 01203 694995

CARAVAN CLUB
East Grinstead House
East Grinstead
West Sussex RH19 1UA
Tel 01342 326944

BRITISH HOLIDAY & HOME PARKS
ASSOCIATION LTD
6 Pullman Court
Great Western Road
Gloucester GL1 3ND
Tel 01452 526911

NATIONAL CARAVAN COUNCIL LTD
Catherine House
Victoria Road
Aldershot
Hampshire GU11 1SS
Tel 01252 318251

Please write to: Campsites Editor, AA Camping and
Caravanning Guide, Publishing Division,
The Automobile Association, Fanum House,
Basingstoke RG21 4EA

Use this form to recommend any caravan and camping park with
good touring pitches where you have stayed which is not already in
our guide.

If you have any comments about your stay at a touring park listed
in the guide, we shall be grateful if you will let us know, as
feedback from readers helps us to keep our guide accurate and up
to date. Please note, however, that the AA only inspects and
classifies parks for their touring facilities. We do not inspect or
grade static caravans.

If a problem arises during your stay on a park, we do recommend
that you discuss the matter with the park management there and
then so that they have a chance to put things right before your
holiday is spoilt.

Please note that the AA does not undertake to arbitrate between
you and the park management, or to obtain compensation or
engage in protracted correspondence.

Readers
Report form

Your name (block capitals) . . . .

. . . .

. . . .

Your address (block capitals) . . . .

. . . .

. . . .

. . . .

. . . .

. . . .

Comments . . . .

. . . .

. . . .

. . . .

. . . .

. . . .

CAMPING AND
CARAVANNING
GUIDE

....
....
....
....
....
....
....
....
....
....
....
....
....
....
....
....
....
....
....
....
....
....
....
....
....
....
....
....
....

Please write to: Campsites Editor, AA Camping and
Caravanning Guide, Publishing Division,
The Automobile Association, Fanum House,
Basingstoke RG21 4EA

Use this form to recommend any caravan and camping park with
good touring pitches where you have stayed which is not already in
our guide.

If you have any comments about your stay at a touring park listed
in the guide, we shall be grateful if you will let us know, as
feedback from readers helps us to keep our guide accurate and up
to date. Please note, however, that the AA only inspects and
classifies parks for their touring facilities. We do not inspect or
grade static caravans.

If a problem arises during your stay on a park, we do recommend
that you discuss the matter with the park management there and
then so that they have a chance to put things right before your
holiday is spoilt.

Please note that the AA does not undertake to arbitrate between
you and the park management, or to obtain compensation or
engage in protracted correspondence.

Readers
Report form

Your name (block capitals) . . . .

. . . .

. . . .

Your address (block capitals) . . . .

. . . .

. . . .

. . . .

. . . .

. . . .

Comments . . . .

. . . .

. . . .

. . . .

CAMPING AND
CARAVANNING
GUIDE

. . . .

. . . .

. . . .
. . . .
. . . .
. . . .
. . . .
. . . .
. . . .
. . . .
. . . .
. . . .
. . . .
. . . .
. . . .
. . . .
. . . .
. . . .
. . . .
. . . .
. . . .
. . . .
. . . .
. . . .

CAMPING AND
CARAVANNING
GUIDE